Trouble in the Flesh

BY MAX WYLIE

Novels:

HINDU HEAVEN — 1933
GO HOME AND TELL YOUR MOTHER — 1950

Non-fiction:

RADIO WRITING — 1938
BEST BROADCASTS — 1938–39, 1939–40, 1940–41 (annuals)
RADIO AND TELEVISION WRITING — 1950
ASSIGNMENT: CHURCHILL — 1955
(Written for Inspector Walter H. Thompson of Scotland Yard)
CLEAR CHANNELS — 1955

Plays:

THE GREATEST OF THESE — 1946
THE FUNDAMENTAL GEORGE (with Milton Geiger) 1949

Trouble in the Flesh

DOUBLEDAY & COMPANY, INC.

by Max Wylie

GARDEN CITY, NEW YORK

1959

All of the characters in this book are fictitious,
and any resemblance to actual persons, living or dead,
is purely coincidental.

For my dear wife,
who waited a long time

I am as a spirit who has dwelt
Within his heart of hearts; and I have felt
His feelings, and have thought his thoughts,
    and known
The inmost converse of his soul, the tone
Unheard but in the silence of his blood
When all the pulses in their multitude
Image the trembling calm of summer seas.
                —Shelley

Part One

1

THE SOUND AND THE SMELL OF OCEAN SAND BEING washed by low short waves, then scoured again as the water receded, formed a complex of sensations, most of them happy and sonorous, that had been visiting back and forth all morning between the beach and the willowy girl in the kitchen.

The house she lived in was an abandoned lifesaving station, comfortably remodeled but remote and masculine and far too big. It had been condemned for further service by the Coast Guard two seasons before, when geodesists reported that a change in the littoral would sooner or later undermine the property and pull this section of the shore back into the sea. A new station had been built a mile down the beach, tucked inside a curve away from the shore currents. It was the only human habitation that could be seen.

Because she was so much alone, the young woman had invested the dunes with a personal obligation to attend and respond to her. It was an agreeable fantasy of companionship that continued over into her adult life from the undisciplined dreaminess of her childhood. By the subtle but constant change in the contours of the sand, by the soft whistling that tumbled down the dune sides whenever the wind combed at their crests, she felt her pleasant meditations were being shared and enjoyed, poked into and commented upon, perhaps even talked over when she wasn't there herself.

Though this part of Cape Cod was empty, it was not silent,

even on mornings like this—the dead center of August. Aeolian whisperings that grooved the sand, the cry of gulls lighting, and the murmurous conversation of the shore came in through the kitchen window with the air and kept her company there.

Gillian Scott Farrier—they called her Jill—was a clean and simple person, unsure, believing, and resourceful. But her situation was not simple. And it did not clear up for her when she tried to peer into its center.

She hoped the men wouldn't drink. Not that day. It would be all right when they got back from New York—she and her husband and the boy. But not today.

Jill looked up the beach where the men had gone toward the wreck. Barrels were still lifting and heaving in the bright water. Far out, a cluster of them winked back at the shore, bright and black and shiny like an accidental spill of licorice drops. One barrel, close inshore where the low breakers curled and turned over, had won the interest of her husband, Seton, and the tall noisy new man from the Coast Guard, Jimmy dePrix.

The two had shed their trousers and were kneeing through the shallow water. The third man, Terry McCabe, was perched in the dry sand, watching. It was about the only posture Jill could associate with the man. He had a whisky still in the dunes. She was not allowed to say she hated Terry, although she did. And more than ever since their son had come.

Beyond the three men, approaching like insects, she could see others more than a mile away, bearing down the beach toward the broken schooner, no doubt summoned there by the invisible yet mysteriously effective telegraphy known to sailors and to a few shore people, and to no others. A pennant on a pole was all they seemed to need. Or a quick wigwag with colored flags. At first sight of these, strange people would start coming to an exact place, never before visited, bringing with them the clumsy colorless gear of salvage, working all day without a word; working with lanterns into the night, going away again across the sand with their rotten treasures and their purposeful backs and fixed eyes; their ropes, barrows, cant hooks, hand winches, mallets, spades, and sand anchors.

In the presence of treasure men behaved as they would in the presence of hostages. Nothing was safe. Eyes tightened. Voices rose.

To Jill, their sudden unquestioning proprietorship—her husband's among them—seemed illicit. The sight of any man gloating over anything always sickened her. If the dead schooner were not so generously giving up her cargo to the fingering lift of the tide, Jill felt these men would rape her for it. That she was a corpse would make no difference now. They had her down; had her down and no one looking, as it were.

Quietly but suddenly the nature of the men's activity changed. Her husband and Jimmy had got a line over the barrel and were letting the waves bring it in. Terry had risen and moved nearer, his duck trousers whipping.

Jill looked at the cot where her two-year-old son lay sleeping, and tightened the netting against the sand flies. Then she turned to the swiveled spyglass that stood in what had once been the captain's port.

The powerful magnification of the glass seemed to jump the men to the very railing of the porch. A lip reader might have followed their talk with ease. Seton Farrier, her husband, had the rope's end, while Jimmy squatted down in the water, rubbing the side of the barrel, trying to read a stencil. Both men were grinning wide. They shouted something to Terry, whose head went back in the brittle but silent acknowledgment he always made when he hadn't quite heard. Then he leaned toward them again, attentive to the catch they'd made and their skill to bring it in.

Seton backed with care toward the shore in a taut crouch of instant readiness, as if dragging a bound but thrashing alligator out of a pen.

Their excitement caught hold of her own feelings. She wished they could all be children for a few hours; that after everyone had had a good time with the barrel they could all be taken to a fine home and given a dinner that someone else had prepared.

They'd be ravenous, all right. This would mean a bigger meal than she planned. And a bigger mess afterward than she wanted. What she wanted seemed minimal: just to be on time at Truro for the train. Nothing more, except she wanted no interference from the others. Terry was supposed to be on his way to Provincetown for groceries. The young Coast Guardsman, dePrix, on active station, was a mile from where he should be at that very moment. No doubt the Coast Guard even here at the Cape didn't get a good wreck every week. No doubt the young man would send in a laconic report that would presently be stapled in Fall River, then mailed to Washington where, like the schooner it told of, it too would founder. But it would save dePrix, because he'd written it.

Him and his tattoo!

The first time he'd come by with the mail he'd waked Sean by tousling his curls and the child had screamed at the stranger. No wonder either, thought Jill, for the red seaman stood over the crib making a face, then exposed the dreadful tattoo of a nude brunette, giddily crucified on the skin of his chest. With the heels of his hands he'd pulled his own breasts apart, stretching the skin and so stretching the tattooed lady and grotesquely widening her.

"Fat lady!" he had roared, leaning down close to the boy. Then he'd straightened up with a shout, looking about for approval. Though naked to the waist, he seemed to have stuck his thumbs through his braces. When his hands fell, the stretched girl snapped back to first dimensions and relaxed there, a hand reaching out to each of his nipples, her tiny feet just touching the hard base of his breastbone.

That first encounter had left Jill with an impression of the man as rough and lubricious, naïvely suggestible, and altogether empty. Her husband knew too many such. Dangerous too, as any mindless but eupeptic vagrant can be dangerous if left unwatched.

She had never read sea stories but she clung to the picture of Jimmy dePrix as the man who was always being thumped by a marlinspike, whatever that was, and never by anything else; always by a mate who was heavy-fisted, and always on the heaving deck of a brigantine putting in for Trafalgar or lying to off the Cameroons. Such men never managed to make ports like Boston or San Diego, but always a place you couldn't find on a map or fix in your mind.

Jill preferred to read about things she already knew. And she liked the ocean the way it was. She respected its unsoundable privacy and used it for nothing but contemplation and a little wading. All the men who drifted back and forth across her life here by the ocean, all who had tried to take charge of its tides and traffic, seemed a sweaty and a loutish parcel, Jimmy the worst of them all.

And certainly there was nothing so disgusting as a blond pink man with a hairy chest.

How her comments had roiled Seton!

"You'd never know a fine sailor if you woke in bed with 'im!" The sharp edge of Irish temper came quickly into his speech with the least appearance of tension.

Though she did not plan to wake in sailors' beds, nor to sleep in them, what her husband had said was true enough: Jill would never know one sailor from another. But Seton saw he'd frightened his wife by rebuffing her so savagely and had made a dismissing gesture with his hand.

"He's handy. He fits in. And we don't have to go three miles for the mail any more."

Fits in! she had thought. Like any other tramp on the prowl he fits in. Wherever there's whisky!

Though she had let it die there by saying nothing, her irritation was more intense than her husband's and for better reason: she did the work while he did the roaring.

Well, not quite that, she amended, trying to be objective, for no one on earth ever worked the way her husband did. But the spat was still vivid, though ten days old by now.

She tilted the spyglass back to its base, picked up her work, and went out to the clothesline. With a handful of wrung diapers and a mouthful of clothespins it was not always easy to be objective, especially with men she didn't want around the place at mealtime. And never a woman to talk to.

Jill was a person of easy motions, quick when she needed to be, as when their son Sean—when learning to walk—might start to topple. But most of the time she was unhurried, almost leisurely. People felt comfortable around her.

She hung up her boy's things, then took in Seton's shirts, sprinkled them, spread them, ironed them neatly, slipping the smooth bottom of the iron expertly over the covered beeswax. Then she put them in his suitcase, all packed now except for his toothbrush. She'd remind him after lunch.

If Terry had gone on to Provincetown and if the bleached man from the Coast Guard hadn't appeared at all, Jill would have been

exquisitely happy in these familiar actions, thinking of her long preparations for the trip down to New York. And this time, for sure, her
teeth would get a good going-over and the boy would be examined
by a real pediatrician. She knew her son was all right, but her own
teeth were terrible and they hurt. Seton's had been fixed the year
before—twenty days, two hours each day, by a specialist in Boston.

There were things about her husband she was forbidden to know;
personal things which, because of her intimate relationship to him
as much as to their being a focus of natural and persistent curiosity,
kept tossing and twisting in new angles of speculation and wonder.

She wondered often about her husband's first wife and about the
son born of her, twelve now, yet never seen by his own father and
never mentioned. The few times Jill had moved to the edge of this
prohibited territory, half answers had multiplied the very doubts she
wanted satisfied.

Had he loved his first wife? Had he had to marry her? Where was
she now? Married again? Was it a quarrel? What did she look like?
What did her husband's son look like? Where was he now physically
and actually? Most important in her own imaginings—since she felt a
human desire to make up for what she suspected his young life was not
receiving—how was the boy getting along?

She considered whether a second wife had any ethical right to be
curious about a first wife. Or was it the best thing to put it out of her
mind and keep it out and just try to be herself? The question alter-
nated with its half-rationalized opposite: would it not benefit their
marriage if Jill were to know a great deal about her predecessor just
to avoid a disastrous repeating of the setting and the set of facts that
had broken up the first?

What could they have been that they should be so painful he
refused to look upon the only living product of their life together?

She was sure, for example, that her husband was not *exactly* sure
where his son did go to school. She had come to this conclusion
much earlier when Seton had not immediately answered whether his
son's military school was on the east or the west bank of the Hudson.

The matter stayed on in her mind with justifiable intensity; supposing this indifference to his first marriage were someday to visit
her own? That their own passionate enfoldments, often sudden and

ecstatic (and to her unbearably thrilling)—suppose all of these breathless intimacies and wild whisperings were as outspent and meaning-
less, once over, as was his breakfast coffee or his solitary nappings in
the sand? Did he love Jill or just Jill's being a woman? Respond
more to her being a lithe and available vessel of convenience and
allure, and never once see the spirit of her, nor the deeps of her,
nor the permanence of these? She felt specially made for him and
for the problems in his special circumference. She felt in many ways
she was more like his own ocean than he was, sunny on the surface
on days like these but always a long way down, while he, more and
more, took on its attributes of austerity, of its vast and voiceless
mystery. There was something elemental at the center of him; and in
the broader spread of his personality something unchartable, un-
answering, and remote. The ocean's uses of him had seemed to make
him kin only to himself, not to nature.

The single thing that struck a terror she could not yet face was her
mounting belief that their own son, waking now on the cot and
arching his head to watch her movements at the stove, was no more
seen nor comprehended nor needed than the first son had been,
whatever the reason there. Never once had Seton sat to play with his
son Sean, never tossed him in the air, never spontaneously reached
down to pat him or to lead him or hold him, never studied him as
he tried to eat, never steadied him as he tried to climb. Sean up to
now was growing up with no *feel* of his father, no scent of him
either. Jill watched the boy's bright eyes, looking gravely at Terry
and Jim and Seton—knowing they had different meanings to him,
yet not knowing how to separate them out. Though a passer-by,
thumbing an album of the Farrier family snapshots, would have been
charmed at the father-son display it held; though these were endearing
trophies for Jill, it was she, not he, who had made them, for Seton,
though not unwilling to stand or sit or swim for pictures, was unwilling to learn how to take them. And pictures in which he did not
appear had no interest for him at all.

She picked up her son and hugged him, took him to the bathroom,
then set him in his cut-down high chair facing the beach. He let out
a squeal of delight at the activity about him, at expectant smells
coming from the stove, then began pounding his tray for more service.

Jill put his lunch before him, in the blue dish that had the hot-water chamber for its bottom half. She'd seen it in a New London department store the last week of her pregnancy.

She felt a faint sense of guilt over the sliding fantasy of conjecture and of reassessment that her thoughts of her husband and her marriage were sending through her mind. When she was alone with him all her thoughts were affirmative. It was the times when men, or some passing rowdiness, intruded and took him away that the fears and the guessing began. It would be a great marriage, a productive, even important marriage, if only she could get some control over it.

But at thirty, with his own work out of the way for the moment and in the hands of others, he was like a kid in a city block, waiting for a game to start.

With something like Roman rejoicing the men were bringing their prize barrel down the beach, back to the house. They'd bound sections of life-preserver cork to the two-wheeled rig the Coast Guard had at one time used to get boats to the water.

Terry and her husband balanced the barrel on the improvised caisson. Jimmy dePrix, the satyr, lunged forward wildly against the lines, his neck cords distended like guy wires.

They were all panting. If one of the men had had an eye patch or a crutch it could have been *Treasure Island*. It was ridiculous and comical. But it was boyishly engaging, too.

They were taking the barrel into the boat room directly below the living room. There they stopped to breathe. Then all looked up at the window where she stood. All she could see was teeth and triumph. Then Terry shouted:

"It's grain alcohol!"

They rolled the trophy out of sight. Presently there was a thump that shook the house. Somehow they'd got the barrel hoisted to one of the gantries. Immediately the sound of hammering began. They were wasting no time.

Shrieks and yowls bounded out to sea from the boat room. Sean pounded his bent spoon on the edge of his high-chair tray. Already he could exult like his father.

Jill turned the flounders and shook the home-fried potatoes. Then she set the table on the porch, took out the stone pitcher from the icebox, pressed it to her cheek to see if the milk had chilled, and rang the ship's bell.

But the men stayed with the barrel. Jill placed the dinner on the back of the stove and went outside to the open doors of the boat room to see what the men were doing. They had found a number of empty glass bottles where the lanterns had once been stored, and they were siphoning the clear alcohol into the bottles.

"Absolutely pure!" Seton shouted to her. "Got the government stamp right on her side! U.S.P.!" He pointed.

It was surely there. And it was sure, too, that the three men had already nipped at the raw alcohol.

"You come on up and eat and do this later. I don't want dinner to dry out. It's fresh flounder."

"We'll be right up."

"Why don't you leave it in the barrel?"

"Somebody'll steal it. Minute we leave."

"Won't it be easier to steal the smaller bottles?"

"We'll bury them," her husband explained. "In the sand."

"Come and eat now."

While the three men ate she put on the powder-blue linen suit she planned to wear on the long train ride. The wagon was coming at two to pick them up.

The wagon was the only way to get over the trackless sand. Its driver fitted clumsy-looking leather bags, tied on at the fetlock, over the horse's feet, a usable sand shoe but tiring and distasteful to the horse. Often enough Jill had seen the animal stop at the foot of a drift and shake a foot, like a cat caught in a candy wrapper. But the ride was an adventure she loved, for it meant change, New York City, the seeing of old friends again, excitement, renewal, a few Broadway shows, a few new clothes, and a refresher for her spirit and her marriage.

She loved staying in hotels too, even the dismal Byzantium. They always went there because of the special rate, a consideration the management extended because Seton's family had lived there themselves for so long. The promise to bring Sean for the first time to see his grandparents was another gay rhythm in the street-piano music her imagination was beginning to play. There were other fresh memo-

ries: of cramped but lively places they went to in Greenwich Village
for meals: the Pig and Whistle on West Fourth, the Samovar just
across the street, the 4 Trees on Christopher, Alice McCollister on
West Eighth for "after the theater," Ferreri's on Macdougal, the
Silver Ship, the Blue Horse, and the Kopper Kettle. She loved Lee
Chumley's on Bedford Street, its darkness and smokiness, the bright
book jackets that decorated its walls, the essence of the Village spirit
and idea in its foyer sign: "Sunday Breakfast Served from 5:00 P.M."

Her thoughts of New York broke off suddenly when she heard the
sand wagon coming up the beach. There was a large crate on it.

It was the new pump and the gas engine. Things never came when
you expected them.

Her husband was in the doorway. She had heard nothing but he
was there. He was barefoot still.

"I'm not taking you. Nor Sean. I'm going alone. You know how it
embarrasses me. When he cries. That trip on the Fall River. Last
month. Everyone looking."

"But he was sick," she said.

Everything went out of joint.

"I'll be too busy. I don't want you."

"But your mother does. So does your father. They want to see the
boy."

She rose quietly, facing him. But she wasn't pleading or challeng-
ing. She had been his wife for four years and was beginning a little
to know him. "We don't need to ride in the same car," she said
softly. "How do you know he's going to cry? He's never been on a
train."

She could see her husband's mind reviewing this, palpating the
truth of it and the probables she was suggesting. He stroked his black
mustache like a fly caressing its own head. But she could see the
twist in the mouth corner, and she knew he had already thrown out
all her plans. She knew he was going without her. There would be
no sense in talking now. It was over.

She knew, too, he'd regret his impetuosity as soon as their house
was out of sight, knew he'd write a letter on the train and mail it
back when they changed engines at New Haven. She knew that in
another day she'd have a letter begging her to understand him, insist-

ing he needed her more than any living thing, that he loved her beyond his power of reason to understand, beyond his power of speech to tell.

And he did need her. She knew this from the day of their marriage, and more the day of it than the night; the spectacular helplessness, the incapacity to plan, to buy tickets, to order food from a simple menu; even to register in a hotel. She remembered that Seton's mother had always "signed him in" when he stayed with his parents in their little suite in the Byzantium, just off Fifth, in New York.

She felt the dull frustration of it now, that her husband did not know how to use her, how to take what she had for him; could not take it in any way that was gratifying to her, or even predictable. Her husband was a person who would suddenly turn his back and disappear.

She turned her own back then, and thoughtfully took off her hat.

A tumult of disappointment chilled her stomach but there were no tears in her eyes, and when she spoke, looking into the mirror to pat her hair, her voice was level.

"You better go down to the wagon. The pump has come."

Seton welcomed the release this news brought and was gone.

Jill was afraid of her husband. She was afraid of the dark impulse that ruled him but she concealed the fear, often concealed it even from herself.

She did not know that he, too, was afraid, that his fear was deeper, that it had no beginning and that it was never to end.

2

SETON'S OLDER BROTHER, PATRICK, HAD BEEN LOOK-
ing forward to Seton's arrival in New York for some weeks. And he'd
been expecting him now, with his little family—expecting his appearance at almost any moment, for a full day.

Patrick was just ten years older than Seton. There was this bright
thing about him, everyone knew Patrick and liked him, but over this
a shadow had fallen: no one believed him any more. He'd thrown
away his chances. (He put it another way, of course: "They took
my square root.") He lived on forbidden handouts from his mother;
he lived on women; and he worked shows in any capacity when he
could find an employer.

Without his personality, which was his charm and his undoing, he
would have been called a bum anywhere else in the world. But Broadway forgave his excesses, knowing his story and his gifts and remembering the brief days of his splendor. So the threat of his being discovered a bum anywhere else in the world was slight since he was the
precise kind of anaerobic germ that would perish in normal atmospheres but that flourished in the airless caves and dank shafts where
he slept, the grottoes and *schlacht* stores where he ate. There was
little that was regular about his eating and sleeping and this was at
times felt to be rather sad. And so it was. But through the center of
the man there ran a narrow corridor of real tragedy, narrow because
his end was near, and tragic because he was still occasionally trying
hard to be useful.

He wanted to mean something. He took his loss and marked it
off without pity. His situation was his own fault and he knew it. Now
he wanted Seton to mean something, to avoid his own mistakes, to
get where he ought to be and get there by the quickest routes. Patrick
thought he knew what these were.

Without doubt he knew some of them, but the very nature of Pat's livelihood, its indefatigable cheerfulness no less than its ineluctable disasters, always filled Seton with as much caution as contempt. Any failure (Seton's mind ran this way) who had the brass to be cheerful about it was suspicious.

There were other dubious areas in Patrick's make-up besides his good nature. He'd gotten mixed up in the taxicab-rate war when Luxor started to crowd Twentieth Century but his activity had had an unusually clandestine flavor to it, keeping Pat all night in West Side garages. It was rumored that he could fix meters to run either fast or slow, that he could even "jig" the new meters to show dimes and skip the stop at nickels. He was thought to get a flat fee of twenty dollars for every meter he fixed and once, when Mogul Checker became suspicious that mechanisms had been tinkered with, he was tailed by a company detective.

Seton was always afraid his older brother was going to be arrested for something and get his name in the paper.

It was true he lived at the edge. But what was affecting to the sensitivities of those who knew of it (there weren't many) was that Patrick recognized his brother's genius and wanted to protect it. In fact, he wanted to manage it, not for his own, but for his brother's gain. He could have, too, for Seton was egregiously naïve. Patrick was a lawyer and just crooked enough, through the fluency of his morals as well as the exigencies of the daily struggle, to be almost impossible to fool. He was a wise guy in the true sense and knew what games to stay out of. And what neighborhoods.

He was attractive to women. In this part of his life he had much trouble and not enough sleep. Pat was a self-spending pagan, temerarious, urgent, knockabout, joyous, amoral, friendly, confiding, disloyal, and temporary. He thought and looked like Jimmy Walker. He had the same social fluidity, the same Irish bounce and easy banter.

Politicians liked him. Through their influence he'd had jobs tending bar in political clubs. He lost them all because he stole liquor. He'd lost night-clerk jobs in West Side hotels for visiting lady guests, sometimes with their consent, sometimes just appearing as (he hoped) a happy surprise.

Patrick knew many of the men who were close to Jimmy Hines, who at this period of municipal evolution in New York City represented the symbol of all ward politicians—men whose power was rooted in personal favors, in the quick "fix," the speedy providing of bail money. Pat hung around the Monongahela Club, hoping more for a Turf Club appointment than a court clerkship, but he settled for whatever fell to him—errands, race tips, fight tickets, or handouts. He was a safe man with large sums of money, hoping to be cited as incorruptible, but on anything steady or anything near a cash register, invisible pilferage would start soon after he hung up his hat. Tammany got him a job at the Phoenix Brewery but in thirty days he'd gained fifteen pounds and, though no one ever saw him drink, few ever saw him outside the men's room. He was let out when too many of the company's trucks that he was checking were showing up "light," a case here, half a barrel there.

Yet no Tammany banquet occurred without his advice and support. He supplied the acts, frequently appeared in them, hosted the parties, and now and then served as master of ceremonies for the entire occasion.

Patrick, for whom Seton was now waiting in the Claridge bar, was no less familiar to the fragmented social patterns of New York City's 1920s than he was to the geography, the mean hotels, and uncertain loyalties of its West Forties.

Many who knew the brothers were occasionally tempted to doubt the blood relationship. For Seton—at least when looked at from the outside—was the Irish reverse of his Irish brother, compressing at all times his inner tension inside a turtled calm, hiding it from the world in a watching but unspeaking look, in an observable tendency to hold back, to scowl, to be slow to answer. Noise bothered him. In his whole life Seton had never slapped anyone on the back. Pat could not pass acquaintances on the street without doing so.

By the age that Seton had now achieved—thirty—Patrick had already been and gone. Now he was nothing.

Everyone knew this, yet his acceptance year after year on and around Broadway—a neighborhood of rubbery accommodation—was a continuing mystification to old Dermod Farrier, father of these brothers. Dermod was a retired actor of great fame whose code, though primarily nonspecific—(a necessary thing for an actor and not unknown among the Irish), was a code that carried the plausible hope that his difficult goddamn sons, who had never said thank you in their lives, would somehow find steady work. It was a good deal more important in the old man's view that his sons should find work than that they should find their way to God, save democracy, or vote the machine.

Whether it was the secret guilt that these brothers wore over what they owed their father yet planned never to pay, or whether it was their ineradicable fear of life and of living, a remarkable quality of brotherness, strange and strong, existed between Pat and Seton. Seton escaped life by being invisible through being absent. Patrick escaped it in the roar and jingle of a great city by keeping himself continuously awhirl. Both were forever in flight.

Now Patrick bobbed his head down quickly into the green window box of hyacinths that decorated the ledge of the Forty-third Street hotel, and sucked in the pleasant fragrance. At the corner he thumbed a nickel into the tambourine of a Salvation Army lassie—he never passed one of them without giving something because their "God bless you" always soothed and strengthened him.

Sometimes he'd snatch pencils from blind beggars and peddle them for half a block in front of the Astor, wave at the doorman, then return them at once with a dime of his own or anything his antic had attracted. Seton had from time to time seen these carryings-on, had hung back embarrassed, but marveling a little, envying much. Patrick had a most disquieting custom of ducking into the Waldorf-Astoria whenever he and Seton were on their way to see their parents at the Byzantium Hotel on Twenty-eighth Street. He said he liked the rich feeling. He said he often saw someone he knew and often got a drink out of it. Or met women of another type who seldom saw anyone quite like himself but who, about one time out of six, indicated they would be willing to see more if the conditions were less open. He had had a few nights between silk sheets without ever exchanging last names.

It was to Patrick's flash and assurance that women responded. He was dandified and titivating, cravatted, summer-spatted, Kelly-hatted, kerchiefed and gusseted with such carefully ill-concealed ostentation he could be seen from an unusual distance. He was not a fop. And he was not a sauntering boulevardier with a white carnation and a hint

of accent. He was a flamboyant cakewalking Broadway *flâneur* who
smelled like a barbershop and gleamed like a toy train. He was held
together by Kum-Aparts, a snap bow, and a quality of nonchalance
so real it would not have left him were he suddenly informed, while
giving last-minute directions for a public execution, that he was
presiding at his own.

But for all the show, Patrick Farrier was not stupid, and though
mathematically close to useless, he was neither unkind nor uninterest-
ing. He merely happened to be no good.

He was whistling now, trilling softly to himself, wondering about
Seton. He thought he'd better scoot back over to the Claridge and coast
through the bar once. If he was anywhere, he'd be there.

It was beautiful weather, balmy, not hot. You could smell ozone
and you could smell the ocean. This was rare, especially in summer.

Seton hadn't shown up yet. Patrick decided to kill a little time
and try again later. He had a young woman—a girl from Peekskill
who had tried to make the chorus line in *Poor Little Ritz Girl* and
failed to do so—tucked away in his hotel room but she was too drunk
to be useful for several hours.

Still whistling, he stepped lightly into the lobby of the Princess
Theatre. *The Mandarin*, a new play and one not doing well, had
opened there the week before. The reservation window was open
but there were no customers. Pliny Bartholomew was behind the
window. Patrick knew him of course. Patrick knew every New York
theater crew.

"Got a pair I can have, Pliny?"

"Sure, Pat. What night?"

"Any night."

"You'll go to sleep in this show."

"Well, it's a girl I promised. Wants to see this new actress."

"Helina Bruzovna? She's good. What's in it for me, Pat? What's
the duke?"

Pat passed him a hotel key as Pliny tucked two tickets into an
envelope and slid the envelope under the grille.

"She there now?" Pliny asked.

"Sure. Had a few drinks. Asleep now. Ravenous little chipmunk."

"Who shall I tell her I am?"

"She won't ask. She'll think it's still me. Wake her up quiet."

"All right. She in a show?"

"Poor Little Ritz Girl."

"Really?" Pliny leaned toward the bars. "What are you leaving a fellowship like that for?"

"Seton's down from Provincetown. We gotta have supper with the folks."

"He's uptown this time, isn't he? His new play? I mean Seton."

"You bet. He could have made Broadway two years ago. He's got the big stuff, Pliny. He's just stubborn."

Pat slipped the tickets into his jacket pocket and stepped out of the lobby. Pat would do things for others but preferred to do them on a fair-exchange basis.

Now he jogged into the sidewalk's tumult and skimbled through the crowd like a hockey player, dancing, side-stepping, slipping neatly between streetcars, trucks, people, buses, horses, beer wagons, and limousines. In a walk of only three or four blocks in this part of New York he always saw eight or ten people he knew. Each one got a flutter or a flurry or a shoulder clap as he whirled by, and a quick spontaneous smile. Pat had flash and people liked it, the people around here.

Patrick, being older, was worried about his brother. Seton was a day late getting to town, so he'd probably started to drink. It was either that or some goddamn doctor. He never could drink and quit. Or drink and get drunk and quit. His drinking was like his working: both were addictions, pursued with a deadly and excluding fixity, both always ending in collapse.

Though he was a theatrical castaway himself, Pat didn't want this kind of disaster to overtake his brother. Seton had had thirty jobs, quit them all, stuck to writing. It was a steaming frenzy, the way he did it. He'd seen the young man struggle out of a liquor slump and grope his way back to work many too many times to be in doubt about the industry and the integrity that went into his written labors. There was a fanatical diligence about Seton when he was at work, a monastic absorption so enveloping and impenetrable that to try to break in on it was disturbing even to think of. He knew his brother had savagely struck Jill a year before, when she'd come out to his crazy work shack with a tray of sandwiches and a pitcher of milk. He just had not wanted to be interrupted.

This explosion, as he'd heard, had been apologized for in a spill-over of such remorse that Pat often felt his brother must be a little dippy. Later, he knew, it had smoothed out intelligently. Whenever Seton was ready for his lunch—if he planned to work on through the lunch period—he'd hang a towel in the window of the shack which Jill could see from the kitchen. Terry would take the trays out. It was the only work Terry did. Yet Seton had fed and housed this bony stiff for nearly five years.

You had to put up with things if you cared about people. That was the trouble with caring, Patrick felt; and you had to put up with the oddness of people if they cared about their work.

Pat knew his brother was important, far more so than himself; that Seton was standing now in the doorway of fame. But Seton had a way of sassing the wrong people. Or of ignoring them. He could walk right through a city and never know he was surrounded by living faces. Never know and never care. Never even look.

He could refuse honors and invitations, and he did, and very annoying it was to Pat. Right now, the Algonquin Round Table was trying to corral him. Why the hell shouldn't he drop in, thought Pat, just once in a while for a slow meal and some real booze and a chance to improve his stock with the very men who, if they wanted, could lift him in a single season to a place in the American theater that other men had spent thirty or forty years trying to find?

He was a goddamn black Irish bastard was the plain reason, and why should he kid himself about his brother!

He hurried on into the lobby and began poking through its garru-lous fleeting friendliness, hoping he'd catch his brother's face some-where. They could have a good talk and some fun and find some drinks somewhere, or a couple of girls—anything Seton wanted to do would be all right.

The bell captain saw him looking. "He's in the bar waiting for you, Mr. Farrier."

Seton was curled up on a stool at the corner of the Claridge bar, next to the cash register, with a glass of something not identi-fiable before him. He was alone. The bar was kept open partly for

reasons of sentiment and partly, as were bars in all New York
hotels, because managements had not yet converted them to other
uses. Customers, too, brought their own liquor, dumped it in setups, then passed the empties to waiters who threw them out with
the rest of the bar's refuse. Prohibition hadn't stopped anything. It
had just made drinking absurd and troublesome.

Seton had something of his own and had just flooded his highball
glass with a fluid clear as white mule. Regardless of seasons, he always
had a smoldering look. His movements, as he reached for his glass,
drank, then returned the glass to the bar surface, were gracefully slow
and meditative. He was a silent person, dark in his moods when alone,
peevish, even vicious, when crossed in the smallest of whims. Because
Pat sensed the hungering loneliness that was the main mark of his
brother, he seldom permitted his sulks or his explosions or his wild
complaints to affect him.

He was Irish too.

He slipped quickly onto the stool next to Seton and squeezed
his shoulder.

"Everyone's talking about your play, Seece. The talk has spread
all over the city. How are you?"

"Fine." He looked fine too, hard, lean, weather-beaten. He rose
almost formally and shook hands warmly with his brother.

"How's Jill? And the youngster?"

"They're great. Be down soon."

"Good. Mother's expecting them both. The governor keeps asking
about you."

"Well, he'll see enough of me, Lord knows. And me of him, too."

"Well, I hope you don't row."

"*Me!*" His disclaimer was almost reflexive.

"He isn't very well. What are you drinking there?"

"Excuse me, Pat. I'm sorry." He waved at the bartender, who
hurried over. "Bring a setup for my brother." He turned to Pat.
"It's gin. Pretty good. Made in a hell of a hurry yesterday."

He told Pat of the wreck of the schooner *Phoebe* and the happy
discharge of its cargo.

"Try a little straight." He dumped out a jiggerful and Pat snapped
it down.

"Real good."

"Government alcohol. Lucky to get it. Even one barrel."

The setup came. Seton poured in the gin, and Pat, after an exploratory sniff, took down a long draught.

"You want to go see Mother and the old man?"

"No. Let's drink a little bit first. I'd sooner visit with you," said Seton.

"You were supposed to be here yesterday, Seece," Pat said after a little. "Where'd you stop off?"

"New London. Thought I'd have Dr. Cedric—Randall Cedric—take a look at me."

"Are you all right?"

"Well——" Pat saw the look of fear, but if there was anything wrong with his brother, it was not visible. He was brown as a berry-picker and his bright dark eyes were clear and steady.

"The old man got any liquor?"

"He sure has! Gets it by the case. From the Lambs. Lord knows what he pays."

"By the *case!*" Seton marveled. His whole face tightened with interest. "What do you suppose he *does* pay?" But he rushed on, not waiting for an answer. "What kind? What kind of whisky is it?"

"Canadian Club right now. But he doles it out like a prescription. You'll never get much. And a long time between. Moralizin' all through it, cross-checkin' your conduct. Catechizin' your behavior inventory. You'd think he was lookin' you over for a cabinet post instead of you bein' his own son lookin' for a thimbleful of whisky that won't send you to Bellevue or burn holes in your tie."

Suddenly the large room boomed with Pat's laughter and he told Seton of stealing a bottle the day before. He'd given his mother a bunch of daffodils. When she went to the bathroom to put them in water, he'd slipped a bottle into a pile of the old man's suits waiting to be taken to the presser.

" 'I'll send the bellhop when I go,' I told her. And I did. I left as clean as a baby. And I picked the bottle up downstairs. For a dollar. Must've cost the old man twelve."

He laughed lightly, then lightly flicked his brother with his knuckles. "Want to go over to Forty-eighth and hear Zez Confrey?" Seton shook his head but he was glad to be with Pat again, absurd fatal Patrick; Pat, the dancing peacock.

He was an object of disquieting fascination to his younger brother and had been for many years. Though Seton had taken girls in and out of both his marriages—and in between them, too—it had never been nearly so gay or so easy, never so conscience-free, for Seton as for Pat. Pat had a tinsel flourish and a gaudy flair. Debauched women wanted his strength and safety, new girls his glitter. With no doubt about it, he had the moxie.

"Mother wrote Jill you had a show in Allentown," Seton said.

"Yeah. Good show too, but a rough town."

"Did you get paid?"

"Sure. Yard and a half." Seton hated some of Pat's slang. It was too Broadway. He remembered this meant a hundred and fifty dollars.

"What's rough about Allentown?"

"Why, man, you can get the clap just pissing into the wind!"

Seton smiled but doubted the Allentown story. At least he doubted the money. Managers would no longer risk him. They'd discuss him endlessly around the quiet tables of Thum's Billiard Academy, buy him a drink, loan him a dollar (never five), or take him to Dinty Moore's for a meal whenever they might collide. He was companionable, inexhaustible, unembittered, ubiquitous, and lusty. But he was not an employable actor. Not any more.

He tapped the bar top now with his yellow gloves. His eyes, like his brother's, kept roving the big room. Unlike Seton, however, Pat seemed to be hunting for the next bright moment, the next adventure. Seton sat hunched forward like a fugitive. His eyes never swept the room. They poked and darted. If he encountered anyone looking right at him he looked away at once, and could not bear to look back until drink brought him the mercy of composure.

"Where's Jill? And the kid?"

"Jill's sick."

Pat didn't believe it. Jill was always sick when Seton wanted her out of the way.

"Too bad. In that case, let's postpone seeing Mother and the old man, Seece."

Seton looked sideways, silent but relieved. He'd sooner drink, now

that they'd started, but he didn't want to say it straight out, that way.
It would be the sort of thing Pat would say.

"All right with me. I'm not expected anywhere. Not till tomorrow."

"You got any money?"

"No. Eighteen dollars." Pat knew better. Probably had sixty or so.
Seton was tight as an air lock in a cellar pipe.

"Well, tell you what we could do. We could go down to Villepigue's Inn for a shore dinner, then walk over to Coney Island and
see the fireworks. It's Saturday. Might pick up a couple of girls.
There's a waltz marathon. I mean after we've had dinner, not before."

"Take some of this liquor along?"

"Sure. Oh sure. Where's your bag?"

"In the lobby."

"Of this hotel?"

"Yeah. I'm not checked in at the old man's."

"Tell you what. You got any more government alcohol in the
bag?"

"Two bottles."

"Let's have the bell captain get your bag up to my room. We can
both sleep there tonight. I promised to take Mother to church
tomorrow. There's four Masses on Sunday now. You can come down
and join us all for dinner, like as if you just got off the train."

The plan seemed simple and agreeable, even though his brother,
as usual, had no money. However, he had to admit that if his brother
had no money, he himself, as usual, had no plan. He could never
"cook up" anything that was fun. It was always Pat who did that.

The alcohol began to bite him pleasantly now. With the sudden
lifting of the strain that visiting his parents had always been, Seton
felt a pleasurable unexpected buoyancy. And he felt safe with Pat.

On the BMT subway platform at Times Square, Seton started
to step into the first train that came.

"That's Sea Beach," shouted Pat. "We take the Brighton."

Seton hadn't been out this way for five or six years, not since the
last race on the Sheepshead Bay Speedway. Half-remembered stations
began to whirl past after they got to Brooklyn: Church, Beverley
Road, Cortelyou, Newkirk.

Pat was carrying the gin, though Seton couldn't remember giving it to him.

"Hold up the newspaper while I take a pull," Pat said, uncorking the bottle. After he drank he set the bottle between them, then held the paper for his brother.

They became very cheerful and relaxed; began to develop new respect for each other's characters. They began to feel capable and talented. And began to think of each other and where life was taking them. Neither man had the faintest sympathy with the other's notion of success, yet each saw the exact flaw that held the other back. But both were Irish—neither would budge.

At the Sheepshead Bay station they got off and walked down to the street. It was cooler now. To Seton the neighborhood looked new and foreign. He would have had to ask his way. But Pat walked down the street like a resident.

Before long they could hear music, a small orchestra with the sound of a banjo cutting through the other instruments like a saw. It was playing "Swinging Down the Lane." A colored voice took a chorus.

"That's Broadway Jones," Pat informed his brother.

The immense parking space at Villepigue's was choked with cars. Patrons were standing about the porches, waiting for tables. The smell of ocean stood in the air. Seton's nostrils responded to it. He began to feel hungry.

Pat saw the size of the crowd and slowed down, considering how to get in. How to get service would be dealt with later. He never hesitated long. Steering Seton by the elbow, he wove through the cars to the loading platform. This ran down the side of the frame building to a small separate porch that the help used, and a screen door on the porch opened into the service bar.

Inside the service bar waiters' orders barked agreeably, and trays rang. Beyond, in the main dining room there was a happy chinking of table silver. Pat peered through the screen, then pushed open the door, stepped confidently in, and went right up to the bar.

Customers were never served here, even before Prohibition. The bartender, a young fellow in shirt sleeves but no apron, looked up with a scowl of surprise.

"You look like the Sunday School Kid," Pat said at once.

"I *am* the Sunday School Kid," the young man answered evenly, wiping his hands and standing up straight. "But you gentlemen came in the wrong way."

"Couldn't get through the crowd. This is my brother Seton. Seton, this is the Sunday School Kid. He's licked everything in the American Legion. Hundred and forty-six pounds."

The young prize fighter shook hands with Seton, then lighted a cigarette, wondering what they were going to ask for.

"This is the fellow," Pat said admiringly to Seton, "who flattened Mangoneri in the Velodrome last July."

"You see the fight?" asked the bartender.

"I saw it," Pat said quickly. He turned to his brother again. "This kid can stand on a dime and nobody hit him. He can land punches with both feet off the ring. Same as Grebb."

"Grebb's inside," said the bartender, now interested. "He's having ten dozen oysters."

"Must be planning quite a weekend," Pat said, grinning. The bartender laughed. Pat moved to the door leading into the main dining room. "Can you see his table from here?"

"Sure. He's at Mayor Hylan's table. Quite a party."

"I'll say! There's Elsie Janis! Say . . . there's a million of *my own friends* out there! Be right back! How about a drink for my brother?"

Pat strode into the clatter as if mounting a platform. One could believe he had come to call a convention to order. On the way he seemed to be shaking hands everywhere. He leaned over to kiss a couple of women. Here and there he cupped an elbow, clapped a shoulder. His head rocked back with his quick wild laugh, his flash of teeth.

"He knows the show crowd all right, don't he?" the bartender said, peeking in.

"He ought to," Seton said. "He was with Leon Errol's company. Several seasons."

It wasn't true. It just came out that way and seemed right.

"What're you drinkin'?"

"I'd like a little gin please."

The Sunday School Kid set down a bottle, with a cordial bang. "Help yourself. What does he do? Perform?"

"Yeah. He's in *Mary*. At the Knickerbocker." Seton drank and filled the jigger again. The active terrors of the main dining room began to depart, though he would have much preferred to eat right there in the bar. He hated being with others when he ate.

The orchestra played "Everybody Step," then *segued* to a medley that included "Dardanella," "Old-Fashioned Garden," and "Love Nest." People picked up the chorus and a roar of half-drunken singing swept out over the parking lot.

Pat burst back into the bar.

"Come on! I got us a table!"

He grabbed Seton and they made their way through the noisy room to a table in the very center. Here Patrick introduced his brother to a large party, all of whom bobbed their heads in some sort of acknowledgment, but those who didn't stop eating went right on singing. "All swill and chatter," Pat shouted in his brother's ear. Then Pat leaned the other way and joined an old woman with a brass voice in a courageous encounter with "La Vida."

It was not possible to determine who their host or hostess was. A tall man, thin except for his belly, reached under the table and poured liquor into empty water glasses. These were passed about. The young woman on Seton's left picked up a round compact of Colgate's Quelques Fleurs, made a mock-dramatic gesture of leave-taking, and started away.

"Where are you going, Priscilla?" the thin man called.

She came back briefly and brightly and gave them another flourish:

"I'm going to Rector's to make a hit and to hell with the rest!" Then she swept off, her feathers flying, to the ladies' room.

The table roared. Seton didn't understand her joke but appreciated the exit. It had style and authority.

"She hasn't had a show since *The Rainbow Girl*," Pat shouted to him over the noise. "She's one of Lou Tellegen's girls."

Two of the other girls had been in the show *Sinbad*. The tall man with the whisky had produced *Fancy Free*. It wasn't Seton's kind of show crowd but it was certainly lively.

The orchestra played "Till We Meet Again." Everyone sang. Dinner came. Seton began to eat, at once began to feel better.

Waiters clanged and spun, unloaded, pivoted, and disappeared.

A gigantic birthday cake came in, aflame with candles, on a table lugged by two waiters. It went to the mayor's table. There was a burst of cheering and clapping.

"It must be Enright's birthday. Commissioner Enright," Pat hollered to his brother.

Seton had never heard of Commissioner Enright, but from Pat's intonation he realized the commissioner had a fixed part in the New York pattern and that Pat knew what it was.

It was a strength Seton drew from his brother.

Pat knew what and where things were, and how to get them. He knew who everybody was and he knew whether they were somebody or nobody. He knew, if they were currently nobody, how soon and through what vicissitudes they might improve their station. If they were presently on top, Pat knew when they might fall, even what it would likely be to tumble them. He knew how they made their money, how much they had, how long they were likely to keep it, how and where they spent it. He knew more about their love affairs than he did about his own.

Pat never hurt anyone either. But then, neither did he ever put anything in the pool. He was like a large bird that followed the great ships, feeding in the day on jettisoned garbage, resting at night on the after rails to await tomorrow's castings.

Outside, it was quite dark now. The bright loom of Coney Island could be seen, puffing and pinking the sky, out of breath.

"Meet me in the bar. We're all through here," he said earnestly to Seton.

"Through? Why? Where are we going?"

"All these girls are taken. Might as well go over to the island."

"But we got to say good-by. Or chip in. Or something."

Pat just laughed. "Hell, no. Just slip out. They're all too drunk to notice. And they'll never remember. Besides, it'll be a hell of a check when it gets here."

Seton got up uncertainly, then moved furtively away from the table and slunk off to the bar. He didn't like this part of their evening.

The Sunday School Kid greeted him cheerfully, with a deference, as if someone had tipped him off that Pat and Seton were important without telling him in what way. Seton asked for the men's room,

and the bartender directed him to the chauffeurs' room next to the
bar.

When he came out Pat was there.

"Seece," he said easily, "slip this bartender five dollars. He saved
our life here." Seton handed him the money, which the bartender
quickly put out of sight. "We're going on over to the island. Can we
get a drink somehow at Feltman's?"

"Naw. Not a chanct."

"How about something on the way? How about the Beau Rivage?"

"Not a chanct. They were raided last Sat'day."

Pat turned to his brother. "We'll have to wait till we get back to
New York, Seton. I don't get out here much, so I don't know my
way to a drink."

Then he flipped the envelope out and twisted forth the pair of
seats for *The Mandarin*. "Here," he said easily, "this is on me. For
the thrill I got out of your last fight."

"Gee, thanks," said the Sunday School Kid. "Here, take this." He
slid a paper bag over a bottle of gin as if covering a teakettle with a
cozy. "Better go out the back. Same porch you came in. You can get
a Brown & White at the corner of Voorhees. Have a good time."

They drank in the cab on the way over to Coney Island.

"I figured we'd get a couple of hookers from that bartender, but I
never figured on a whole bottle. Here."

Seton paid off the cab.

They walked over to Feltman's. The waltz marathon was in
progress. Interminable renditions of "My Buddy," with only the
trombones audible, rolled about a dance area big as a meadow. They
sat down and ordered ginger ale and began to work on the gin. Pat
got up and circled around after his second drink. Presently he had
two girls at their table.

"No, I don't know how to waltz," Seton said nervously at once,
though no one had said anything.

"I'll take you both," Pat interjected easily. "By turns." And he
was away with one of the girls, bowing to the other as he left.

Seton had half risen. Now he came over to her, smiling, half confident. He held a chair.

"Why don't you sit down in my brother's place?" She was a pretty person, he saw swiftly, with steady eyes. She took a quick look about, then sat down. She did not look to him like a Coney Island pickup, though the girl his brother had taken seemed unafraid of anything, as Pat was.

"Thanks," she said. Then she smiled. "Gee, your brother—is he really your brother?—he doesn't wait for *anything,* does he?" She looked over sideways as the couple went out on the dance floor. "I mean . . . we were just watching. Does he always go around balling-the-jack that way?"

She looked out over the sea of swaying bodies, twirling and swirling and dipping. Half the girls closed their eyes when they passed the judge's booth. Some with coy grace kicked up a heel at the end of a turn, or coquettishly averted their faces, pleading with the world to see their laughter, their gay mouths, their vibrance, their legs, their swiftly passing, never-to-be-seen-again succulence.

It saddened and exhilarated Seton. And his companion stirred him uneasily.

She looked back from the dance floor and directly into Seton's eyes. They held her own a moment. Everyone took a second look at Seton when his own eyes were upon them. They shone, and they held much.

"We just came out to see the fireworks," she said.

"Oh, that's why *we* came," Seton told her, remembering.

"Do you come out often?"

"Well, not me. No. I—I've never been here before."

"You must be out of town then."

"Well, I am, yes. My brother—his home is New York. He's an actor. He's a very talented actor."

"You don't say! You mean—he's in a show?"

"Well, it's closed for the summer. But he's not one of these actors that's always 'between engagements,' if you know what I mean."

"Yes, I know. It's what they say when they can't get work."

"My brother's not that kind. We just left a lot of his friends. At Villepigue's."

"No kid! Gee—I was there once."

"Here. Have a drink. I haven't touched this one."

A waiter passed. "We need two more chairs, waiter. And some more ginger ale. That is, if the lady . . ."

"That would be very nice."

The waiter shuffled off. "It's nice of you," the girl went on, "not trying to be fresh right away. I'm sure my friend appreciates it the same as I do. With your brother, I mean."

Seton said nothing. He watched the dancers, his eye circling the immense floor, hoping to spot his brother. Waltzing was another of those things his brother could do and do with almost miraculous grace. Had he indeed officially entered the waltz contest—he had told the party so at Villepigue's—he might likely have won it. But he took the day's pleasure, or the evening's, as he took his life; as he would no doubt take the end of his life: by improvisation.

Seton thought, sadly, in the blinking quivering false sunset of Feltman's Emporium, and of Henderson's Vaudeville just by, how everything his brother did was so altogether typical of him. What a degrading waste to have so much and fling it away so shabbily.

That was his brother's sin. Not the borrowings, not the bills, not sleeping with women he didn't know, nor eating food he didn't pay for. Not the drinking either.

The sin was richness, richness held in contempt.

Pat had abandoned the law, suddenly and forever, on the very day he'd proved his competence to serve it.

He was still pretty to look at, but he had become a soufflé—a rich, foamy, neat, one-helping soufflé, now sinking.

Seton had a ludicrous flash of fear that if his brother fell asleep under a lamp in a barbershop he'd dry up and turn to powder, leaving the chair empty and the barber screaming.

Seton felt his companion's eyes on him and his mind came back to their table.

"I was looking for my brother," he said, and smiled shyly, not knowing how to get acquainted with her; not knowing how or whether to start.

"You know what you look like, Mister whatever-your-name-is? You look like a poet! In a book or something. Really!"

Her sentences, unexpected, pleased him quickly and strangely soothed him.

A burst of female screaming, in sudden unison, lighted the room like sudden heat, then swept off and away like sounds flung about by a sea storm. It was the roller coaster. The dance floor was adjacent to one of the drops in the wild scenic ride called "Drop the Dips." After the metallic clatter of ascending cars had died away, the girl looked over at her companion and cocked her head.

"You're a million miles from me. Aren't you going to drink anything?" Her question had a cordial matter-of-factness.

"Well, I—I'm a little drunk, I guess," he said quite honestly.

"No kid! Well, I'd never know. You sure don't look drunk. You look like a poet. Honest. I never saw any brothers—so, well, so *different*." Her expression had the oddly straightforward ring of admiration mixed with apology, as if she shouldn't be so personal so soon.

All of a sudden Seton realized she was sweet.

"You look so serious," she said, her eyes still on him.

"Well, I was just thinking—you know how they say, a person does this thing or that thing, and isn't it just typical of him. . . . But *I* was thinking—you know what *I* think? . . . I think that *everything* a person does is typical of that person."

"Gee, well maybe you're right. I never thought. You know, maybe you *are* right. . . . But I . . ."

"But you're not going to accept it. . . ."

"No . . . what I was going to say . . . you can understand a girl saying it. . . . I mean . . . what a strange thought for, you know, *around here!*" She looked at the great swooning room. "How could it ever . . ." She reached for the glass, unable to finish her own thought.

"Occur to me?"

"Well, yes. It would never occur to your brother, would it?"

"To Patrick? No, he quit thinking. A long time ago. It's too bad. He was very good at it."

"You know, you won't believe this but I've never been here before and nobody ever picked me up before. And it isn't at all the way you read about it. I mean in a magazine. Or hear the other girls say." She sipped from her glass, then just setting the glass down she lifted it again and took several quick little swallows. "It's the

way you *look*. I can't get over it. I'm sure your face is going to stay
in my mind. But I guess you hear that a lot. Fellows with dark eyes.
You know . . . fellows that don't talk much and all. You sort of
make *me* talk to *you*. And make me *want* to."

"Do I? I just feel that you're kind. That you're a kind person."

"Oh, do you? Oh, I'm so glad you feel this. Let me read your palm.
I can read palms."

Seton was immediately intrigued and extended his hand.

"No, the other one," she said. "My, you *are* strong. And very tan.
What are you, a life guard or something?"

"No, I'm a writer but I'm outdoors a lot." A pleasurable feeling
ran through him as she lightly bent back his fingers, exposing the
palm. He tingled slightly when, with her nail, she traced the main
lines.

"What's your name?" he said.

"Holly," she said, looking intently into the hand. "Holly North."

"Do you work in New York, Holly? Are you married or anything?"

"I work in a travel agency. It's on Fifth Avenue. 'Far Cathay.'"

"Yes, I've passed it."

"I hope the next time you'll come in."

"Thank you, Holly. I'll remember. What does it say in my palm
about us?"

"About us? Nothing about us. My! Your love line certainly wanders
around. Like Pearl Street. Goodness! And you were very sick. In
your early twenties, I'd say."

"Can you really see that?"

"See it? It's right here."

"You know, that's astonishing. Because it's absolutely true."

"What's astonishing? It's here, I tell you. And you've traveled a
lot, too. *I* know what you are, you're a sailor! I mean a ship's officer
of some sort."

She turned the hand over, then skillfully reached for the other,
drawing the two hands together to compare them.

"You're very strong. Good life line."

She handled and bent and turned his hands—testing their pressure
resistance—with quiet competence. She had a strength of her own
somewhere, from a source he couldn't determine. It wasn't that she

seemed so sure of herself as a palmist as it was that her acceptance of the infallibility of palmistry was so matter-of-fact; as if, to her, it was neither art nor science but a mechanical construct, simple as direct translation of a living language, plain and patent as a blueprint reading.

"You have been married two times," Holly said, a little surprised herself, as if she hadn't seen it in the face but there unmistakably it was revealed in the hand.

Seton tightened up. He hunched up his shoulders in a spasm of surprise and lifted his elbows, his hands sliding back over the table top like small rakes pulled from behind. He was frightened. He dumped his glass full of gin and drank it down, his startled eyes on this slight little travel-agency clerk he'd never seen before. But all he could see in her own eyes was a quiet faraway hurt and a faint embarrassment, an expression she might have taken if he had slapped her with no one looking, or whispered something rank or obscene.

"You plain scare me," he told her honestly.

"I don't mean to. I don't see why. Millions of people have been married twice."

"But nobody *knows* it!" He half rose and shouted at her. "And nobody's *ever* to know!"

"But I'*m* not going to tell. I don't know who they are! It means nothing to *me!*" she said with firm but innocent emphasis. "Neither do you . . . now. I . . . I guess you *are* a little drunk."

"I'm sorry. I'm mighty sorry. Mighty, mighty, mighty sorry. Whole thing is ridiculous of me. Miraculous of you. Ridiculous of me. But I can't say it any other way, Miss—uh—Holly—like getting hit in the head by a pole. Why I've *been* to fortunetellers—lots of times. Professionals. The real thing. Big fees and all. Where you have to telephone first and get an appointment." He drank again, then rose quietly and steadily and walked the two steps to her side, where he bowed soberly, keeping his head low and his voice low, and said close to her ear:

"Madame, please have the generosity to overlook my rudeness. I would like to be your friend. I would like to be able to enjoy the evening with you as a lady and a gentleman and I have not behaved well."

He straightened up then and smiled down at her from his full height. He was very serious. Then he moved back and sat down again and smiled across to her, his deep brown eyes electric with sadness and a bright strange interest. What he was making her feel she could not tell, but she did not want the evening to end.

"They're coming back," Holly said, half relieved, half irritated. She was seldom apologized to, she reflected quickly, and as quickly knew there was seldom reason for apology—given or received—in her life. Not much happened.

"I wish . . . I wish we could see each other," she said. She wished he could have said it, or that if he couldn't, he might have wanted to. "I wish you'd come by the Far Cathay."

"I wish you'd come by the Claridge."

"You mean the hotel?"

He nodded and gave her the room number and it was so sorrowful it just escaped being comical.

Patrick and his companion—Holly's friend—were upon them, Patrick howling and singing something in his partner's ear that had kept her laughing clear over to their table. Seton caught a strain of it. He knew the song, a ribald roaring thing Pat had made good use of for a long time: "Mother loves me but she's got the syph," was the way it began. He had her arm tucked tight under his own and he held one of her slippers in his hand.

"Busted the strap," he said at once, holding it up. The girl sat down—her name was Nancy—and Pat picked up his brother's drink, waving a waiter over at the same time.

"What's the joke?" Seton asked.

"You tell them," Nancy said. "The joke you told me on the floor."

Patrick finished his brother's drink, then hiked up his knee and began untying his shoe. "I'm going to give you my shoelace, Nancy. Only way you can keep your slipper on."

He bent forward to remove the lacing from his own shoe, then firmly grabbed Nancy's leg at the calf, placing her foot in his lap with the familiarity of a cobbler.

"It's about the house dick in Boston," Pat shouted over the noise, his eyes tight, "and his first day on the job. This young house dick is passing rooms on the tenth floor, his morning beat, stopping every so often at closed doors to listen, peeking into open rooms. Just checking. At Room 1022 he stops when he hears a woman say: 'You get on top, Eddy.' " Patrick took both parts of the dialogue, giving a strong falsetto to the woman. " 'No,' he says, '*you* get on top.' Even though this house dick is a vigorous man, this was new to him, so he quick opens the door with a passkey and there they are—husband and wife—jumping up and down on the trunk lid!"

Holly was relieved at the unexpected innocence of the finish. Patrick bound Nancy's slipper to her foot, tying his shoelace across her instep, raised the foot to his lips, turned it over, kissed her ankle, then, with her leg still extended, he reached under her skirt and ran his hand all the way up, then lightly patted the inside of her thigh with three or four friendly little slaps.

"That's my pay, Nancy." He gently set her foot on the floor.

"You!" she exclaimed, twisting away coyly, touching the edges of her large pink hat. Then, "I'm sorry it put us out of the waltz. God, you're a swell dancer, Pat! You're great!"

The waiter lumbered over once more. Pat asked for another round of setups and the check.

Holly saw that Seton had now become quite drunk, that his eyes only occasionally related to the activity and talk at the table. But talk was still gushing out of Patrick. Though purple with the exertions of the dance floor and the drink he'd taken, he was impatient to get more liquor passed about.

He offered to pour for her, but Holly shook her head. Something was beginning to break up now, her instinct told her. She felt no fear, only a quiet disappointment that the younger brother by whom she had become so soon and so unreasonably fascinated, and whose attitude but a moment before had been one of shy and appealing entreaty, was now withdrawing from all sense of her presence, surrendering the table, even the whole evening, to his older brother, a man that Holly could regard only as foppish, loud, and cheap. Gay, surely, for Nancy was enjoying him, but no good.

She guessed that his next joke would be quite different from the sample they had just heard.

"Let's kill this and get over to Steeplechase or Luna. Get a seat for the fireworks," Pat urged.

"All right," Holly said, turning. Then she looked back at Patrick. "I know you're Pat, but I don't even know your brother's name."

"It's Seton," Seton himself answered. "Seton Farrier."

"Let's finish the bottle, Seece. We can't lug it around."

"Can't you just leave it?" Holly asked, a little timidly.

"Sacrilege," Pat shouted, raising his glass, then draining it.

"Sacrilege," echoed Seton, trying to do the same, but Pat blocked his arm playfully.

He rose and held Nancy's chair. Then he fumbled with money, his eye running down the bill. Seton took the girls to the street. Pat counted out money, then, realizing he was quite alone and the waiter not near, tucked two dollars back into his own pocket and rushed away gaily, catching up.

They were immediately lost in the sift and howl of sidewalk traffic and side-show confusion.

Spiraling away before them ran the illuminated tracks of scenic railways. The molten epiphany of Luna Park spluttered and shimmered and shook the night with brightness.

Suddenly right before them, and roped off, was a dead whale lying on a flatcar. It was seventy-five feet long.

An altercation of some sort was taking place. Police were questioning a couple of young men who were planning to exhibit the whale. A protecting screen was being dismantled. The mammoth corpse of the animal lay dead as stone right in front of them, exposed free and awesome to the multitude. People were running. There was no booth, no barker.

Pat crowded right up, excited. In a moment he was himself involved with the altercation, gesturing, jerking his head this way and that, being persuasive to the police about something, talking with great force to the men who had brought the whale.

Then he rushed back to his friends.

"Board of Health! Police killed their permit! Great act! Great! Real sin to give it the hook!"

He was instantly back among the police again and the strange hectic crew that had brought the whale, arguing as if he himself owned a principal piece of the act.

"Its tiny dead eye is looking right at me!" Seton shouted to Holly.

"You know who you look like?" Holly became abnormally alive with her discovery. "You look just like Edgar Allan Poe, only bigger!"

But Seton could only stare at the majesty of the whale, imposing in its death, gigantic, bold, still regal and serene and mighty beyond them all.

The flatcar began to move, inch by inch. When Patrick with one leap was aboard the car, Nancy's face lighted up in a kind of amazed but exulting approval. Holly felt Seton's arm go across her back and she felt the tremble that went through his muscles.

Someone had passed Pat a cane. Sassy little tootlings came out of the air whistle of the donkey engine as it warned the crowd it was going to nudge its way through.

"This greatest of the world's cetaceous monstrossssities, ladeez and gen'lemen," shouted Patrick, leaping about, "this beached leviathan! Never before in the history of public entertainment! Never before in the history of scientific instruction——"

Nancy had taken off her hat and was following the car, her hand actually on the edge of it, to hear what Patrick was saying to the crowd. The whistle kept bleating. Then the sound of police whistles broke in over the rumble of the crowd.

Pat plunged from one end of the car to the other, selling items of interest that were spread over the immensity of this improbable cadaver in a richness of selection that challenged not only his eye but his imagination. He was having an enormous time.

He seemed to have hypnotized himself with his own enthusiasm.

The flatcar shouldered steadily through the crowd and took a diagonal in the tracks that led to the other side of the street and into the confused lattice that was the understructure of the Ferris wheel.

"Why doesn't he jump off!" shouted Holly.

Then she felt Seton's arm grow limp and fall from her.

"*He's going with the whale!*" Seton screamed. He was suddenly and dreadfully sober. He had the look of a man watching devastation.

Nancy waved her pink hat, bewildered by the boldness of her new escort. She tried to go after him but she couldn't reach the flatcar now. A spill of excited people filled in behind it, sifting into the hole like running sand, chasing after, choking the road. They caught one more glimpse of the absurd creaking catafalque when it crept past the arc lights of the Little Tornado. Then it disappeared in the recesses of Coney Island's carnival debris and was gone, its sassy tootlings cut off from hearing as if the car had fallen down a mine shaft.

Seton had turned white.

"Won't he come back?"

But he did not hear the girl. His glance darted up and down the garish bobbing litter of Surf Avenue. The whole region seemed suddenly swollen, suffocating, savage, oriental, and malign. His ears locked themselves against the sounds that beat on them. His nostrils rejected the night's messages. He was in panic at the sudden disappearance of his brother. His arms went out in a quick testing of the air, with the epicritic sense of an animal threatened. Had he been a snake, one would have seen his tongue come out.

In a tense half crouch, leaning forward like a ski jumper at the top of his leap, Seton Farrier hung motionless for a second, then started to run. Then to race.

He left everything behind but his terror. This went with him up the long flights of stairs to the subway tracks. People turned to stare. Those he bumped or jostled swore at him and spun around.

3

BACK IN HIS BROTHER'S HOTEL ROOM, ACROSS FROM the Astor on Broadway and just above the tip of the Times Square island, Seton peered out of the window, sucking in the cool air, trying to steady his mind.

"God! God!" he breathed aloud, looking down. Anyone seeing the face then would have felt the young man was considering a leap into the street below.

Lord knows now, his mind ran, when there'll be word of Patrick again: what day, what city, what situation. Death itself might be in it this time, for the man seemed bent to burn himself out with every escapade.

Seton hadn't seen his brother for nearly a year, but it was obvious now, though Patrick's health seemed good enough, that his occasional periods of gainful work with touring shows had come to a real terminal. There was now nothing left but escapades, all as crazy and impromptu as tonight's. And he'd counted on his brother to ease the tensions that always flared up whenever they got together with their father. These occasions always began well, even jovially, but they always wound up bitterly, sometimes with such Irish screaming their own mother fled from their sight.

Patrick had a way of calming them all. But where was he now? And what kind of inquiry could be made? You couldn't ring up the police and tell them a forty-year-old bachelor had run off on a flatcar with a dead whale!

The long ride back had cleared Seton's head, but his nerves were piercing his skin.

He turned back into the room, unlighted by any of its own bulbs but dancing in a jangle of light from hotels, restaurants, and theaters below. From straight across Times Square an immense display for Adams California Fruit Gum kept flaring and going out, turning the room into a choppy chiaroscuro of quick light and delayed shadow.

He had had just enough liquor to set up a craving for more. He opened his suitcase on his brother's bed and took out one of the quarts he'd brought down from Cape Cod. He mixed the pure grain alcohol with water from the bathroom tap. It made him feel better at once. His eyes watered but his courage lifted and he began to try to make sense out of the present disorder.

Perhaps things were not so awful. He had no positive commitment to his mother and father, no agreed-upon afternoon when he was expected to appear with his wife and child. He'd phone his parents in the morning that although he was in town, he was here alone. He'd already written Jill, on the train the day before. He'd conceal that anything had happened to Patrick—who could show up as unexpectedly as he could vanish. He began thinking of the girl he'd seen earlier that evening—the one he'd paired off with, only because

Patrick had so quickly taken the other. But that much had come out right; he'd liked her better. Her name wouldn't come back to him now. He remembered only that she looked real nice and liked him and that she was a clerk somewhere.

From Broadway closer sounds brought him to the window again, and he leaned on the sill, stuffing a pillow under his elbow so he could rest and reflect in some comfort. He tapped the edge of the glass against his forehead, sipping away at his makeshift powerful drink. Taxi sounds floated up to him, and the clang of the Forty-second Street cross-town trolley, and from time to time the deeper and more civilized sound of limousine bulb horns, chauffeur-driven, no doubt, and Long Island or Westchester borne, with Wealth and Influence and Power in the back and a trim Jap at the wheel. Pierce-Arrow had a bulb horn with a pipe coiled like a cobra, and a cobra's mouth to deliver its warnings. It seemed somehow the most perfect symbol of Position, the most dramatic proof of Arrival, that a man could own. He envied and resented all of it.

As the liquor took hold of his ego and began to shred his mind, a fascination, half curiosity and half disdain, took the place of ordered thought. In his assessments of what he saw spilled out there before him, his inner contempt for Broadway and the commercial theater "uptown," developed a pitying, almost noble condescension. This happened whenever he started to drink. But drunk or sober it was a fixed idea.

Lightnin' was right below, now in its second year, and a most successful melodrama, *The Bat*, next door to it. Theater crowds, as he watched, were beginning to pour out onto the sidewalks. Electric call boards above the marquees were flashing signals to chauffeurs waiting along the curbs, their motors already running.

It was New York's greatest theater season. Though the Armistice was long since signed by the Germans, the tourist traffic had not found its way back to Europe. Hordes of Americans with nothing to do and millions to spend were crowding into theaters usually dark for at least another month.

Over twenty plays had opened in the month of August that very year. Half of them were sprawled out below, the worst of them advertising their excellence quite as brazenly as the mediocre: *Dulcy,*

*Abraham Lincoln, Happy-Go-Lucky, The Famous Mrs. Fair, Smilin'
Through, The Tavern, Déclassée, The Hottentot, Enter Madame,
Ladies' Night, Mary Rose,* this last being the most sickening fraud in
the whole pack, in Seton Farrier's opinion.

Seton hated Barrie's plays altogether but hated Barrie's successes
even more. He hated him with such irrational violence his hands
sweated when he thought of it.

No wonder the theater was in such dismal condition, when the
awfulest kind of acting, the worst writing in the U.S. and Europe
combined, were being unloaded in every house in town by the most
cynical of managements, for the disgusting purpose of making money
and no other purpose whatever.

Drunkenly, insultingly, he stuck out his tongue, a lean and jeering
Quasimodo pouring his unspoken venom from a cheap room in this
commercial mid-town Notre Dame.

When he straightened up finally and walked over to the bottle for
more alcohol, he heard a tapping at the door. Though his senses
were blurred and blunted, he was sure it could not be Patrick. Patrick
would bang and kick, rattle the knob, scream through the keyhole.
Even so, Seton had a sudden hope it would be his brother. Hurt,
maybe, or ill, but back again.

He wrenched the door open.

It was Holly.

Shy, questioning, tentative, very neat, she clung tightly to her little
poise as if it were a new reticule she carried for the first time.

She didn't smile. She just looked at him. Perhaps she was relieved
he was safe. Or that she had found him. He stood with slightly
awkward stoop, the doorknob in one hand, his drink in the other.
Though devoid of natural courtesy, his diffidence in a strange situation had a protective disguising civility that now notified him to
open the door more widely. Holly stepped inside.

"Were you sleeping?" she asked, seeing but ignoring his drink.
"No."

She looked about uneasily. "I mean, your lights are off."

"Oh well. Yes." He set his drink on the bureau. "I don't even
know where the switch is."

"Well, leave them off. It's all right." She smiled quickly. The smile left her voice but stayed in her mouth corners. "You scared me. Running off that way. You scared us both. Nancy's still looking for him. Whatever made him *do* it! Whatever made *you* do it!"

He didn't answer for a moment, then suddenly sat down on the bed. He realized he was almost frantically glad to see her without at all knowing what quality or sense of relief her coming there had brought.

An apology of some sort was forming in his eyes and she saw the mechanical production of it beginning to build in a sentence he seemed unable as yet to deliver.

"I—I guess—I must have been scared. The whale! My God, it was *terrifying!* And then——"

He began to tremble. Holly feared if the man did not at once control himself, he would become hysterical. She picked up his glass from the bureau top and handed it over to him.

"Here, you better have a bit more. You really *are* in a state."

"I mean—then when my brother jumped on that train——" He sprang up in great agitation. "It *was* a train, wasn't it? I mean—didn't we see it together? *Weren't you right there with me?* I didn't make it up, did I?"

"Yes, yes. Please don't worry so about it. Please! You're beginning to frighten *me*. You already *did* frighten me once tonight."

She walked over to the window and looked down into the quivering incandescent basin that Seton himself had been so long staring at. "I never did anything like tonight. I never *met* anyone like you. I never met anyone made me *feel* this way. I—just couldn't get your face out of my memory—I—I just had to know you were—all right."

He was disturbed and touched by this, and deeply flattered. "Well, I'm mighty glad you came by," he said, his voice lifting slightly. Still seated on the bed, he ran his hands over the cool spread and looked across the room, enjoying the dark silhouette of her against the window, the lights dancing behind her head and constantly changing the color of her contours. She seemed a bright benign ghost, keeping him company in a dream that had been shattering once but was now clearing.

Her name went away from him again—something to do with Christmas, he knew—he thought of berry, of mistletoe, wreath, Yule.

"I didn't remember that I'd told you where I was. Or even *who* I was. Not that it's very much. It's my brother—*he's* the one the girls can't leave alone."

He felt very weary and he yawned, locking his jaw to hide it. But her being there was strangely peaceful. He remembered where she worked now—a travel place on Fifth Avenue—the Far Cathay. Must be a hell of a slack office these days, he felt. What would she do in it? Show people booklets of ship's interiors? Diagrams of routes to Shanghai? If they were going to China, it wouldn't be the way they thought when they got there.

Nothing was.

"I have some liquor. It doesn't taste any good but it's safe." His fine head went back slowly and he seemed to enjoy a joke of his own. "Right off the boat, too. More ways than one."

"You mean you got it from a rumrunner?"

"Well, yes. Indeed I do. But not quite that *way*." He rose up slowly and walked over near her, looking past her into the nighttime climax of Broadway's activity. He was right beside her. Without extending her arm she could have touched his shirt. She wanted very much to do this; wanted his touch in return. But he kept looking down.

"It was a schooner," he said, not turning. "She broke up on a bar near my place on the Cape. The barrels just floated up out of her."

He looked back into the room now and asked her what time it was.

"Eleven-thirty, I guess. About."

"Is it Saturday?"

"Yes, it is." Holly came over to him then. "Why don't you get something to eat? Or why don't we get some coffee?"

"Yes. Maybe I should." (She wished he'd said "we.") "But I can't stand it around here. I hate it around here."

"Well . . ."

"Let's go down to a place I know. It isn't pretty. It's just a sort of plain hangout really."

They left the hotel and took a Brown & White cab, a long ride, disturbingly long to Holly and into West Side atmospheres that kept getting worse and more deserted. She realized the cab driver was himself uneasy. He kept half turning his head as if on the point of asking if his fare was sure of the directions given.

They were in a section of New York she had never before seen or imagined. It was open, yet except for the cold glare of scattered street lights, altogether dark. Vans and wagons banged and wobbled over the cobblestone street—hardly a street either, she saw, for everywhere she looked it was wide as a plaza. Though Holly had never been to Europe, down here it looked European. And it looked spooky.

She could smell the river. Unbelievably a locomotive passed them, dinging a bell, backing a string of cars into the cavern of a riverside shed, impudently tenting their whole cab in a blast of steam from her cylinder blocks.

In senseless contrast the smell of fresh fish—not quite a stench—swept through their open taxi, struck them hard and swept on, yielding to the unmistakable pungency of horse urine. She could smell livestock too, and damp straw. The muted gutturals and melancholy cluckings of aroused chickens, the belligerent exploratory snorting of penned-up invisible hogs, floated in and out of her hearing. Men slept on wagon seats, reins looped over their necks. Untended wagons, their shafts empty and erect, waited in the dark like field guns for tomorrow's bugle. From the shuttered eyes of storage sheds, from the open mouths of warehouses, from black heaps of careless spillage on the pier headings, odors strong and muscular and mind-moving came to her. Smells of tar and cargo, of used rope, guttering oil, covered lumber, leaking machinery, harness, cooperages, stale beer, and cement bags accompanied their motion and their silence.

If the neighborhood was disquieting to her, its effect on Seton was quite different. He was relaxed. His voice, very deep and soothing, was pleasantly confiding, his words unhurried, coming forth with affection and interest.

"The cobblestones came as ballast. Ships' ballast. This is West Street. The waterfront." His voice was assured and comforting, but the pictures that came up were strange to her. She'd always felt at home in New York. But this . . . This place, this *man!* "You never see cobblestones down the main drag of a city. Always next to the piers. And always a port city, too. An empty ship is a tender ship. Rides too high in the water. She'll broach to in half a sea. All these stones, worn smooth by the drays and carts and wagons of another American age"—here he waved his hand as if indicating a bed of rare and interesting flowers—"were laid down before 1820." Then he leaned forward slightly, peering at signs and crossings.

"Here we are, driver."

They pulled up at the curb. It was an unmarked saloon on the corner of Fulton Street. Seton paid the driver. Holly saw him look queerly down at her from behind the wheel as he hunched back to put the money into his trousers. She felt a twinge of fear—not her first—when the taxi's gears engaged and the machine pulled away. She felt suddenly as her companion must have, when the whale unnerved him and took his brother away.

But there was no running now, not for her.

She had never been in a saloon. Considering the depopulated look of the street outside, it had a surprising number of men in it. The bartender looked up with a quick calm eye, then smiled widely.

"Hello, Mr. Farrier! We been missin' you! You want a table in the back?"

"Been working, Tommy," he answered, his eye going over the scene with slow pleasure. "Yeah, we'll go in the back, I guess."

Seton put his arm carelessly around Holly's waist and she passed a row of standing men, all of whom had turned to stare.

"I *am* a sort of sailor, you might say," he said to her, leaning down, talking quietly. "Or I was. Been dropping in here for eight or ten years."

In the back there were six tables, only one of them occupied.

"You can get a good drink in here. That was terrible stuff we had earlier." Then he seemed to stumble in his thought. "You know, I don't think you ever *did* tell me what your name was."

"Yes, I told you. It's Holly."

The bartender came out to them. "This is my friend Holly," Seton said easily. "This is Tommy Hennessy, Holly. Old friend." The bartender nodded and turned on a wide-open smile. "Got any Irish whisky tonight?"

"Sure, Jameson's."

"Let's have a couple. Is that all right with you, Holly?"

"Yes, that's all right, I guess. I don't drink much," she said simply, looking up with a smile to the bartender. But he already knew that.

"Yes, ma'am," he said, and went out.

"What does your father do, Holly?" Seton asked. "Do you live with your folks?"

"My father—he works for the Schermerhorns. Summertime he's mostly out at Old Westbury. But we're together the rest of the time."

"You mean Schermerhorn, the old millionaire widow-robber?"

"Well, he's a millionaire, all right. I don't know about the rest."

"What does your father do for him?"

"He's the Schermerhorns' chauffeur."

She told him this with the same disarming candor with which she spoke of the Far Cathay.

" 'I'm a clerk.' 'He's a chauffeur.' You're very honest, Holly. Very honest girl." He patted her hand.

Tommy came in, set down their whisky, and left.

"Why do you say that? How do you know?"

"Not trying to fool anybody."

"Why should I? Are you trying to fool anybody?"

"I'm trying to fool the whole world, and me along with it." He passed her whisky to her, then extended his own jigger to click their glasses together.

"Here's luck, Holly. Luck to us both." The whisky had a smoky fresh-bread flavor and a doughy smell that Holly liked.

"This is nice."

"Of course it is. It's Irish whisky. Have you no Irish in you?"

"A little. I'm a quarter. Mother was half."

"Good for her! She'd have been the pure thing left alone to it, no doubt."

His eyes roved the walls, and her own followed his. He seemed to be taking inventory of remembered stock, ship models, five or six of them on projecting shelves out of reach, and a dozen pictures of ships, eye level, in varying stages of maritime disaster.

Seton could leave her suddenly, be suddenly far away. The physical nearness but the strange spiritual aloofness that was a part of the record of her little experience with him at the table while the other two danced in the marathon; the strength of him, at least the suggestion of strength when he moved; the dearness and the diffidence; the

brooding in the back of the eyes but the incredible obsidian brightness of their lenses when he fixed his regard directly upon her, or
upon anything; the unpredictable alternation between his being close
one moment, remote the next—all this attracted her powerfully and
drew her feelings to the surface, and though these feelings were
tumultuous, they were not confused.

She wanted to love him and to mother him. She wanted to be
needful to him, to feed his hungers, calm his fears, dispel his brood-
ings, lift the darkness he built in the space around himself.

She did not know how many women before her had wanted these
things too.

Women wanted love affairs with him without being able to say it
out loud in the privacy of their own thought. Yet astonishingly few
women saw him for the involuted mechanism he was, and Holly,
though she had the rough sophistication of her class as well as a quick
perception in most of her first guesses, did not see it now or guess it;
did not see he was a man who had to be asked, who waited to be
taken (and who could be) by the women who would go after him;
that he was a man who *was* taken by those who had.

All responded to the masculinity beneath (while speaking to him
and to themselves of the poetic projection he presented to the world),
thus assuring to their primal urges the social safety of a cultivated
overlay. Yet few women went beyond this, baffled by a brusqueness
they did not see as defensive, deceived by an independence that was
not independence at all but a self-isolation bred of fear.

What had he done that he was such a hero here? The war? Something of ships quite obviously. But there was something wrong about
it all. There was just too much man there for a place like this.

The more she dwelt on the incongruity, the more it intrigued her
mind. She had been stunned by the sight of him when the brash
Patrick had tipped and twirled his straw hat and cakewalked up to
them. How many million times had such a thing happened at Coney
Island? What was different here then? One thing: Holly's quick eye
had caught the younger man's embarrassment at the instant of it, and
from that instant the look of him had flooded her imagination and
infused her and stayed in her.

Here by the river, with diminishing reason, the seizure of her mind and thought was more leaping than it had been; stronger than it was when with gathering purpose she had rushed back to the city and run down the empty corridors of his Forty-seventh Street hotel, hunting for his room.

What had she been seeking? And for how long? What had told her, this time only, to pursue?

Why *him*?

More than anything it was to satisfy his thirst, not hers (she thought), and though she was inwardly conscious of the sexual fascination he could hold for her if he sought and wanted her as a woman, she was sure—she told herself she was sure—that her response to his strangeness could be just as strong, just as real, if, upon knowing him more openly, she found he did not need her as a woman at all but only as a vessel of human sympathy, of attentive and affectionate companionship, of response to fun, the kind of fun they'd all been struggling to find when they met.

She knew a little of this kind of fun, its unprepared moments torn from the day or out of the night—as this day was, and this night. She knew the frantic little fragments of excitement, of junkets to parks, Sunday ball games, Bear Mountain excursions, parades—of furtive short-lived love-making that lonesome city dwellers of small means and spotty leisure must accept as the allotted pattern for normal living.

Holly didn't think she was much. She didn't seek much, or expect much. While Seton prowled about, reviewing the prints and chromos and the framed gravures from Sunday supplements of days past she finished her drink.

It was quite late now, she knew, but her uneasiness did not seem to be building up. Surprisingly it was beginning to go away. The whisky? Whatever it was, it was welcome. She didn't have much fun.

When she forced herself to be as calculating as she could, she decided that Seton—whoever he was—was of her own class, or nearly so, economically. (She had noticed his hands, his clothes, his use of money.) And she made a guess at the source of his nervousness, putting up in her mind that he might have been orphaned when halfway through his education. Something had been interrupted somewhere. At least she felt that if not that, something *like* that could explain her present impression of him as a man who was lost; a man whose intensities were not of his making but were riveted there by the circumstances of his life; that his adjustment to these had become so complete, they had now become protective.

He didn't belong in this saloon, yet he was, or had been, well known here. Holly decided he was temporarily separated from his second wife; that he was just returning to an old haunt, a sentimental or runaway visit, innocent anyhow.

She tried to interest herself in guessing what it was that Seton found so absorbing in the old pictures. All ships looked alike to her, like all pictures of hunts and hunt meetings, all baskets of flowers on hotel walls, all Currier and Ives and all Audubons, all boxers and wrestlers, all prints of famous race horses, weddings, graduations, grandparents, views of European capitals, and portraits hung in banks.

But you could walk down a line of a thousand faces, one face after another, she felt, or pass a thousand pictures and pick out the face of Seton.

It was this one fact about him that kept advancing itself before all others: emphatically, irresistibly, Seton Farrier was different; he was unforgettably different. He was a special man, of what sort she could not imagine for he seemed a law unto himself.

The quick look given him by the men in the bar, the frequent covert peeks that were raised to him by the table in the corner, more especially the deference shown by the bartender all accented the special quality he carried, the special notice he earned on sight.

He was accompanied by a definite though unstatable competence. He was tall but a little stooped, and both sat and walked that way. He had a sad look and Holly guessed he'd been offered much, but the spare severity and the frequently forbidding overcast in his manner suggested that of the much offered, little was ever taken. Physically he looked weathered and capable, and though he did not look danger-ous he seemed one who had looked past danger as a man used to it, accustomed to survive it from having met it, from having turned it.

Altogether he had a quiet look, but a look of unused yet available agility and self-account.

She wished she could study the palm once more. There was death in those hands, and not far from him in his private life, a long-running parallel to madness.

With her finger tips she tapped him lightly on the back of his hand, calling him back into her life again. When he turned she smiled.

"Please talk. Please come back. It is dark. I am lonesome."

"Tommy!" he roared. Tommy was instantly among the tables. "This time, Tommy, bring the bottle. How's my credit?"

"You know it never runs out here, Mr. Farrier."

When the bottle appeared Seton leaned back.

"I've been terrible company up to now, I know. I was hoping I'd pick up." He smiled on one side of his face only. She extended the small shot glass and he poured. "I guess I was hoping some of the old gang would show up. Shipmates. Maybe an actor or two, not that actors are fun." He drank then and poured another and drank that too. "You're mighty sweet to come all the way down here, Holly——"

"If you want some money——"

"No."

"You asked Tommy about your credit."

"No, it's still good. It ought to be. Money I've dropped here. Men I've brought. Dump really, isn't it?"

"Not if you like it. The way it makes you feel."

"Yeah."

"You were a sailor. Now you're an actor."

"No. I write. I don't do anything else. I have a hell of a lonely life." He drank again, refilled the jigger. "Will you stay near me?"

"Yes. If you wish. But it's you, not me, who keep going away."

"I'm sorry, Holly. Every time I get in one of these moods—not knowing what is to come right away—I drink. I'm afraid to drink and I'm afraid not to drink. I find consolation. But always—I find despair coming soon after. I keep hoping it won't happen. Keep hoping"—he tossed off the full jigger with a quiet cold pleasure— "this is the way out, the way to peace. But I feel in a trap. Like I've fallen down in a hole and there I am at the bottom with my leg broken and my voice gone and nobody passing. I need something. Something I haven't got. I need you, Holly. Don't go away. Don't leave me. Promise to not go away." He held out his hand toward hers.

There was some shouting in the bar and the outside door banged. It startled Holly but she remained still.

"Paper boy," said Seton, not moving. "Sunday papers. Drink your drink. Want a paper?" She shook her head. "Let's have a bit of a night, Holly. You and me. Forget the world and the misery. The dreary unbearable."

"All right. I think we're pretty well started. Suppose you tell me— since you're a writer—*what* you write."

"Plays. Just plays. Tried poetry. No good. I felt it. But I couldn't put it on a page." He drank again. "Not very often."

"I knew there was something like that in you. I *said* so!"

His face lighted with pleasure. He got up again, went over to the wall and lifted down a ship's model from its shelf and placed it with a strange pride on the table before her. Holly had never seen one before, at least never to look at one with any knowing. It seemed beautifully fitted together.

"Did you make it?" she asked quickly, her eyes running over the exquisite trim, the scored planking of miniature deck, the tiny blocks and grommets.

"No. I sailed on her." He began wiping dust away with a handkerchief, and blowing lightly. His hands seemed to love the places they touched. They trembled with excitement.

"She's the *Great Admiral*," he said, his teeth showing. "Named for Farragut, you know."

Holly didn't know Farragut. She had heard of him but she couldn't remember which war he'd fought or even which side he'd been on but she said nothing, for Seton was embarked now.

He forgot his whisky.

"Eighteen sixty-nine. She was the finest merchant ship afloat. Lost in a southwest gale off the coast of Washington, December 9, 1912, year after I berthed on 'er. All these works were smashed to pieces." His strong hand passed over the rigging as if he were blessing bowed heads. "They cut away her masts to prevent capsizing. Kept taking soundings."

"What would they do that for?"

"See how fast she was going down. How fast she was taking water.

Seventeen inches every ten minutes. She was going down fast. Cold, too, you know. December. The crew huddled here, on top of the after deckhouse. This part right here. A great wave lifted the structure right off the sinking ship." He made the wave with his hands, opening them majestically, and he looked into the ceiling as if he could see the mass of water coming down upon them. It frightened Holly, and strangely exhilarated her.

"Didn't they all die?"

"No. Miraculous. Two days after the wreck, the *Barcore*, Captain MacKenzie, Liverpool, sighted them. I've seen the log. Sailors never use big words. The awfulest calamities they describe in the most sparing way. But Captain MacKenzie was moved. It was in latitude 47, North longitude 128. Daybreak. 'Sighted a mass of wreckage,' he wrote, 'broken lumber and broken spars. Close observation found people clinging to wreckage, in perilous condition——' " He broke off momentarily and looked right at Holly as if she were a listening child. "Sailors are in peril much of the time but they almost never use the word. '—the sea breaking right over them. Exhausted pitiable condition, insane with thirst. Had it not been for the wreckage acting as a breakwater to the crew, they must all have perished.' That's what he wrote, Captain MacKenzie. Five years later, five *years*, the backboard of the *Grand Admiral's* gig—that's this boat here, the captain's longboat"—he touched it with his nail and it rocked lightly in its doll-like davits—"was washed ashore in Hawaii. I found it. And how do you suppose? A Kanaka was using it to patch his hen coop. I bought it. Gold. Sailors were always paid in gold. It's over my fireplace on the Cape. She was the noblest ship ever to sail under canvas. God, look at 'er! Look at the copper on her! All her exterior fastenings, from keel to monkey rail." He drank quietly, then went on.

"I was on the schooner *Gemini*. Grounded at Waikiki. Daylight. Calm water too. Salvagers got her off but she'd pounded. Broken up for firewood. Think of it! No sailor could ever do that—break a ship for the heat in her timbers. Like burning violins to cook a meal over. What a world! God!"

His eyes seemed to dim over with a mist of a sudden hurt. His words began to slur, to slide. His cheeks twitched.

"Ships are better than people. They matter more. I was on some Gawd-awful tubs too, I'll tell you. Cattle going and hides returning. Sulphur, oakum, nitrate, gypsum. Bones, too, once. Fifty-seven days. Worst stench in the world is cattle bones. Dead flesh in their hinges still. God! Worse than the slaver stench. Couldn't wash it away. Stayed on my skin like an open sore."

He picked up the whisky bottle then and poured a full tumbler, looking lovingly through its amber translucence, then sipped, his eyes far away but focused on something fixed in his mind.

"You should see my place!"

"Tell me about your place."

"High dunes, right on the ocean. Like a flying bridge all to myself. I've got two figureheads. One of them's a Mediterranean fruit girl. The other, the Scots Black Watch. Englishmen are better about ships, not better at building or sailing 'em. Better names though. Americans name their ships after their goddamn landlubbing money-grubbing owners, God stiffen them all!"

He swayed a little. Holly realized he was very drunk. She was afraid he wouldn't be able to return the ship's model to its shelf. He finished the tumbler of whisky, holding the empty glass steeply to get the last drops. He set down the glass with an absurdly careful thump, pushed his chair back, gripped the table edges, and rose unsteadily.

"You need any help? With the *Great Admiral?*" she asked, nervously anxious for him and for the treasure of the ship.

"No, no, no. I'll put 'er back. Place of honor. Sooner drop a baby. Sooner drop a newborn nursing little baby."

He could be a priest, she felt. It might be the elevation of the Host. It was ritualistic and slow, and he carried the burden with reverence. The eyes of the people at the other table were as fascinated as her own.

He set the model on its shelf, then rocked back a few steps and did a mock salute. Holly rose up and put both her hands around the biceps of his right arm. She held him tightly, almost lovingly.

"Can't we go now, Seton? I'm getting a little drunk. I'm afraid I am."

"*You're* getting a little drunk? Why you beautiful blue-eyed larrikin! Could you think of a better place for it? Or a better mate to be drunk with? Could you?" He picked her up lightly and set her down. "Sure, we can go. But you can't *leave* me, and you got to do me one favor. *Tiny* favor. Pure as the driven snow!"

"All right, Seton. What is it?" She picked up her small purse from the table.

He grinned foolishly, leaned forward close to her ear, and whispered loudly: "I want you to cut my hair! Ha-ha-ha-ha! Will you do it?" He tweaked her ear then, and winked, as if he had just consummated an innocent conspiracy in a cavern of elves.

Hennessy came then.

"I got him a taxi, miss. I saw him put up the ship. You get him uptown all right?"

"Yes. I guess so. Thank you."

"One on the house, friend Hennessy! One for my friend. One for me. One for thee!"

"Next time, Mr. Farrier. Come soon."

Holly and the bartender gently herded him to the sidewalk. Hennessy held the cab door. Seton made a slow semicircular sweep of his arm, an affectionate gesture that embraced the whole bottom end of Manhattan, then crawled into the cab.

"We're going to Forty-seventh and Broadway," she said. She didn't quite feel like a woman. Seton didn't seem to help anybody *be* anything in particular, not the way Patrick did; didn't prepare or encourage them to feel any particular way.

Now he dozed. At the hotel she shook him lightly and he roused, came docilely forth, came quietly across the street, and stalked through the lobby without stumbling.

The elevator boy looked at him, then quickly to her for the floor number, looked at Seton again, then looked back to his work. It was nothing to him.

Holly steered him gently down the hall to his room. Seton explored his clothing for a key, finally produced it and gave it to her. She unlocked the door, pushed it open, urged him in, snapped on the light, and looked into his face for some kind of answer to her next action. She was not cross, just tired, and she'd be happy to give in to something, provided it were definite, provided it were restful.

"If you're all right, I'll go now."

"You promised me!" he said, suddenly alert and protesting. "Cut my hair! Remember?"

"Yes. . . . But it's half past three in the morning!"

"What the hell of it?" He waved her into the room, and she came. "Here, have a drink," he said. He held up something he'd left on the bureau.

"Not for me. After that wonderful Irish whisky . . ."

He grinned and looked at her drunkenly, nodding agreement.

"Wonderful drink. Bes' there is."

Now he was rummaging in the suitcase. She caught sight of a manual for body development. He swayed and hiccuped and tried to hum something.

Finally he extracted a small bag of green felt. She'd seen one like it years and years before but couldn't remember how or where. Then she realized it was the same kind of bag that young boys carried marbles in. Her brother had had one. Seton began to seem like her brother.

He was opening the bag now with a befuddled patient earnestness. He had a boyish look of keen triumph when he pulled forth its contents.

Unbelievably it was a pair of barber's clippers.

Nothing this man did made any sense.

She began to laugh. She found it hard to stop. Seton smiled, entirely pleased. He stepped into the bathroom and at once came back, tucking a fresh face towel around his neck, and sat down on the corner of the bed with his back to her. She had never cut anyone's hair and thought it a poor time to try. She realized he must be nearly tired out, besides being full of alcohol. She began to massage his head and the back of his neck. Soon the head bobbed, and he slept hard. She turned him over on his side, straightened his legs, took his shoes off, and unbuckled his belt.

She felt very alone and unsatisfied. She had been stood up often enough and misinterpreted too, a few times. She'd been on dates when her escort passed out. With so much bad liquor around and so many of the young men knowing nothing at all of normal drinking; young men who did all the drinking they'd ever done under the strained unnatural conditions of battle or of Paris cafés, or nervous billetings in French farmhouses—one made all sorts of allowances for the young men these days. She'd heard the talk, knew many of the men who'd been through it, all younger than Seton was by five or six years; or ten years. They did better, every one of them, as men, than he did. She'd been in bed with some of them, quite a few of them really. They'd made love to her and perhaps they'd gone away soon after and never been seen since. But they'd made love, real love.

It wasn't quite true she'd never been picked up. But she certainly was no saloon girl either.

What could she ever tell Nancy about tonight!

And what a horrid place they'd been to, she and Seton! What could it mean, his knowing it so well? Maybe he was a rumrunner himself. He had the look, sure enough, tan and lean and a little mysterious. *Quite* mysterious, not just a little. His being a rumrunner made sense. He lived on the coast somewhere, too. And he knew boats of many kinds, knew small boats, and sailors. And he had astonishing strength in his arms. She felt, when he picked her up, he could have tossed her.

She looked at him again. He was quite pale, and though his sleep was deep, there was still the sad look clear across the forehead. She poured out a little of the clear liquor that was in the bottle he'd brought, and tasted it with the tip of her tongue. It was too strong to drink.

She thought she'd go home. What a dumb night! Perhaps some other girl could have made a different evening out of it but Holly couldn't think how. She did think that after the chasing around in Coney Island, after the long subway ride to find him, she might have become a little untidy herself. She went into the bathroom and looked in the mirror.

Well, she was still pretty, she decided, but you sure had to look sharp. And she needed a bath, so much running around. She felt she'd at least earned that much.

In the doorway she peered back at Seton. He hadn't moved. She closed the door quietly, turned on the water in the tub, and began to take off her things. She laid them out neatly, one by one, her panties going up last on the hook on the back of the bathroom door.

She stirred the bath water with her hand, then stepped into the
tub and began to soap herself. The water comforted her feelings and
began to relax the ache in the back of her legs, down the Achilles
tendons, into the arches of her feet. She'd had a good deal of standing
and a good deal of sitting and that was about all that had happened.
She soaped her breasts, looking down at them as she did so. A
pleasurable tingle ran clear down into her abdomen when she passed
the washcloth back and forth over her nipples. Sourly, her mouth
curling slightly in tonight's disappointment, she thought of some
of the men who had lain with her on other nights, and of their
delight were they to come suddenly upon her like this. And an
image of her own delight in being so caught came into her eyes
and tightened them, flickered up the column of her neck and
seemed to be cresting her ears, pulling them slightly up, pointing
them, while the privacy of her thought and the warmth and release
of the water worked on her and seemed to open her thighs, filling
her young body with a concupiscence it would embarrass her to
confess but thrill her to share, if the seeker were only there to take
it.

If, if, if!

She reached forward, pulled the stopper, then lay back against the
cool inclined surface of the tub, rocking very slightly to keep the
water from settling a deposit on her skin. Finally the water all ran
out, sucking lightly down her back and across her bottom, fingering
past her calves, gently tapping last at her heels.

Outside, it was very still. It was four in the morning. There was
no sound at all, no trolleys, no automobiles, no sudden voices, no
whistling. She couldn't even pick up the sound of laughter.

She was quieter now inside herself and she forgave Seton. In a
moment she'd get up, dry herself slowly, dress quietly, and leave.
Would she leave a short note? Her name again? Or forget all this?
Then she heard the first sound. It was Seton turning. Then a silence,
then the bathroom door opened firmly, slowly. She didn't move, even
when he looked at her and came over and knelt down. But she
relaxed. Slowly, she lifted her hand over and touched his head.

4

SEPTEMBER

ARLEIGH BRAYCE KNEW ALL THE WRITERS OF HIS day. And he knew what they were, as artists, better than they did. He was as quick to urge Sinclair Lewis to quit writing for the stage and stick to his novels as he was to remind Booth Tarkington that light thinking paid better than heavy thinking. The Tarkington play, *Poldekin*, had been a recent and a wretched failure.

"A Bolshevist is a bore, Booth. Keep them off the stage."

Now Arleigh was sitting alone in the sunshine, inside the locked gates of Gramercy Park, reading the *Telegraph*. He was a tall shining person with silvery hair and black eyebrows. He sat very straight. On the theater page there was a delightful story by Reinold Wolf—a nostalgic piece, accurate and full of bright remembrance—about Dermod Farrier, about his accidental introduction to the American stage (he'd been yanked from a Canal Street pool hall in Buffalo in the 1850s), his astounding energy, his more astounding success, his eclipse, his gusto, his loyalty, his humor and decline. Then at the end there was this indeterminate question about the Farrier sons: "What will they do? And what are they doing now, with a heritage so splendid?"

Well, that was a good question.

Arleigh was going to produce Seton Farrier's first long play and do it on Broadway and before this experience was over, Arleigh would know somewhat more of the answer. About Patrick he cared little. It was Seton who mattered. Arleigh knew the young playwright was a binge drinker. He'd known many such. There was never anything to be done about it. They had to have their binge—a week, three weeks, six. With Seton, all that Arleigh had to do was to be around—

calm and unnoticing—when Seton had had enough and wanted to go to work again.

Just never mention it.

Arleigh was very good at this. He needed the time anyhow.

As to Patrick, if he were to kill himself it would be a clean way out of a dirty life.

Arleigh was never thanked for any of his guesses, especially if they came true. But he was everywhere respected for them, for a reason Americans everywhere understood: in pursuing his own guesses he made a lot of money. He was a success, a big one.

In comfortable health at sixty-four, he lived without ostentation in a red-brick house at the Twenty-first Street corner of Gramercy. He was the richest producer in America.

He ran his office and his life and his special corner of the theater world as calmly and methodically as he might have run the village library in Old Lyme where he came from.

Without seeking it, he had distinction. Without trying, he kept his friends (though here he had a secret that he kept to himself to the end: "Friends are people you don't see too often").

Dermod Farrier was his best friend and had been for forty years. In fact, it was Arleigh who had gone for the doctor when Seton was born.

Seton hadn't come along as most young men come along. No Farrier had, or would. They were all different, all mulish, and all of them as dangerous as they were brilliant. Seton was the problem now. Arleigh, who was about to undertake its solution, ran over in his mind some of the items that would in a few weeks begin to show themselves. He could look forward to some. Others made him shudder.

One thing was sure: Seton wasn't going to be an easy writer to produce.

There was a quality of kindness that made it possible for Arleigh Brayce to endure the splenetic femaleness of male authors—and most of them were more female than male, theater writers especially —to endure their rudeness and their towering conceits; to pass over their glacial ingratitudes. There was also a less kindly quality in him that enabled him to sit still with all these troubles, outmaneuver them, and convert them all into money.

With these two sides of his mind and instinct—the kind and the icily practical—Arleigh reviewed Seton for many minutes. Seton wasn't going to be easy to produce, not only because his drinking upset production calendars, but because there were certain things you couldn't do "uptown" that Seton had been doing in the theaters around Greenwich Village for six or seven years. And getting away with. The Village crowd had certain leniencies. There was one particularly— not caring whether a play made money—for which Broadway managements had no patience.

Even so, the problem was going to be fascinating. The play already was. It was fascinating because Seton was fascinating, without knowing it, without trying for it. For most of the years he'd known him Arleigh had had no feeling for Seton but contempt. This was all over.

The quick, summary end that Seton had put to all the sprawling inconsequence of his life had amazed Arleigh and won his admiration. The steady flow of hard work, of finished and professional work that had taken the place of Seton's meeching aimlessness seemed to the producer to be more than admirable. There was a miraculous quality here. Seton's unannounced self-burial in the deeps and privacies of his own mind—especially the suddenness of all this—was unlike anything in Arleigh's experience. So indeed was Seton. He was the most remarkable of all three Farrier men.

But down went the scenes, day after day, play after play, the bold and the bony and the bravely new, the brassy and the sad and the seamy, until now, Arleigh realized, it was becoming a matter of years, not seasons.

Seton was a writer who couldn't stop, who could never stop, who wrote because he had to.

He was worth a risk and Arleigh had taken it.

Now his thought turned to what Seton had done in the Village. Surely the Village was the most knockabout of places! There were always some frantic love affairs, informal stranglings, an occasional suicide. The people who really wanted to kill themselves used a gun or jumped, Arleigh noticed. The pill takers and wrist openers always woke up or stopped bleeding and were back again by Saturday, dull as ever. And most of the parties were as pointless and constipated as the people who threw them. They were good only after they were over.

Seton definitely belonged in the Village. Only two summers before, Arleigh had attended a Charles Street party where Seton had been and where an argument had broken out over the killing, in Berlin, of Rosa Luxemburg and Karl Liebknecht while under arrest. An avowed pro-Spartacist, angered at defenses brought forth in favor of German moderates, had crawled into the fireplace and sat with his head up the flue, like a post-season Santa Claus stranded and unfrocked. And there he'd stayed the rest of the evening reaching out from time to time to grab gin or hurl obscenities.

The main trouble with the Village wasn't the people so much as it was their inability to go home. Or to wash every day.

There was consistency about very little but there was one big fact: Seton got his work done and his work was everywhere considered significant whenever his name came into the talk.

Whenever he himself came into the talk—and it was usually only among men, Arleigh noticed—a remarkable thing happened. Seton was not a good talker but a notably poor one. Yet the spectacle of him trying to discharge a thought, trying to time its delivery with his trembling, almost somnambulistic gestures was such an arresting sight—it presented such a struggle, such a desperate hope to communicate, such determination to be heard and comprehended—that he held the floor. He was never interrupted. The give-and-take of most conversations was never present. It was Seton alone, almost as if he also were trying, along with his listeners, to understand what he was saying; and seeming to hesitate over sentence formations not because the thought was unclear but because it was new.

Like any other man who lived detached, he was hard to know and so, by being remote, enhanced the legend about himself by contributing nothing to it.

Perhaps the item contributing most to the legend of Seton Farrier was the strange manner of his comings and his goings. Without knock or bow or the careless tossing aside of a hat he would suddenly be in a room. In his impact upon others there was something preternatural; to many, something metaphysical as well. For a special few he delivered the shock of the revenant beheld, of real and visible metempsychosis;

of one who though he might appear and be seen at a place where others met, would, upon being seen no more, be thought by many to have made a visit that was in the imagination only. To those who saw Seton only a few times, this illusion (and their insistence upon it) was left intact, for Seton never left any marks, never carried messages, and never said anything that was later repeated or—as time swept on—seldom said anything that was even remembered.

He was as hard to bag as smoke. His comings were more like materializations than arrivals, his departures so swift and silent they were spooky. With no clatter of exit, with the stealth of evaporation, the rooms that had just now held his voice and substance, held the glint of his visage and the smolder of his eye—would be seen to contain these no longer. And there was none who could remember when he had gone or through what door or by whom his leave was taken. He did not pass like others, but dissolved into the dark where the leafy envelope of night, sensing another passenger on the lonely journey of transmigration, turned her branches to let him through.

Even before Arleigh quit producing shows in the Village, the paradox of Seton was an established one. Arleigh recalled now that Otto Kahn was anxious to meet the young rebel, perhaps put money behind him. He'd already shored up a couple of creaking theaters south of Sheridan Square. Seton's closest friend, High Casey, very different from Otto Kahn, was a hortatory but defeated fellow who sold string. Casey was a skinny person with a spattered look and the sad, affectionate, deceitful eyes of the cocker spaniel. Arleigh had seen him many times and knew he loved Seton with the unasking devotion of a disciple for his master; he had vague Lake Michigan origins, no address, and several missing teeth.

He was known everywhere as Five-Below. Though he had no connection with the theater, or with anything at all save a nameless twine concern on Thirtieth Street, Five-Below was often at the same bar with Seton, often in his room, and he never missed a rehearsal when one of his shows was building.

In a true sense, these extremes of Otto Kahn and Five-Below were Seton's world. Arleigh saw it as part grubby and part fairyland reverie; a dislocation between the social level his fantasy sought and the company he kept there, and a world of influence quite willing to accept, perhaps subsidize, the artist he so surely was.

Throughout his life, Arleigh noted, Seton had been nervously impressed with great wealth. He identified it with virility and identified virility with infallibility.

In the dives and diners where he ate, pictures of Tommy Hitchcock, now a ten-goaler, held his secret interest, melding and diffusing and dissolving in a slowly passing processional: footman, fountain, horse, whipcord, tack room, foreign holdings, sail, and cellar. Arleigh had pretty good glimpses of Seton's daydreams. He knew the Farriers better than they knew themselves, the immemorial advantage reason holds over caprice.

Sitting on the stone bench in the sunshine, close to the shade of Edwin Booth's statue, Arleigh realized that Seton's work from the very start had shown both range and authority. From the day he'd set down his first scene (and Arleigh had seen it) Seton had never been anything but a dramatist—often awkward but never unsure.

In scene after scene, from the one-act plays to the present three- and four-hour monsters, Seton had jarred and staggered new beholders with the impact of human collision, shaken them with gashing displays, with twisting ironies of the pincered reach of fate; of a fate that caught his actors at the end of all his plays and tweaked off their heads or plucked their hearts out, sending them down to unsoundable despairs, with life broken apart and lost forever, its meanings charred and blown away. And the same despairs, the same ironies, sending his audiences out onto the hot sidewalks, or into the January slush, unable to say anything, unable even to weep.

Just a few blocks from where he sat, down on Irving Place at Seventeenth, Arleigh had heard a sentence two years before that he would never forget. It was uttered by an old woman who had just seen an experimental production of Seton's *Sun Lovers:* "I feel like the inside of my stomach has been scoured with a wire brush."

Arleigh had heard it, had looked right into the woman, had beheld a woman drained, a woman tortured beyond further feeling. This is what happened to them all after Seton got through with them. Seton went for the viscera.

And that is what so powerfully shook the mind of Arleigh.

These were the things he saw and remembered in the sun that day in Gramercy Park: Seton's capacity to shatter, to shrivel, to annihilate. The appearance of this had uncovered a skill close to full growth the day Seton first applied his powers to the unfeeling discipline of a page. This was thrilling. But the fact of the new direction of Seton's mind, the new occupation of his time, this was the most amazing turnaround of energy ever witnessed in the New York theater, or indeed ever heard of on this earth before. And it wasn't a reversal, not quite. What was it? A reversion? Or was it the readjustment of a power already present and now streaking for an objective newly seen?

Seton was an artist. He would be great. He was now and he would be greater still.

Probably the *man* had not changed at all.

Arleigh got up now, folded his paper, patted his pint of scotch. It was his conviction that people never changed. The Farriers never had. Seton would be hell to handle. But he'd be worth it.

He started up Madison. He planned to swap theater gossip with Dermod and give him the news about his son.

Arleigh was a person whose action was controlled more than anything else by a great self-belief. He had made a few mistakes, even a few big ones, but everyone connected with the New York theater had done that. This was a good season, and Arleigh felt safe about it. He had a successful revival of an old musical going at the Vanderbilt. He had two companies touring with a new Western melodrama of Willard Mack's, and a real smash with Tarkington's fine new comedy.

There would be plenty to talk about with Dermod Farrier. They could discuss Helen Hayes, the new star that every producer had just now discovered. People all over the East were beginning to talk about her compelling versatility and though Arleigh made no claim to having found her—this belonged to Lew Fields—it was he who had slipped her into his current hit.

Cutting across Madison Square for the Byzantium, Arleigh began looking forward to the drink. Dermod would, of course, be crotchety. He'd been reported ill but "coming around." No one had seen him at the Players or the Lambs, his main hangouts. Ten years before, he'd quit the theater for good and for all those ten years he'd been cross as a bear with loose teeth. If he hadn't heard in advance about the piece in the *Telegraph*, he'd be delighted to have it.

Nothing revived old actors like fresh publicity.

If Dermod already had seen the story, Arleigh still had the unusual news about Seton. And an unusual proposal to make in regard to it. He was going to try to persuade the old actor to return to the theater in his son's first Broadway effort and to take a principal role. There were suggestions in the play that Seton had picked up and elaborated frictions out of the family atmosphere (there was an ugly indigent father and two warring sons) even though the setting was a farm, something that no Farrier had ever physically beheld. Between the three of them, Arleigh mused, they couldn't get a bean into the ground.

Ahead he saw the Garden Hotel, where Dermod for several years had permitted his son Patrick to spend two weeks at Christmas time. This gesture, ferociously resented by the giver and meanly spent by Patrick, was insisted upon by Molly, Dermod's wife. It was proof of Dermod's "sense of family" and his Christian love.

What a family!

Now Arleigh turned west into Twenty-eighth, the last cross-town street to lose its horsecars. A pity too, for now a trolley banged through, dinging its foot bell in childish impatience at a Wanamaker delivery wagon, impervious to sound.

It was getting to be a real noisy town.

He thought Dermod would be interested to hear how he had found a theater for Seton's play.

Finding a theater these days was more than a real-estate problem. For one thing Arleigh was a Shubert hater and never would, never did, take a show into one of their houses. This cost him money but gave him satisfaction. Arleigh didn't like the way the Shuberts made you do business—neither did Dermod—so he solved this part of the problem by doing no business with them.

Nor did he like the way—nor did Dermod—the Theatre Guild spent its time lugging in odd imports from Europe when there were Americans beginning to show creative strength, young skills worth substantial notice and a strong risk.

Of such Americans, Arleigh Brayce felt Seton Farrier far and away the most deserving.

As he neared the marquee of the Byzantium, Arleigh knew his decision about Seton was right. Like everything else in his life, it was supported by evidence, not by hunch. He'd seen all of Seton's stage-craft that had been produced in Greenwich Village—in the barns and remodeled carriage houses, in the upstairs cul-de-sacs, in the alleys, the cellars, and the side-street oubliettes where make-do zealots and per-spiring tyros flung their starveling productions together with joyous irregularity and noble mismanagement.

They had an odd strength, the Village crowd, and long before they got it, they deserved a good deal more than they were given. And they never did get much. Arleigh knew it, but could never get Dermod to go.

Yet every week or two something real, something haunting, some-thing altogether new, reckless, broke out and ran, carrying the energy and the fine frenzy (and contempt) of small revolution.

For Arleigh, who was a respecter before he was an enthusiast, the excursions downtown had paid off. He felt entitled to some of the scorn with which he viewed many of his colleagues, scorn for their not knowing what was down there by their being too lazy or too preoccupied to go. Writing names they should respect—E. E. Cum-mings, Hatcher Hughes, Philip Moeller, Edmund Wilson, Sherwood Anderson, Gilbert Seldes, Stark Young—were delivering new ideas in new frames.

To Arleigh Brayce it seemed not only silly but unnatural that skills so alive and productive—so potentially profitable to any man whose sole purpose (like Brayce's) was to make money out of the theater— were not even known to exist. The tubby Woollcott got down from time to time. So did the sprawling Broun, but north of the Empire Theatre, Greenwich Village was nothing but a geographical enclave not unlike the republic of Andorra in that everyone knew where it was, none knew why, and no living man had ever been there.

When Arleigh called his old friend Dermod on the house phone in the lobby of the Byzantium, he was told to come up at once. "My blessed wife Molly has gone to the Aquarium!" he shouted. It was apparent at once that Dermod had read the piece about himself for it was already cut out neatly and put to one side, probably for mounting when Molly returned. But the glow of it was inside him and his pleasure in seeing the producer was large and demonstrative.

He set out glasses at once and ran downstairs for a pitcher of ice.

"I've got some Petlochrie scotch," his guest said, putting the bottle on the reading table in the center of the room.

Then Arleigh told Dermod right out what his plans were about producing Seton's play.

"You mean Broadway?"

"Yes, I do. Have you read your son's play?"

Dermod got up then and opened the door a crack to let in a current of air and to have it open for the bellhop.

"No, Arleigh. It sounds wrong . . . but I haven't been offered a copy. Seton never sends anything. Never writes, for the matter of that."

When the ice came, Dermod poured each man a huge drink, then offered soda to Arleigh by holding up an unopened bottle, but Arleigh shook his head. They sat sipping the cold clear whisky in silence a moment.

"Why would your good wife want to go to the Aquarium, I wonder?"

"Why, to see the fish, I suppose," Dermod answered, his eyes mournful.

Both the men laughed at this. They had no advantages to seek of each other, had been friends before the Gay Nineties without ever being professionally involved with each other, and appreciated the slow comfort of time that was passing but not wasting.

"You should go downtown and see what he has there now, Dermod. Truly you should. I am serious."

"I should not and I shan't!" Dermod contradicted sharply. "I can wait till he's famous. So can his mother. You'd think he'd want *her* to see what he's up to. But not him. Never a ticket. Or a telephone call. And not ten letters a year."

"Arleigh," he said, trying to control his severity, "do you know, I do think the whole family is crazy, me among them, with all this misery going on and no reason for it at all? Do you know I've never laid eyes on my own grandson and the boy nearly three years old? Nor seen my lovely daughter-in-law in nearly four? Now it can't be that hard to get out of New England even if you live on a damn crag with no companion but the auk and the foghorn! Is my son afraid of trains? Or is he stone drunk in the cellar the past year? Who knows, who knows? Only God and his missus can say. Or some of the barefoot sea pirates grinning in the snapshots! Where can he find a devil today that is barefoot! But Seton, he can dig up the damnedest!" It was obvious that Dermod had heard no rumor of the present circumstance of either son—that Seton was likely going to stay drunk until his brother showed up again. If Dermod knew nothing of it, so much the better.

"What's the missus like? Seton's wife?"

"Now there's a lovely lady, Arleigh." Dermod crouched forward to touch Arleigh's knee and to pour out a little more of Arleigh's liquor. "And fair, too. Eyes like a child and the color of the corn-flower. How she stands him—how he got her—'tis unknown. But the little boy—my, look at him! There now! It's me all right! I was the same exactly! My! It curls that way by itself!"

There was a shower of pictures, snatched from a bureau top, hurried into his hands, hurried back out of them into the impatient fingers of the grandfather. Dermod transferred them, shuffled them, treasured them, cocked his head, cooed, rushed to the window for better light, groaning and gurgling like a frightened man going under ether.

"It's a good thing the boy's not here," Arleigh said, impressed with the beauty of him. "You'd ruin him."

"A grandfather's duty! The only good thing left in a bad world!"

"Well, maybe. Not the *only* good one, I hope. But I didn't come over to hear you complain about your sons. Or brag about your grandson. I'm just makin' a visit. I'm happy to find you in. And so well."

"If you had my sons a few minutes, you'd complain worse! Have you seen Patrick? Now *there's* a reward from heaven! He's a movin' piece of Purgatory plaguin' me when I least expect it, like a blow-out in a heavy rain ten miles from town. And where the hell is he, the traipsin' flycatcher? His mother's frantic."

"Oh, he'll be back all right," Arleigh answered easily, as if he knew.

"God stiffen him, he'll surely be that! Whores, whisky, and a new hat! That's all there is, he says. Well, it ain't quite. He should mention the water closet for he's half the time in it!"

"Oh, now, Dermod . . ."

"It's the truth. Liquor goes through him like the police were behind! His kidney's a sieve. His liver is carborundum. Was there ever a man with such straight pipes? And so crooked a head! The doctors don't know what's goin' on in 'im. His gizzard, they say, is a kaleidoscope whirlin' with bottle caps. 'Tis unknown what keeps him alive but I wish it would stop soon."

"He's a drinking man but he's got his talents, Dermod. And he goes to church, too, doesn't he?"

"When he isn't too blind to cross the street, he'll sometimes take his mother. But it's God's wonder we don't have lightning every time. Or an eclipse!"

To Arleigh it was both sad and funny—it was always so much the same when he was with his friend. Dermod went through life with the same worries and complaints, rejected and baffled by his sons, grieved anew with every cut and slight, as anxious over their silence as he was upset when they appeared in his doorway. Was there anything, indeed, that could still be saved? A glimmer of affection stood in Dermod's eyes. He looked miserably down into Twenty-eighth Street, across to the church his wife attended, trying to blink back the tears.

But there were too many years of them.

A tower chimed.

"I've just had lunch at the Players, Dermod. You should come oftener."

"That I should," answered the old man, not turning. Arleigh heard him snap out a fresh kerchief, then blow his nose.

What a curse was on the Farriers, he thought: the sad and horrifying suspicion that Molly had for years used the needle; the theatrical end of the old man, a great actor his whole life, and a great spirit, self-ruined now, sunk in a sea of disappointments, smothered in the wasting dreams of days now gone forever.

Was he really ruined? Who said so? Himself?

Though at the moment he seemed broken and solitary and something that could not be reassembled, Dermod Farrier was surely spry, even ageless, and when the fun was in him or the fever of a swift interest, he was as alive as a man of thirty. He was more alive indeed than Seton had ever been, more alive than Patrick when he was still an apple on the tree, before he fell and rotted.

"Dermod, my old friend. I want you to listen now and nothing else. I don't want you to answer. I'll wait for that."

"You sound very ominous, Arleigh. You sound as if you were going to propose a new act! What is it, a Sunday balloon ascension at Hillside?"

Damn the old man! He always knew what you intended. Why did the sons ever feel they could fool him? Because he couldn't handle his money? Well, neither could they.

"Yes, it is, Dermod. It's a balloon ascension of a remarkable kind. And I want you to do it."

"Really now. Maybe we should finish the whisky first."

"Indeed." He poured out a large splash for each of them. "I want you to read your son's play."

"Never," he said instantly, his glass halfway out.

Arleigh went right on as if he had heard nothing. "You are the finest actor since Booth. And it wasn't only Booth who said it. A man could go to his grave in some comfort with a judgment like that, Dermod."

"It is true."

"I've shown the play to Richard Bennett and to Edward Arnold. They want to do it. We had lunch together. Helen MacKellar wants to do it too. So does Louise Closser Hale."

"But you have them working in other shows, right now, haven't you?"

"Some of them. Edward Arnold's doing a great job in *The Storm* at the Broadhurst. Some of the others are in *For the Defense* at the Morosco. I want you to see both of these shows."

"No. It only saddens me."

"Even so. There is a reason."

"What is it?"

"Your son has written the most important play I've read in ten years."

Arleigh saw the father shrink back from this threatened association.

"What has my son's play to do with me?"

"This is his first full-length work. It's a story of tremendous power."

"A tragedy, no doubt."

"Yes, it is."

"You could count on it. He's been gloomy since he was ten."

They drank in silence a moment. Dermod hoped Arleigh was finished yet knew better; knew he hadn't yet heard the main feature. What could it be? That Arleigh wanted him to co-produce? To put up some of the money? What was he *at*?

"How can you get a theater?" he asked, pointing at once to a fundamental and hoping to scatter interest.

"I'm already *in* the Morosco."

"What of it? You going to move *Defense*?"

"No."

"Then I don't see . . ."

"I'm going to do Seton's play as a series of special matinees. And I'm going to amalgamate the casts. Make them work two shows. I'm going to give Seton an uptown tryout that really matters. I'm spending money. Of course, I'm taking chances. But I've done it before. Who hasn't? If it's a failure, at least it's had an honest chance."

"But Seton spits on Broadway. He snarls at everything."

"He wants to make a living in the theater. He'll never do it where he is."

"He'll never thank you either."

"No one has ever thanked me for anything, Dermod. I'm not in business for thanks."

"Have you ever been through a rehearsal with Seton?"

"Of course not. How could I?"

"Or hear about one?"

"Yes. He's very stubborn about his lines."

"Stubborn is a soft word, Arleigh. And the cast, do you think he'll be satisfied you're delivering the best? He'll find them the worst. Seton is a man for whom the best in Barrymore is a bit less than tolerable."

"Well, he's a writer, by God, he is! I don't know anyone who isn't difficult. Everyone interesting is difficult."

"I know all this."

"You don't think of it in the right way."

"Perhaps not. Maybe I can't. What is the right way? Do you know?"

Arleigh reflected a moment before answering, wondering indeed if he did know. It was so easy to rile the Farriers. Yet they'd botched so much that others handled so easily. They could do all the hard things, but the easy ones they couldn't do at all.

"What you mean is, how can I know when I don't have sons of my own. And the truth is I don't know. But I do know that one of your sons is greatly gifted. His gifts, in a way, are as rare as your own. So, I want you to accept your son as the writer he is, not the *person* he is or isn't."

Arleigh set down his whisky glass and looked straight and hard at the watching Dermod. "And I want you to take the role of the father in your son's play." Dermod flinched and began to redden. "There's no sense in this retirement of yours. It's immoral waste. It's unnecessary and dishonest. You'll be dead in two years, Dermod, if you don't get back in the theater. You'll live twenty more if you work."

Dermod began to stroke his ribs with his hands. He stood up nervously and looked out the window again. Outside, the day was full of sun, and the sparrows chattered. His mind raced back to the day sixty-five years before in a bleak pool hall in Buffalo when a perspiring man under a gray derby and behind an unlighted cigar had tapped him hard on the shoulder and offered him work in a traveling show that was leaving that night for Cleveland. And he'd gone. And been a player ever since.

But Dermod shook his head.

"No, Arleigh. I shan't read it. And I know what you're trying to do for me. For us all. But I won't do this. Suppose I was right for it and my son didn't see me so. Or that I wasn't right, and he being my son couldn't say so to his father. It's impossible either way."

Arleigh saw it was useless, for those were the center risks.

"Either of those ways," he said, correcting him, and mildly rebuking. "But Seton isn't going to freeze in one role, the way you did. And to hell with money. Do you know this young man has five new plays? Not one. *Five!*"

He rose, not looking to see what reaction this news might carry.

"I'm going to Atlantic City, Dermod. I wish you'd motor down with Molly."

"Atlantic City?"

"Yes. I have two more of Seton's plays. I'm going down there to read them. And I'm going to get Charlie Westover to direct. He's there now. Give my kindest wishes to your dear wife."

"I will do that, Arleigh, and thank you."

"I remember the night I ran for the doctor. The night Seton was born. Maybe that's why I feel so—so favored." Dermod's eyes dimmed. His own mind went back. Then:

"Have you really got Westover?"

"I really have."

He went out quietly before Dermod could hold the door for him. And Dermod remembered too, the wild October night, the slant of the table lamp, the crying, the morphine.

Then Dermod muttered the number to himself as if there was magic in it, or necromancy: "Five . . . five."

He had the curiously shaken feeling of an event, of the sky opening —the feeling he'd had when he stood on the ground near this very hotel and heard a roar and felt the earth tremble and knew there was a tunnel below him and a train going through it, going through it for the first time. With those short words of Arleigh's about Seton's plays: "Not one. Five," something irreversible had been said. Something irreversible was set in motion.

Band music found its way to his ears, floating among the buildings from Madison Square Garden and bearing with it the pressure of an unutterable regret, the trombones piercing and pricking at his vitals like whittled sticks, sending alarms and signals up the column of his neck, grabbing at his hair roots.

The music was so clear and carrying, it stopped his breathing for a moment. He wanted to fling himself down and sob. He wanted to hurl himself into the street and die quickly, hearing no more, being no more. He was old, old, old, old! Why, why did it all have to be over? When he'd gone so far and striven so hard! Why could there be no peace at the end? No splendid reward, no honor, no transfer of the flame?

He felt shriveled and split open. He bent forward, pressing his elbows into his belly and in this position he rocked oddly. Strange Gaelic words, half pleading, broke forth and mixed with the transporting mightiness of the music. Did anyone care he had ever been great? Would any stand at his stone and, standing there, instruct the young to be silent? Of the millions he had thrilled, was there one, only one, please, who might uncover his head, drop a flower, write a letter, light a candle, buy a prayer?

What a dismal, disowning place—this world, this age, this city!

He heard the ice settle in the pitcher. He went to the closet to get a bottle of his own.

5

JILL, THE DAUGHTER-IN-LAW THAT DERMOD LOVED, was on the beach.

Sean, the grandson he had not yet seen, was sleeping after his lunch. Terry was in Provincetown until Seton should return. It was one o'clock. Jill had put on a yellow bathing suit and a floppy sun hat and walked down the slope to the water's edge.

She'd write Seton here. She'd keep her temper in the letter, tell him where things stood financially, urge him for the tenth time to send some kind of note to Sean, tell him a little bit about the trouble with the damn pump.

Being down here on the beach when the men from the Coast Guard came up with the Farriers' mail—if there was mail that day—would at least keep them from coming up to the house. Often she had trouble getting them to go away. With Seton off in New York, she didn't want them hanging around at all, especially if they decided they were part owners of the alcohol barrel.

She never thought of reporting them and it did not occur to her now, but she felt uneasy at the thought of their coming.

They were mighty in their way too. She knew they'd go into the sea day or night (do it in the blackest January weather), launch boats from right here where she was now sitting, be very cunning at sea, tow back a raft or a ship's boat, snatch things from the wild water, cleverly outwitting death, then joke about the frostbite their exertions brought to their hands and feet. She'd seen one of them die. They were nerveless men, all right, most proficient boat handlers in New England. Crafty, too, when fighting the ocean, but laconic and dangerous ashore.

They were like cowboys in cities. Ashore they got into child's trouble, not man's.

She leaned back against the winch post, wondering what she would write her husband.

She could remember every detail of her first seeing Seton. She'd met the two brothers in New York and at the same time, Seton waiting to intercept Patrick to get a loan of ten dollars and Patrick appearing, hoping for the same. It was the day she had sold her first story. Street and Smith had paid her a hundred dollars. It had appeared much later in a magazine called *Live Girl Stories*. When she'd gone back to New London the eyes of Seton had stayed in her mind. Then a letter and a poem had come to her from him, forwarded by her publishers, the only way (and flattering) he could think to reach her.

No girl could have resisted what came after that. He kept a small naphtha launch two miles up the Thames River. He wrote her, suggesting he come down some Sunday afternoon and pay her a visit. Her father had two mahogany rowing canoes in their little boathouse, and they had a good pier for landings. No one ever used the facility or rowed the boats. It was right at the foot of Connecticut College for Women and right across the river from the submarine base.

When she was not able to explain who Seton was, however, except that his father was a famous man in the theater, Mrs. Scott said no. She was suspicious of Jill's growing competence. Mr. Scott went on painting. He had no suspicions. He was a happy man who lived in his own spirit. He was doing a portrait of Eugene V. Debs, who sat before the open window, shyly watching and listening to this immemorially intimate family fuss.

It was adversely settled. The young man is not to tie up at the Scotts' pier. It is not proper. We don't know him. Surely it is nothing for a nineteen-year-old girl to be doing on Sunday. Going to New York alone to sell stories was already more than enough and this was the kind of thing that came of it.

But every Sunday, Seton came anyhow. And every Sunday, Jill brought a small flat basket of sandwiches and a checkered napkin. Each time she'd hide this in the mailbox on the post at the corner, a safe place on Sunday. And Seton tied his launch right in the middle of the Thames River, fastening its painter to a tidal boom. Then he'd swim to shore—and what a royal romantic look he had! With a book of poetry tied to his head to keep it dry and towing a bottle of wine behind him on a cord, he'd swim strongly, silently in.

That summer, every Sunday, she met him. She got so she could recognize the sound of the naphtha engine over all the other sounds in the river. Just thinking about his coming, about his being only a few hours away, made her heart pound so hard in church, she couldn't sing the hymns. She had to stop and simulate a voice that wasn't there, straining her mouth to make it work. At two o'clock she'd leave the porch for her "Sunday walk," go down the hill and through the broken gate of the old Anselmo School, burned down in 1900 and never rebuilt. She'd walk through the weeds and past the ruined walls to the greenhouse near the water. Here, where he would so soon appear, her heart would start to pound again just as it had earlier in church. Real pain tightened her stomach when she thought of him.

She'd hear him in the water, then hear the dripping and light splashes as he came out, hear his feet on the gravelly beach, the soft thud of them on the bank as he rushed up the rise to the greenhouse. Then he'd be there, furtive, piratical, terrifyingly masculine, gloating, sly. He'd hold her hands, standing off, till his body dried, looking about, crouching to peer suddenly, then rising, finally taking her and holding her. Always he held her a long, long time before he kissed her but holding her tighter and tighter until they seemed locked together as one person.

He'd come even in the rain, but on the wet days they couldn't meet in the greenhouse for it had neither roof nor glass now. It was a shell of ribs. Inside, its tables were tumbled and its tubs split and in the corner was a heap of shard, smooth now with the years' passings. Phoebes that nested on the shelves whirled in and out, objecting. When it rained Jill and Seton went to a little shed where the Anselmo girls had dressed and undressed for swimming. But it was a gloomy place and it had a moldy smell like a cellar.

Mostly the days were soft and bright that summer. They'd lie in the deep grass outside the greenhouse. Jill would spread the napkin, Seton would open the wine. They'd eat the sandwiches she'd brought, and drink the wine, Seton pouring it out carefully into a folding silver cup Jill had been given as a child. They'd pass the cup back and forth, always leaning forward, for it leaked.

Then they'd lie back in the grass and he'd read to her. Later he'd make love to her.

This was the most exquisite memory of him that Jill had.

The war with Germany filled all the newspapers but it seemed far away to them then and not important, especially when they could look right across the Thames into the submarine pens of the naval base and see men lying around, leaning and loafing. When there was no wind you could even hear their voices. The submarines were all lined up side by side as innocent as the fleet of bright red delivery trucks at Ward's Fine Cakes, right next to the base. Anyhow, no matter what happened, they'd never get Seton. He'd had some lung trouble, nothing serious; "Just right," she'd said once to her father. Swimming had been prescribed to keep him strong and his lungs clear, and he'd become the finest swimmer she ever saw.

It was there in the grass, that summer, when she could resist no more, when she gave in to him and to herself too, embarrassed and thrilled at his tumescence, the blinding hot thrill of feeling him, of having her fingers guided to him, the paralyzing thrill of being pierced. Shyly she'd shrunk away from him when it was over, spent altogether in a feeling of long slumber, lost on the shore alone as she watched him enter the water again, peeking through the trees to see, proud of the white glint and the sinuous ripple he made on the way out; held by the sight and wishing so terribly he was taking her with him now wherever he might go, returning slowly to her house in the quiet dignity of procession, in stealthy triumph holding her secret, not knowing how to bear the full week of nothing, nothing but waiting for the next Sunday, nothing but the suffering of her sisters' shrill and shredded talk, the marble front of the town's Episcopal desolation. A great thing had happened—love. How inappropriate now became the bouncy sounds of her young sisters, always eating or howling and their problems no greater than colored pencils or Friday night Castoria, the shrill traffic on the stairs, the scarred banister, while *she*—

There were moments when she was sure her mother knew. It certainly had made a difference when that first story was sold. And it wasn't that her mother had lost something of Jill then, though the levels had changed. It was more as if she and her mother were now the same age. There was an adult, knowing calm.

Jill put on sunglasses and looked far out into the ocean. There was always a ship or two, going down to Boston, going around the tip of the Cape for Plymouth or on up the coast for Portsmouth, or to the ports of Newfoundland or Labrador.

She realized, trying to write him, that she had been worrying a long time about her marriage to Seton, a marriage now nearly six years old. She was quite sure he slept with other women when he went to New York. She was quite sure that Patrick, without wanting to be, was a spoiling influence on her husband. But these were the worries that all women had, she supposed, and to her they were surface worries. Her real ones were deeper.

If they *lived* like other people, Jill felt she could make the marriage work the same as any other marriage was supposed to work. For one thing, most married people had other people around them, near them; friends they saw, acquaintances with common problems. There was exchange, and regularity. There was church, stores to go to, conversations to have and to look forward to having. Invitations. Laughter. When she was a girl in New London people had Sunday-night suppers.

Sex had changed in her marriage too. She wasn't being taken

any longer the way he used to take her those Sundays at the side of the Thames. There was courting then, covert *oeillades*, delighted squeezes, waitings, pleadings, sudden boyish lovable friskiness. Now it was hot or cold without warmth in the intermissions. Now there would be long droughts and sudden downpours. But there was no rhythm to their sex life, no happy warnings, delightful surprises, no leadings up.

She realized for the first time that a passionate man could be a cold man, and she had her first presentiment then that her husband could never *be* a loving man. Perhaps he didn't love his son Sean because he couldn't. Perhaps he couldn't love anything.

Yet often as she sat in this very spot and leaned against this same post, the same form and face of Seton, the same exterior virility, the exact picture of him swimming in from the middle of the Thames, would reproduce itself before her eyes. He'd approach the shore—here at the Cape he always swam stark naked—riding powerfully in on the shifting water, at home in it, never breaking the beat of his stroke, come up out of the sucking foam and stand here, marvelously healthy, somber, his exercise behind him, his troubles before, his mind away.

All the externalization of it was the same here at the Cape as it had been before on the river. So were the beauty of his motion and the lean beauty of his body. Her own, too, she remembered shyly. Oh, with what ravishment his eyes had gone over her those days! His mouth!

But he was apart now. He was all to himself.

The swimming itself had become different, almost ritualized. He'd begun to take a set number of strokes, both crawl and backstroke. He was even keeping a record, a kind of daily chart that included time (he brought a watch to the beach now and wrapped it in a towel), the distance covered, the actual number of strokes taken. And pulse before and after exercise. He kept a chart in the kitchen, changed it each day, studied it, then hung it back on its nail.

Jill could be here with Sean on a thousand mornings or afternoons and neither she nor the boy be seen by Seton, nor spoken to—while he dried and thought and checked his timing and burrowed into a silence you could touch. And these accumulating memories and the almost unvarying sequence of each happening: the long look at the water, the long swim, the long, mute rest—began to set up in her a psychic separation she didn't know how to fight, how to discuss with him, even how to define to herself.

She couldn't discuss it with anyone else either, for she saw no one else, or nearly no one. It made the New York trips that much more precious. In New York, if she could find no answers, she could find human companionship, all of it very cheering and sustaining. It didn't take a lot to lift her up. In New York she'd see the movies, she'd see her husband's family, see her own sisters. All her sisters were fun, they were all "doing things."

She could buy a couple of dresses too, always, of course, with Seton's vague and wearing protest at her ear: "I thought you had something" (why did men say that idiot sentence!), and bring back some things for Sean.

She picked up her pencil.

Dearest Seton,

I can't resist writing you (I would have much preferred to tell you, here on the beach, and sort of casual as if it might be something I was able to manage without trouble whenever I had the time for it!) that Biograph seems to have bought a story I did for one of the pulps nearly two years ago. In fact, when the story was mentioned (the publishers wrote me, not the Biograph people), I could not immediately bring back its plot. You did not read it, not liking my title. Not my title really either, for I took it direct from the old ballad: "Mother Will I Be Pretty?" You may be a man-of-the-world but you don't know a damn thing about women (You know I'm joking!) even though I realize you are destined to be famous! (You know I pray for it, too, dear, don't you?) But I knew women would love the story, and I was right.

But sometimes I think: famous? Famous for what? Him?

Not for the way you take care of things! You've gone off again, leaving me without any clue about our money situation. I don't know the balance (if any) at the bank. And you have either mislaid, or taken with you, the checkbook.

I wish I could take the same comfort that you do here, in

*the distance between ourselves and our creditors. To me it is
quite false, that we don't feel we have to do anything ever—
at least never do it in a hurry—about money we owe to stores
here on the Cape (or that you owe in New York)—just because we are too remote to be got at! It seems altogether
childish that you can actually feel* safe, *and that your credit
will take care of itself somehow, if you can somehow manage
to avoid a face-to-face encounter with the people whose bills
you can't (or won't) pay.*

*My own feeling about this will win neither thanks nor
respect from you, but I want you to know what that feeling
is. In it, you may get some glimpses of what I am too; or what
I like to think of myself as being; of what I would like to see
Sean grow into; of what I think you yourself should have
tried to be—just in terms of the realities—the dull realities if
you wish—of daily living. You have got to stop running away
from these dull daily realities or something is going to snap.
Maybe me. Maybe you. Maybe this marriage. It's already
mauled enough.*

*My own feeling about our being so far away from things
is quite simple: it puts a greater, not a lesser, obligation upon
us to pay up promptly. Only in this way can we quietly show
we are not (and will not) taking advantage. If your own
attitude about bills (that you can go on and on getting
away with everlasting postponements or actually beat people
out of what you owe them); if such became more than a
personal attitude with you and became, instead, a general
practice, this world would stop.*

*I know this sounds unladylike. Let it. There is little that
is ladylike in the stories I am selling and there is good use
for the money they bring, even if it is small and irregular.
(And I know it will all seem absurdly small when your
own ship comes in!) (Don't ever get the notion I am com-
peting with you! I couldn't! You know it, and you know
that I know it. So let us forget that part of it, since it does not
exist.) What does exist is this:* we are in a terrible situation
right now and we have to get through a certain place.

I am going to let you worry about the bills in the stores at Provincetown.

About the magical Delco system (and thank God for it— I'll bet farmers all over America, and farmers' wives, say a prayer every Sunday for the wonders of it and the convenience!), I have paid out a substantial amount, just to be sure we are going to be able to keep it. I paid this out of my own money, not out of yours. (I hate that phrase—"my own money." It isn't mine, it's yours. Or at least Ours.)

But you know you had not been meeting payments on it. Rigging its power to the pump, getting new wiring done, new insulating, that new tank for oil storage—all this is very important! Reason: you didn't have to lug all that water to flush toilets with. I did. (Again, quite unladylike! but not of this lady's doing. Nor am I complaining. I'm just rejoicing that we have some power on the place, some running water.) For things like Sean's bath! To have running water in the kitchen, instead of that weary old hand thing!

A very decent chap from the Navy Base at Portsmouth— now transferred to the C.G. Station here—has made everything "go." The people who sold us this equipment claim you never warned them our place here was hard to reach by truck, and they have been insisting we are "outside free delivery and maintenance territory." I even shouted at Jimmy the Tattoo, much as I dislike him, and he stopped, looked at the engine, tinkered and cussed and wiggled the pet-cocks, spun and the fly-wheel, and got a hell of a bang and a cloud of smoke to come forth but that was all. Also, when he saw the padlock on the door where you had stored the alcohol, he was annoyed as the devil. He didn't quite have the nerve to say anything about it but he sloshed the barrel and it gave up one more pint, which he put in a milk bottle.

(A boy just came down the beach with a pail of squid. I bought enough for supper for 10¢.)

Oh, Seton, my darling, what is happening to us? I won't talk about the way you left us, so suddenly, alone. But it is doing a great damage to me. You have hurt me too much.

When you just walked out and left us flat, you took away a little more of something I thought I would have for you forever. But it is not true. It does not fill up again. Oh, darling, why do you feel close to me only when you are gone from me? Why do you feel near to me only when you are far away? Why do you do these things—you have been doing things just like this ever since we were married—when you know you regret them as soon as they happen? You can't know the feelings you left behind after the wagon disappeared. It's been a long time now, but I still see it. I feel punished and degraded. You can't understand this but you would if you could see the look I get from Terry. He knew we were all to go together. So did those men down the beach. I feel humiliated before them. But I have to look right back at them when they look at me. What do you give me to do this with? I feel very unprotected.

What have you told your mother and father? To hell with me on this one. They are crazy to see Sean and you have known this since he was born. Have you told them again that I am sick? Aren't we all getting tired of this childish lie? If you don't stop using me this way, I am going to clear it up myself.

There, I've been very cross again. Take it or leave it. I do so terribly hope that this time something really splendid happens for you and for the thousands and thousands of hours you have worked alone. And it truly does look like it now, doesn't it, darling? Also, we must be able to put disappointment to one side again, if we have to face another, but with so many things to show, and so many interests seeking you, I know it is going to be a great thing for you. Be sure not to catch cold. Summers are the most dangerous times.

Sean sends you all his love. Please remember to get him a little something. Anything. How about a sailor hat with a ship's name?

All my love, darling, all the love I have for any man is yours always. Jill.

Reflectively she tapped her pencil against her teeth, not trying to anticipate what might be on its way to her from him, but actively seeking a solution to their problem of communicating.

One fact came forth—writing to her husband had become a torturing thing: a gentle letter would cross a harsh one in the mails, and misunderstandings just composed would start again.

Thinking of his susceptibility to colds, she added this short postscript:

Hot milk? (Before bed?)

Part Two

6

IN THE SPACIOUS ROOM HE HAD TAKEN IN ATLANTIC
City's Traymore Hotel, Arleigh shoved an easy chair to his front
window to look out over the same ocean that Jill, three hundred and
fifty miles north, was looking at. In some ways their concerns were
about the same: both were conjectural and dealt with Seton.

The mail had come, and with it a revealing, and to some extent
encouraging, letter from Seton. He needed more advance money.
That was good. In a man who threatened to be difficult, this could
be a control.

Since this was the first letter of consequence from Seton, Arleigh
turned his left shoulder slightly to the brightness of the ocean and
read the pages very carefully a second time. In his exquisite miniscules
Seton had set down the following:

Dear Mr. Brayce,

    *I fear it is not possible for me properly to express my relief
and gratification that you have looked with favor upon some
of my work; upon enough of it, at least, to urge you to want
to see the whole of it and to be willing to proceed right now
with a contract and a production.*

    *For me—for my name to be associated with your own is
also something that gives me real pride. Though you have
known who and what I am for years—(I have a very level
view of my abilities, considering them to be real and, I hope,
expanding)—it is to my mind (if I may be permitted this*

*aside) probably not at all the real "who" or the real "what"
to the person you may currently entertain as the image of
me in your mind.*

*I am aware of your long friendship with my father, whose
capacities still seem to me (in those rare occasions when we
see each other at all) to be intact, while his career, by what
perversity of mind or nature I will never know, seems cut
short, voluntarily ended in fact. I mention my knowledge of
your friendship for a reason: I assume you see me through
his eyes, as well as the eyes of your personal remembrance.*

*I doubt if either estimate is close to the true one. Com-
bining them can only blur the image more. Father has
lumped together his two sons, making us equally deficient
in that quality and degree to which we seem to him—in
today's accounting—to have fallen short of his own accomplishment.*

*I can say quite bluntly that my father brought his own ruin
upon himself. With equal bluntness I can say that my father
is morally unable to realize he has himself accelerated the
ruin of Patrick—most versatile of all the Farriers—a ruin far
sadder than Father's, for the collapse came while the temple
was building. Father's temple tumbled down long after,
and it fell of its own Samsonian vanity.*

*All I wish you to know of me—all you need to know—is
that I work every day, that I permit nothing to interfere.
I badly need a second payment on the play you have bought.
May I have it?*

*Belasco, the self-frocked god of his tinsel synagogues, is
fishing for me. I realize the merit of what I have done is
unrelated to his curiosity. If you are considering other plays
of mine, actively, I will send nothing over to him. I loathe
all he is and does—plays, audiences, quality, integrity or
obligation being no concern of his. He's the nearest thing
to Wagner we've ever had here, and without a tune to his
head. Let me know now.*

*I have brought my father into this letter because, since
you and I are about to work together intensively, I suppose*

*he will, as your friend, from time to time materialize. I
wanted you to know at the beginning how it stood between
us. That is all.*

My sincerest good wishes,
Seton

Arleigh now folded the letter and put it aside. He had read a good
many such from many kinds of authors in his years in the theater.
Most authors, he knew, were not what their reading public thought
they were. And it was good for the authors that this was so. It was
even better for the public, thought Brayce, whose concern for
audiences was somewhat sharper than Belasco's.

That part about Belasco amused him, though Seton had no idea
how funny he'd been.

Arleigh looked out over the ocean. He was not one to putter about,
wondering what to do first. He rose quietly, sat down at the writing
desk, and wrote out a check for another thousand dollars for Seton
Farrier, Author. On the face of the check he also printed in the
words: "Second Advance: *The Rim of Chance.*" It looked impressive and clean and official.

He wrote a short note on the Traymore stationery, telling Seton
of his great hopes for the play, his great belief in it. He asked Seton
to be patient through more weeks of delay. He suggested the sense
of the idea in a beginning series of special matinees. He acknowledged
that this was not ideal but that it would ensure them a fine cast and
a good theater; that, except for infrequency of showings, it was the
most intelligent solution he could bring to that part of a new season.
Then he signed the check and the letter, put them in an envelope,
sealed it, wrote a note to Dermod, and sent both letters to the
Byzantium in New York, in care of Seton's father.

It ought to ensure that at least this one visit to his father would
be happy, picking up a check for that much money. And it wouldn't
even have to be mentioned unless Seton wished to mention it. It
would be money, it *was* money, that Seton had earned. Arleigh was
happy to pay it. He suspected the payments were the largest amount
of money Seton had ever had in any year of playwrighting, and he
was right.

He went out into the bright morning corridor. Fat women were beginning to greet each other in the elevators. They would eat too much, rest too much, spend the day riding in the chairs, get manicured and marcelled and massaged, forage ahead joyously toward the grave, exchanging diagnoses of ailments that would mend by themselves if the management would merely shut down the soda fountain.

Arleigh was a lean person.

Waiting in the hotel lobby he began to feel an impatience to see Charlie Westover. He wanted to talk to him about Seton. Now that Charlie had read the plays—at least Arleigh presumed he had done so by now—he was most anxious to hear if Charlie had decided to take on the direction of the dramatic tragedy Arleigh planned to do first.

He got a little fidgety. If Charlie didn't get here in the next few minutes, all the rolling chairs would be gone.

Anticipating this, Arleigh hurried over to the bell captain's desk, asked to have a numbered chair sent over and held. Since this was against custom, he paid him a dollar to make sure. Then he went back by the cigar stand, snapped open his paper, and sat down.

Charles Westover, usually punctual, had a number of special qualities, the most noteworthy being that he was, so far as Arleigh knew, the only professional theater man in America who was always up and in motion before seven in the morning, irrespective of last night's disasters. Arleigh considered him the most brilliant director in the American theater.

His thoughts turned to Seton again, but he kept his eye out for Charlie, tapping his paper lightly against his kneecap. If Arleigh planned to make money out of Seton's plays—and that he definitely did—there was one large area that was going to need altering. This had to do with what was then coming to be known as public relations. Seton had no instinct for this.

If it were conceded that Seton's contempt for opinion was genuine, it could also be suspected of a shocking unbalance somewhere, just because the contempt was so massive, so all inclusive, so manic. In his mind now, when Arleigh tried to pin down the exact reason why no one really *knew* what Seton thought or planned, he realized suddenly that there were never any quotes in anything that was printed about him—that he had not been interviewed at all.

It wasn't that Seton hated the press. It was just that he refused ever to receive it.

This refusal to talk to newspaper people Arleigh would insist on adjusting. Even if Seton were serious in his flouting of opinion, he would nonetheless be forever at the mercy of opinion. He was now. If producers held a poor opinion of him, they wouldn't produce him. If audiences did, they wouldn't go to his plays.

But Arleigh knew that the more obvious the truth, the more resistance Seton would bring to it.

His play was going to Broadway now not because it fulfilled an author's dream—Seton's contempt for Broadway was genuine—but because Arleigh Brayce was a businessman whose business was the theater.

His thoughts of Seton broke off short. Charlie Westover came whirling into the lobby.

He never wore a hat, summer or winter—didn't own one—and seldom had a coat either. His eyes looked at everything quickly and directly like a puppy in a new barn. He was big and blond and hurrying, always just missing collisions. There was a rosy journalism about him too, as if he approved of most of what he saw and couldn't wait to report it; or perhaps couldn't wait to eat it.

When he saw Arleigh he ran right over to him.

"I'm late! Your fault! Farrier's fault! Been through them all! Couldn't stop! Come on out! Get a chair! Grand morning!"

They were in a chair, moving over the smooth boards, slow, pleasant, inviting of private talk. They stayed near the oceanside rail, away from the Skee ball, the tattooing, and the taffy.

"He's great absolutely! I want to do all three! Sign me now! I'm on fire with him! I mean it. He's *tremendous!*"

Well, it was a nice way to start.

"He's clumsy. Real clumsy. But it doesn't seem to matter somehow. He mislays characters. A lot of his speech is forced, even archaic. His people move around badly too. But God, Arleigh, think of what's at the core! Of every *one* of them, too! What do *you* see there?"

They had the chair stopped and they sat quietly, looking into the bright immensity of the Atlantic.

"A sort of universal immaturity. He's a fear-ridden fellow, all right. I never knew how bad until today. And through his fear and his pity and his sense of hovering hopelessness, he takes you where he wants you to be. And where he wants you to be is right in the middle of the human predicament. What does anything *mean* —what does it really *mean*, he says. He puts it right at us. Lashes us across the face with it."

"That's right, Charles. That's very right."

"I would think, too, that his intellectual weakness is going to turn out as theatrical strength. Theater strength. Give his people playing power. It's that very *immaturity* that will hit audiences right in the belly. *They're* immature. They know it. They won't say it but they know it. We're all scared. We're all confused. We all try. We hope. We seek. We weep at night. We love. At least we try. We get up with a plan and struggle all day with it but something breaks the sticks or flattens the wheels before we can get it running. Deeper and deeper into these confusions Farrier takes us. Our frustrations thicken, our fears harden, our dream breaks up. Pieces of it stay on top for a moment, like those beach balls. But it all gets scattered or goes down or gets taken by some other. I feel *wrung!*"

"Is it too much?"

"For an audience?"

"Yes."

"No." Charles seemed sure of this. "The imma*tur*ity! That's the key, Arleigh! His plays have *victims*. Not heroes who struggle and fail. Nor villains who conspire. Things break out. The gas leaks. You'd think Farrier was a Jew, a brilliant, jog-minded Jew. Like Walter Hasenclever. It's impossible he's a New York Irishman."

"They're much the same, I find."

They were silent a moment. Charlie was Dutch. His real name was Veshoefer. His father was an Amsterdam grocer.

"What will make Farrier a million dollars in three seasons"— Charlie was pinching his eyes as if trying to see into the seasons he spoke of—"is the biggest, fattest, most undetected, unsuspected, one-man epidemic of self-pity ever seen outside an insane asylum. But it's such a masterful mixing of all the age-old miseries of the world, every man and every woman can pick up their own package and bawl and slobber all evening, with catharsis by the double handful, with denial of any possible salvation made fashionable, inevitable, and shocking. And the soul cleansing! My God, he's a naphtha plant! And there's just enough raw talk to bring North Jersey across the Hudson, and enough repetition to carry his points in Boston. But I wouldn't give you two cents for any of his shows in Chicago."

Charles leaned back, poking about for his Old Gold cigarettes. Arleigh could see by the intensity of the expression that he was still in the midst of his thought, so he said nothing.

"You see, Arleigh . . . with your friend Seton . . . he demands one very positive thing from his audience—you got to *not be afraid* to feel and to suffer. You got to go with him. This means you sometimes have to go with absurdity. Sometimes the man is just foolish. And this is going to be hard. And another thing: he says everything forty times. He keeps tossing it around the stage like a conductor who's stuck with a score where the composer gives the same tune to everything from the triangle to the bassoon and he keeps poking his damn stick at everybody in the band. Only it's *me* now."

Here he leaned into the light breeze and lighted his cigarette. "He's not going to say it forty times. We'll have to throw out a lot."

"That's not going to be easy."

"Maybe not." Then he was quickly suspicious. "*Why* not?"

"Well, Seton seems to feel what is written is down for good."

"But, my God, Arleigh, his *Rim of Chance* will take *four hours* to perform!"

"Well, I don't know. I'll help all I can. The trouble with Seton— the trouble we'll have—he thinks people *have* four hours! If they don't, they can stay the hell out."

"There's been shows where people stayed the hell out."

"I've had some," Arleigh said with a little heaviness.

They enjoyed, in the midst of the day's clean brightness, the dark remembrance of their share of play burials; post-mortems, and cineraria in places far from the spacious invigoration of the Atlantic coast. It was invariably a hotel room in a gloomy city. It was invariably eleven in the morning.

The room could be silent, yet hollow, even booming with the un-
voiced sound of faraway jeering. Half the men who showed up after
a play's collapse had less business around a theater than the jungle of
consumptive simians who sprang out of the cracks in the Garden
after a fight and jammed cigars at each other. They were the same
men.

Where the hell did they come from?

They weren't the whole of the problem either. Producers were
pricked with many thorns. There were reviewers with a built-in love
of disaster. They weren't numerous, yet how they loved to ram in
the probe and tampon. How strong they seemed to feel, skinning
the weakness off their tied-up victims! How public-spirited!

Arleigh had learned to be philosophical about all this. Charlie was
still bucking and lashing back at every printed sentence he disagreed
with.

He was a great director but he was no show-off. He was a believer,
an arm waver, bold in all his living. They'd suffered together more
than once—Arleigh and Charlie. They'd had triumphs, too, but every
theatrical occasion, for Charlie, was a brand-new experience. It was
a quest, a crusade, a transfiguration, a battle, or a fall.

Arleigh felt he had been that way himself at that age. Experience
and a capacity for productive contemplation had brought him an
adjustment and a balance. Age had brought wisdom. Though quick
in his protection of any skill, Arleigh was ice cold in his appraisals.
And he did more asking than talking.

"Seton would do better," Charlie offered, the chair in motion
again, "if he had a little humor."

"He has a little."

"No. He just tries. But it's got the clank of scrap iron. His jokes
don't scoot in and scoot out again. He lugs them in by ropes. Like
busted farm machinery. They're cranked up while we're watching.
And left there. There's a lot of cutting to do, Arleigh. And some
rebuilding too."

"Yes."

"The best *play* of the three—not the best piece of drama—is the
sanitarium story. He ought to throw out those horrible sputum cups
and spray the room and the heroine's breath. People with active

tuberculosis can't run around kissing each other. Audiences won't stand for it. They'll rush home just to get X-rayed. They'll be plain horrified. Love affair in a leper colony. Jesus! He ought to turn the whole damn thing into a modern *Romeo and Juliet*. But it comes out right. Very moving. Great hope. Great lift."

"Yes," Arleigh agreed.

Charlie turned and asked abruptly, "Did Seton have t.b. himself?"

"No. But he was threatened. Successful arrestment. But it scared him. He's scared stiff today. Old woman about his health."

"Really? He doesn't look it. Why does he smoke so much if he's scared?"

"Why does he call this the silliest season in Broadway history when it's the greatest?"

"Is he a little crazy?"

"Well"—Arleigh decided to let it roll away—"he has opinions. If you had your pick of the three, Charlie, would you take the one I'm offering you?"

"Of Seton's plays? What a question! Let me think." A strange agitation went through his body. He might be a duck with the weather changing, not knowing which way to fly or where to light.

"Let's get out of this damn chair and walk, Arleigh." He was already out. Then he peered in under the top and grinned. "It's an irresistible morning out here, Arleigh! You should come out and see it. Enjoy it." He reached in. "Come! Use your legs! You're a notorious walker! You know it!"

It was true. Arleigh could outwalk any man in New York except Bernarr McFadden or Charlie Paddock. It kept him young, too. It was the Shuberts and the Seton Farriers who were aging.

"Is Seton Farrier off his binge yet?" Charlie asked suddenly.

"He's coming out of it."

"How long does it take?"

"He can stay drunk for a month."

"How long has it been now?"

"Well, it's *been* a month. Damn near. But he's got a strange idiot sense of responsibility to his brother Pat."

"Is that the brother that won't work?"

"Yes. Besides, nobody knows where he is. He's run away."

"With a woman, I s'pose."

"No, not a woman. A huge embalmed whale."

"You can't embalm a whale."

"Well, I've had very little experience."

"It would take all the juice in the U.S."

"Yes. It would be better to take just a little and embalm Patrick."

"A carnival or something?"

"I think there was a flatcar. But it's going to delay Seton's return."

"Where'd you hear?"

"Down at The Players."

Arleigh paid the chair pusher and they started back toward the hotel, two miles away by now. Then Charlie laughed, bending clear over to the boards he was walking on. "A whale! Jesus Christ! A *whale!*"

Now he bought an Eskimo Pie, offered a stack from the cart to Arleigh, who shook his head, and began chewing happily, waving the stick as he talked, spattering pedestrians. From time to time Charlie would duck into a stall, buy something, send a post card, grab a .22 and empty it at a row of clay pipes, missing them all.

Everything delighted him this morning. Life had jumped the fence and there was no roping it.

But Charlie had a good set of exasperations, too. Arleigh hoped they'd never collide with Seton's.

They swung on up the boardwalk.

"I'd like to do the farm tragedy, if you're really doing it, and *if,* and I *mean* if"—here he stopped to sign his wife's name and address and to put down two dollars. "She's crazy about this salt-water taffy —if you can get Richard Bennett to play the younger son."

"All right. Anything else?"

"You have no theater, have you?"

Arleigh told him of his plan for a series of special matinees.

"Well, maybe. What does it give you?"

"Richard Bennett, for one thing. And two or three others from Pace's melodrama, Pleiades Hooker, Beryl Cutting, Aspasia Roundhill Hale, Adrienne Morrison. And I'm tapping the cast of *The Storm,* too. Edward Arnold wants to play the older son."

"That's great. Great. *Real* contrast! Real theater! Who you thinking of for the twitchy woman that makes all the trouble?"

"I've sent the play to Jennifer Bigelow."

"You could do worse. She's gifted. She's a comer. There's quite a few coming along now."

They passed the marquee of the gaudy Bijou. "Betty Compson and Neal Burns, HER FRIEND, THE CHAUFFEUR. And LOU TEL-LEGEN, in person, in a DARING DAZZLING NAUGHTY NEW SKETCH."

"If you don't get Jennifer Bigelow?" Charlie asked.

"I think I'll get her."

"You've paid a lot of attention to Helen Hayes."

"So has everybody."

"There's Bankhead. Tallulah Bankhead. A lot of stuff comes in when she comes on."

"She's not for Seton. Too city. Too sophisticated. The woman in *Rim of Chance* is too complex, too variable. She's Lilith, primal. Destructively notional. Unsatisfiable. Bankhead is too feline for any of that. Bankhead will always have to play women that are contemporary to her own time. She's present. Modern. Today. She'll be that in thirty years, whatever's going on then. And Helen Hayes—she's no good for this either. Too happy. Too cheerful, too loving, too perceptive. Seton's woman"—and he went back into his mind trying to compress his thought—"she's a devouring primitive."

The phrase stuck there like a yellow tile in a brick wall.

Westover re-examined the image of the woman. He always paid sharp attention when Arleigh talked about the fugitive problem of acting and of actors, for the man had the most sensitive casting skill of any producer Broadway ever had. His colleagues all admitted this. Most of them, in fact, before their own rehearsal plans were set, had a habit of calling him or arranging to lunch with him, in order to get his opinion of their judgments. It had become a Broadway superstition ("Does Arleigh think she's right?") and Arleigh would always take the time out to say what he thought, if he felt the person worth it.

Arleigh spoke again. "All Seton's women are devouring primitives, Charlie. Haven't you noticed that?"

"Devouring? You mean willfully destructive? What do they eat?"

"They eat their men. Bite out their insides. They unsex them. They suck their blood. All his women are extinguishers of the living fires of the spirit."

Irrelevantly he wondered why Charlie had not mentioned Tanager Bolt. Arleigh had been there when the affair began. Charlie's love affair with New York's most beautiful woman—a lady of more adhesiveness than principle, in Arleigh's view—had salted the tables and buzzed up the chit-chat of many thousands during the previous three years. Perhaps it had cooled off. Or perhaps Charlie had escaped. (Arleigh always felt this way when love affairs came to an end. He'd had four wives.)

He decided not to ask about Tanager, though any time her name came up a new excitement came into the talk. Instead, he smiled urbanely at Charlie, and shook his hand. Their talk was about over. There would be nothing but work from here on, and the battle to control temper.

"Thank you, Charlie. Very much. Don't be proud of it yet. You've never had anything like Seton. It'll be more difficult than exciting, I'm afraid. He'll take the fun out of your work. He's bitter and he's mean and he's a weeper."

"What the hell are you doing it for, then? You got more shows than you can handle anyhow."

Arleigh glanced up and down the endless boardwalk. His eyes were steady, his voice matter-of-fact.

"It's time this happened to him. It's more that I want to see it done than that I want to be the one to do it."

He smiled quickly, his hair blowing in the soft air. "Read his things again. Have you seen *The Storm* yet?"

"No," Charlie said.

"Go see it. Then think over the people I've suggested. Start fitting them into your own mind, if they'll go there. Throw them out if they resist you. Call me at The Players day after tomorrow. At one."

7

THE MEN WHO OWNED THE WHALE WERE CALLED Cleat and Boomer. Patrick saw at once that both the men, young and industrious and full of good ideas, very much believed in their whale. Far from being defeated by their Coney Island experience, they were already planning to clean up in what certainly appeared to be a professionally thought-out series of one- and two-day stands in the string of rich little resort towns on the Jersey shore: Deal, Allenhurst, Asbury Park, Ocean Grove, and Avon by the Sea, all in a neat line close together and full of people with nothing to do. From there, Cleat, who paid the bills, was now thinking of jumping inland to pick up the summer crowds in Mount Holly, Toms River, Lakehurst and Barnegat, using the little Tuckerton system wherever the Jersey Central couldn't take them.

Cleat didn't seem like a carnival type to Patrick. His speech was all wrong. For one thing it was grammatical. And he had a real good suit. But he seemed sure of his mission, and the railroad had not only taken his money but had expedited the transfer of the whale on its flatcar clear across New York's lower bay to the classification yard at Perth Amboy, a distance of thirty-three miles.

They'd been shoved across by a big tug, with a bargeload of freight cars on each side, arriving at the docks as the sun came up.

There they were hooked into a string, mostly of empties, going to Mays Landing to pick up melons. The speed of the coupling up and the unusual attention of the yard crew were unnatural, or so it appeared to Patrick. Then a chance remark told him why the crew hurried so: they were all afraid that animal would start to stink as soon as the sun got strong.

Yet Cleat had insisted the whale had been embalmed the very day it died.

In motion now, rattling down the fields behind Sandy Hook, Patrick began to consider how he might run this present project into a chisel that would pay him a little money. The men were naïve. Cleat seemed well financed. His mother owned a large cemetery in Nashville, Tennessee, and sent him checks as he needed them. She had been doing this since his graduation from Vanderbilt University in 1901 so he could "get experience."

He had had a good many experiences. But he did not know how to put them together. It was in this area Pat thought he could be useful. As the train clattered happily through the sweet air, Patrick learned that Cleat had been a member of a bobsled team in Zurich, that he was a great attender of games of all sorts, that he had bought an orange grove in Fuerteventura in the Canary Islands which had failed commercially but where he had nonetheless learned to play the guitar and had married. His wife and children were there now, and Cleat's mother sent money to them also. Everything had been pleasant and unsuccessful.

Boomer turned out to be an Italian who had owned a boat Cleat had purchased earlier that year when he wanted to visit the Italian islands off the Yugoslav coast.

Boomer spoke no English but was a quick pointer. And he had such intensity of eye and such simian flexibility of face that he could convey almost any idea, sometimes with many intervening subtleties. From time to time Cleat would translate a little. Patrick realized they were a pair of amiable homosexuals, that such experiences were not part of Boomer's primary nature, and that the man, besides being very strong, could be violent.

They kept hitting pretty little towns that had no people in them, towns Patrick had never heard of, Parlin, Old Bridge, Englishtown, Tinton Falls. Outside of Shrewsbury the train stopped. The men jumped off to look around. Patrick realized his clothes were getting dirty and rumpled. A switchman told them they were breaking the train to pick up some more cars. They'd be there till noon.

A few automobiles passed on the main road parallel to the tracks. It was still early. Next to a general store, not yet opened, there was a shack with a sign "Job Printing" and a man working inside. Patrick thought they could make the whale seem more commercial if he were to get some business cards printed. He suggested this to Cleat and asked for twenty dollars. He promised to return it all if the job could not be done.

Patrick strolled over and went in. It was a tiny place with one hand press. The owner was setting type, working near a window. He was in overalls.

His name, Higginbottom, was on the door.

"Good morning, Mr. Higginbottom."

"Morning," he answered, his smile ready but not yet showing.

"We're going to sell shares in that whale. Not the whale herself, but the ambergris in her. Atlantic City. We got 'er on a special train outside. Could you print me up some cards? Some business cards?"

Then Pat's quick eye saw something far more convincing: a print-up of bonds of ten-dollar denomination, on yellow-gold paper. They had an imposing cheap look like circus promotions.

"The church ordered them. It was a raffle. But they never come for them."

"Could you print a heading in that empty rectangle?"

"Sure. Why not? They're not real, o' course."

"Well, how much?"

"Oh——" Higginbottom took a quick look. "Nine dollars a hundred?"

"Okay. Call it 'Consolidated Ambergris.'" He wrote out "Ambergris." The printer dropped type in a large stick, tied it, set it in a frame, packed it with the odd-shaped blocks of furniture, pulled a proof, recentered, then methodically began to pedal.

When he was done he wrapped the stocks in a piece of linen.

At the train some children had drifted over from the town and were grouped near the flatcar in relaxed postures of openmouthed gravity. Boomer came out of one of the truck gardens with a zinnia sticking out of his hat. The Italians who farmed this part of the county had sold him two bottles of liquor. He passed a bottle to Patrick, who took a pull and handed the bottle back with a quick hard Irish smile. Cleat was seated on a box at the forward end of the flatcar, watching them. Patrick realized he was sizing him up. He opened the package and gave him a quick peek. Cleat was impressed.

"We're legitimate now. We can sell stock." Then he winked. "If we don't stay long in one place."

"How much?"

Pat was ready for the question. "Fifteen." He handed over five and kept six. The only thing that worried Pat now was the condition of his clothes.

The train jerked without warning. A light tug on its whistle cord produced a moaning sound. They were moving.

The Guinea-red was no good. It wasn't doing anything. Patrick felt uneasy. His sense of identity broke down whenever he got beyond city limits. Insignificant symbols of city living, like gum boxes or penny scales in the empty depots they passed, brought him faint breaths of reassurance, but this left him each time a station or hamlet fell behind.

He teetered along the edge of the car, leaning into the great carcass, and took another drink from Boomer's bottle. Wherever they wound up for their next stop, he hoped they'd have no trouble finding liquor.

Maybe Atlantic City would be next. Patrick never thought of his own drinking beyond the coming need for the next one; beyond the ingenuity or luck that would bring it in. But he thought of Seton often enough, and of what drink and drinking did to him; thought of it as a problem to Seton as a man, what it did to his work.

Dangling his legs over the edge of the car, leaning back against the tail of the whale and looking at the endless meaninglessness of New Jersey he thought of his brother's fearsome industry, of the meanings and the honors, of the money too, that could emerge from this. The thought was both bitter and exalting to Pat. In some ways the brothers were not unlike, yet Pat knew it was in work alone that their main difference lay; knew he had perversely, even cruelly, wasted his life and substance and all his gifts from the exact instant he had walked off the Fordham campus with a Jesuit education behind him and nothing on his mind, not a thing, but the show girls on Forty-fourth Street.

He drank from the bottle again. He could have been something too. Once, in a twitch of shame and a sudden impulse to win her regard, he'd confessed the whole sorry thing to Jill.

Yes, without drink he could have been something too. Married even. Had a home. Pat had never been in a private home. He'd been in a few apartments but not once in his whole life had he ever been in a private home. Like many men who knew her, he had always been in love with Pauline Frederick; and there had been that early autumn, with him about, sober for once and the actress hospitable to his conversations while she waited for a show to ready— Then he'd gone on another one.

He'd even dated Jeanne Eagels, the only full season he'd really ever had. Oh well. It was silly to think of it now.

Yet if Seton failed, as he himself had so enormously done, that would be tragedy everywhere. If liquor caught him. He kept thinking back over their little toot around Villepigue's and Coney Island. Surely Seton, while drinking, was different from most of the rest of the Irish. Not all, but most. If most of them wound up drunk, and surely they did that, or wound up fighting, and surely they did that too, they'd had their fun on the way to it anyhow. Good fun. They'd had their moments, not quite so rich nor strenuous as Pat's were (he felt), but always somewhere along the way and before final collapse or explosion or police van, always before anyone got marked up, there'd been some roaring fun all right. Songs, too, and wild noisy stories. The bang and the sprawl and the happy what-the-hell.

But Seton, he was a black drinker.

Seton the mealy, Seton the moody, Seton the crafty, the self-preserving holdout, *he* never had this kind of fun. Never had *any!* "Like he was all over scales." That's what that Coney Island girl had said (and what the hell was *her* name?), the girl he'd waltzed with, that he'd given the million-dollar feel to right there on the dance floor, and again right there at the table with her leg up and her foot in his lap when he tied on her slipper—when he'd gypped the waiter at Feltman's.

"All over scales." That sure said it about Seton. What kind of a drinker could endure an evening in Seton's hangouts, the Hell Hole, the Taffrail, Jimmy the Priest's? And the dead company he could dig up! Porters and cab drivers and the jug-headed Five-Below that sold string. Jesus! Was *he* nothing but a nothing! The whole pack of them, bindle-stiffs and birkies, Tenth Avenue Arabs, West Street ragpickers, churls, chuffs, Pier Six dingoes! Fun? Hell, it wasn't fun! It was hell itself! Who could have fun in the embalming parlors, in the fish-market smells where his brother spent his hours just staring into the bottom of a glass, staring into the dull misery of imaginary men struggling in the bottom of a well of cheap whisky.

A great truth about his younger brother burst over him then: through his whole life Seton had never had friends, just cronies.

Why the hell did Seton have to be a bum too!

Patrick was a bum, all right, and he had his own grief: he knew he was a bum. He had his own fear too: he knew he was about through. Nowadays—the last year or two—every bout and collision had about it a shrouded eagerness, a seeking, a haunted urgency. The little-boy-at-the-mouth-of-the-cave respect for the darkness just here, so close you could poke your hand into it; Death just here in the dark, and the hot-and-cold fascination to know this resident in the black shadow, to behold Him, to glimpse in that blind entire instant His mighty claw as it came out for him, came out with no sound coming with it; coming out for the neck, for the shoulder, of Patrick.

Sometimes, half drunk as he was now, he'd wince, run his hands over whatever he might be sitting upon, spring up with a gasp, a despairing half prayer to do better. Now his fingers went back and forth over the rough and splintered floor of the flatcar.

"O Jesus! O Jesus! What'll I do when I'm dying! Where'll I be! Is it all too late for work? Too late for church even?"

He drank again, thirsting, fearful, his eyes hard.

At the shore town of Deal the police wouldn't let the men stop with their exhibit. It was the same in all the towns till they got to the yards at Atlantic City. It seemed almost as if their arrivals were being telegraphed.

Patrick for the first time began to worry about the future of this "tour"; of the possibility of getting any money out of it. Or any fun.

If they could only get down toward Barnegat where they'd be sure to find whole communities that appreciated what a whale was. But Patrick knew Atlantic City. If nothing were to happen there, at least he wouldn't be lost. And a great town for show people. He was pretty sure Sam Bernard had something going at the Fortesque Pavilion.

"I've got a police pass in this city," he said importantly to Cleat, opening his wallet. "I'm going to phone the Pavilion. If the police come, or the board of health, tell 'em we have a ten-day permit. Remind 'em the whale is embalmed. I'll be back as soon as I find a public telephone."

If nothing good turned up, he'd merely not come back. Pat took a heroic pull from Boomer's bottle. Then he picked up the linen package of printed stock and nimbly left the yard, his head bobbing in all directions, watching for trains.

Already people were beginning to show up at the siding. There was pointing from the boardwalk. Parasols stopped. Rolling chairs turned inland away from the sea to regard this unexpected arrival.

Patrick followed the sound of an electric piano.

Inshore, with provision trucks unloading at its rear, a huge ramshackle hotel spilled forth a jangle of holiday wakefulness. There was a weedy tennis court for the help, converted now to indifferent croquet. In the parking space a big Packard touring car was being driven slowly around and around while mechanics endeavored to find a squeak in her tonneau, one of the men lying on his belly on the front fender, peering under. Pat could smell the hot black leather of its cushions. Money.

A man putting on a tie leaned out of a third-story window and sang out to all the world: "In the land of Oh by Jingo," then moved in out of sight and hearing.

The bar of the hotel was cool and full of men in their shirt sleeves. There was a good smell of beer. Nothing was visible on the shelves but soft drinks, Apollinaris Water, and blue bottles of Bromo Seltzer.

Pat went right to the bartender.

"We've got quite an exhibit coming in. Giant killer whale. You can see it if you just turn to your left."

Before turning, the bartender made a swift invisible assessment of Patrick Farrier: Irish, drinking man, well educated, promoter, ladykiller, momentarily on the bum. Then he looked out the side window and marveled.

It was something to goggle over. Crowds had already begun streaming to it. The giant corpse was arresting. In size, immediacy, and unexpectedness it had the fascination of a grounded dirigible.

Others coming to the bar saw at once the preoccupation of the bartender. They too just stood and stared. Finally the bartender looked back at Patrick.

"That yours?"

"Me and a couple of partners. We're exhibiting her. Three-four days. Then we're selling her. Oil and ambergris, you know."

"You mean it's worth money?"

"My, yes. 'Bout seventy thousand. That one carcass." Having won his interest on the point of its value, Pat left it there. Nonchalantly he knifed a slice out of the cheddar wheel. Then he leaned slightly across the bar, spoke quickly, lowering his voice.

"Could you sell me a drink?"

"Sure. What'll you have?"

"Bourbon?"

"You bet."

"You couldn't tell me where I could go in this town for a case, could you?"

"Couldn't sell you a case from here," the bartender answered, wiping out an ash tray. "But I might steer you to one."

"That would do." Pat knocked his drink down and passed the jigger back. The bartender wrote a name and address on a card.

"That's right next to Fortesque Pavilion, isn't it?"

"Yeah."

"Thanks. Thanks a lot."

"Sure. Pavilion where you takin' your whale?"

"Yes. Last stop. Then down to Barnegat. For the oil and ambergris. Just showin' her for the fun of it. And to make her pay her own fare, of course." He laughed easily. The bartender liked him, his light manner, his light acceptance of the rackety world, his nonchalance over the dramatic dreadfulness of the whale outside. He set the bottle of Early Times on the bar.

"Help yourself."

"Why, thank you. Thank you very much." Pat picked it up lovingly, read the familiar label, and poured.

A flash of the face of his brother Seton came into his mind now, Seton who couldn't stop drinking once he started, who hated it altogether but who was powerless once he started. Pat had no problem.

He just never stopped drinking. He had never been on the wagon in his life. He never would be. Drink was fun. Drinking was a part of all his crude escapades with women, it was part of the fights in the Garden, the bike races, and the track when he had the money to go. A drink was like a woman—no matter when or with whom, it was something one never refused. The only two great satisfiers. The only two real pulse-kickers. He would drink anything with alcohol. He would sleep with anything warm.

But Seton!

What a cockeyed way of looking at things Seton had!

Patrick now opened his linen package and slipped out one of the certificates. It looked rich and impressive in the cheery gloom.

"We're selling shares in the whale. At the Breakers. But you've done me a favor. This is for you. What's your name, bartender?"

"Coyt. Willis Coyt. Call me Bill."

He looked at the certificate admiringly.

"That'll be worth about three hundred and forty dollars by the end of summer, Bill. Don't leave it around with the loose change."

He snapped down another whisky, shook hands with Bill, and went out into the cool sun.

He could hear the ocean now and he could smell the strength of it. He wanted to be out on the boardwalk. He wanted to strut a little.

His appearance held him back. Patrick had a horror of being seen, especially by women, in shabby clothes. He needed a shave too. A shave was the only physical attention he could still pay for. He stepped into the barbershop behind the Fortesque Pavilion, asked for a once-over-lightly, paid and tipped and went up the rear stairs to the boardwalk and into the side entrance of Weber and Heilbroner.

He found a Panama hat he liked and a light gray ready-made suit that fit his shoulders pretty well and hung exactly right.

He flashed about in front of the triangular mirrors, then told the salesman he wanted to see this shade of gray in the morning sunshine.

"I'm with a show here," he said with pleasant dismissal—tapping out a few steps on the cool floor to prove it.

"Sure, go ahead."

Patrick went outside. He had transferred his wallet with its Lambs Club membership card, its New York City Police Department courtesy card, signed by Enright, its hotel credit cards, and eight speak-easy cards. All were valuable to him and everything about them was genuine except the signatures.

He knew what he'd done was dangerous and that he could not hang around Atlantic City long.

He walked up the boardwalk to the exit next to the Pavilion, left the crowd of strollers with a sense of regret but a larger sense of relief—he had never been "picked up"—and walked into the parlor of Daisy Glad's theatrical boardinghouse where he'd stayed a few years before when touring with Phil Sheridan's *Marathon Girls*.

There was a loud yawn, then some sleepy laughter in the dining room. Pat stuck his head in. In a corner table by the window six or seven show girls had finished breakfast. Except for them and a pale man, badly mottled with liver spots, the room was empty. The man was reading *Zits*. Patrick felt he might be in the right room once again, perhaps even at the right time. There was a bang of crockery and a chinking of cutlery in the kitchen. Pat took on his look of amiable unconcern, whistled the opening bars of "I'll Build a Stairway to Paradise," and sauntered into the room.

One of the girls looked familiar to Pat. He ran back in his memory. From the middle of the floor, where he looked neat in his fresh dandyism and where he felt pleasantly spotlighted, he called gaily, holding out his Panama in vaudeville salutation.

"Aren't you Marie? Marie LeVon of *The Merry Whirls?*" He had not fixed on any one particular girl but had passed over them all.

"I'm Pat," he went on. "Pat Farrier. Don't you remember me?"

Here in the middle of the bare dining room of Daisy Glad's boardinghouse he went into the first few steps of the "Jenny Cooler," a complicated routine developed by Fred Stone and admired by show people everywhere, but little performed on stages. Its intricacies were too swift and subtle to be appreciated by vaudeville audiences.

Pat realized the spotted man had put down his paper. That was all he wanted. He gave the girls a breathless fifteen seconds, gave them a cute little vaudeville bow, and came over to their table.

They all applauded. One rose, holding out her arms, and kissed him. Now he sat down expansively at the table, flinging an arm about the shoulder of the girls on each side and leaned back, enjoying them.

"Gee, you're some dancer, Pat. I never seen you."

"That's a mean step. Do it again, will you?" said the girl at the end.

"Not before breakfast," he said, smiling and picking up a roll. One of the girls passed him her coffee. "Say," he said conversationally, looking at all the raddled midmorning wreckage about him, then at the hard but theatrical prettiness of the brunette right across from him, "Weren't you one of the 'Jersey Lilies' with Leon Errol?"

"I sure was, Cupid. I'm Gwennie Durgan."

"Gee, of *course!*" He rose gallantly, leaned over the table, pulled at her as if taking in kite string, and kissed her hand. "You were great! You were *tree-men-jous!* You should have been starred from there on, Gwennie!"

A happy flurry went through them all and the talk became a burble of joyous self-interest and excessive claim, of wildly embroidered reminiscence. Big names, intimate contacts, seraphic notices fluttered over the table like birthday confetti. Some of the statements were true. Two girls, still pretty in a deathless defiance of chronology, disappointment, and bad food, had obviously once been with Nat Fields in *Girls from Happy Land*, and one, the soubrette of the present company, now leaving (as he gathered) for Cincinnati, had been briefly starred in *The Merry Whirls* with Jay C. Morton. He had been right about that.

All the girls had a battered but durable look—like stage soldiers coming to, stretching and batting their eyes open in comic reveilles.

The pale man came over from the corner, folding his paper. He was young, about thirty. He had all his hair but you could tell somehow he was soon going to lose it.

"Bus will be here in forty-five minutes. Be on the porch."

They nodded with disinterest, all looking as if they wished he'd just go away. He sensed this and screamed with unexpected savagery: "Well, *move!*"

They all rose then, and walked stonily out of the dining room as if conducted by a matron. In the doorway Gwennie turned and thumbed her nose at his back, but flounced her bosom for Pat and grinned at him.

"You with a show here?" the man asked Patrick.

"No. Just a vacation."

"You seemed to know them. I'm the road-company manager."

"Yes, I figured so."

"I saw your soft-shoe just now."

"Oh." Pat shrugged slightly. "Just a memory. I did the whole routine once. Hurtig and Seaman's. But it doesn't go over. Anyhow it's Fred Stone's. It isn't mine."

"Well, it's good. You want to try it on a better-class audience?"

"Where you goin'?"

"Cincinnati."

"People's Theatre?"

"Yeah. Ever played it?"

"Couple of times. As an actor though."

"What in?"

"*Adam and Eve's Daughter*, for one."

"Who were you workin' for then?"

"Sam Bernard. I played the same theater before the war. I was road-company star in *The Travelling Salesman*."

"Any burlesque?"

"Oh sure. Vinnie Henshaw in the *Bowery Burlesque*. And I was in a rough show—a real hairy-ass show—in the Albany Spit-Box before the governor closed it."

"Are you bonded?"

"No."

"Equity?"

"No."

The pale man took this in silently.

Then Patrick did the thing that made him special.

"I'm not looking for work, Mr. Whatever-your-name-is," and he got up from the table. "I'm going to manage my brother. His play is in rehearsal. Morosco. His name is Seton Farrier. You may have heard of him. Or Dermod Farrier, the actor. He's my father." He walked away from Fisher then. "I'm going to wait on the porch. I want to say good-by to one of the girls."

The road-company manager followed him out, taking quick steps.

"But I—I could *use* somebody like you. Even if you could only

give us a week. It's a good show. We got a great jig-and-biddy. We
got a good line. And a Jewish comic that's funnier than Lew Palmer.
I'll give you a hundred. Just for one week."

"I'm not performing any more, Mr. Whatever-your-name-is," he
reminded him, looking off toward Europe, looking a little irritable.

"Fisher. Fisher. Sammy Fisher. If you're on vacation anyhow—just
a week with the show. They can't be needing you at the Morosco, if
you can take some days off here. I mean—since you already know
some of the company——"

Pat opened a pack of Fatimas, snapped a match with his thumbnail,
and tilted his Panama.

"What else you got?"

Fisher told him quickly, routines, sets, special music. They talked
back and forth a few moments. Then Pat slipped a hip over the
railing of the porch.

"I'll go with you for one week for one-fifty. All expenses and
seventy-five cash right now. Pullman and lower to Cincy."

"All right," Fisher said after a moment. "But it'll have to be fifty
now. I got to hit the bank before we leave. Trunks have already
gone down."

"The other twenty-five in the diner then?"

"All right. In the diner. Here's fifty. Where you staying?"

"At the Traymore. With Arleigh Brayce."

"Brayce? The producer?"

"Sure. He's doing my brother's show."

Fisher looked again at Patrick, as if trying to spot something in
his own memory.

"Say, aren't you the Farrier that can whistle?"

"Yeah. Sure." A flutter of flute sounds filled the porch, and Pat
grinned, suddenly pleased. "But I do it just to entertain myself.
Or at a party now and then. I never whistled in a show. Doesn't
belong."

"Well, maybe. Let's do a number and see. I got a good music man."

He told Pat how far ahead they were booked. Pat decided on a
week with them, more to get out of Atlantic City and to spend
nights with Gwennie than to work.

"The girls are going ahead with Choppy Handel," Fisher was

saying. "I'll meet you on the platform on the four forty-five. You'll have space in Car 88."

Mr. Fisher left the porch and went to the phone booth under the back stairs, and asked the operator for the Traymore.

"Traymore? Is Arleigh Brayce registered there?"

"Yes, he is. May I connect you?"

"No, never mind." He hung up and went out.

On the porch Pat smoked enjoyably, slipped back into the dining room for another roll, greeted the girls when they came down. He told a few jokes and picked up a few first names. Then he announced he was joining the company. A happy squeal ran out over the sand.

Pat sauntered away then, filling the air with melodies, romantically departing toward the boardwalk while the girls watched.

8

ON THE BOARDWALK HE THOUGHT HE'D TAKE A chance, a brief one, with Weber and Heilbroner. If they had police scanning the passers-by already, he'd merely acknowledge the truth of the report against himself, say he couldn't find his wife when he walked out into the sun, and that he was right then on his way to pay for the new suit and pick up his old one. "What the hell is this?" he'd ask in gay innocence. They'd shut up soon enough the minute they saw him peel off a few tens. And apologize all over the place.

He approached the store's front. Staying close to the building so as to shorten the moment of his visibility, he walked right past the store at the shoulder of another man moving the same way, took off his hat when in full view and dabbed sweat from his temple, obscuring his profile.

He was safely past. He was on his way for the whisky. He'd thought of whisky as a way to survive the uncertain vicissitudes of a journey with the whale. But it was all different now. Much better now. He had abandoned the adventure with Cleat and Boomer the very instant the Fisher approach had become real.

A little farther along, at the address that the bartender Coyt had given him, he found he could buy all the whisky he wanted. The liquor was put ashore near Cape May, then brought up the truck route to depots for fresh vegetables and to warehouses where commission merchants received and retailed fruit, poultry, eggs, and green groceries. All the truckers handled such liquor shipments as their connections and their nerve permitted.

Everyone knew, no one cared, and nobody much got hurt. The whole system fitted in very well with Pat's own pattern of living.

With perspiring industry there was a legitimate laundry business going on all about and directly behind the liquor business. Thinking of the train ride to Cincinnati, Pat could see there was no way to take more than a couple of bottles. You couldn't tuck a case under a lower. And in any event he wanted to stay sober long enough to see what might be in the show for himself; if nothing, see what there might be that he could take out of it for himself, a girl, or a stepping-stone to another show. Perhaps a fouled-up manager that New York might be canning by Western Union. Something good might turn up. You never knew. You had to be there and you had to be sober enough to see it. That was all.

His bottles were cheerfully wrapped, then tucked in tissue paper and tied up in a blue laundry box.

He had five hours to kill before his train.

He walked back to the bar where he'd talked with Willis Coyt, set down his package, and asked Bill for another shot of Early Times.

"Get your case all right?" Bill asked, interested. Pat could hear the group laughter of women behind him, shrill and peppery and a little out of the ordinary.

"You bet."

This time, Pat noticed, Bill poured the whisky behind the bar and below the level of the beer drain.

"And I got a couple of spares for a friend." He showed the bartender the laundry box. He turned around to look at the crowd in the bar now. It had changed a great deal. It was now mostly women, and from young to middle-aged, with a couple of real old crocks, he noticed, at the head of two of the tables. They'd taken over the place someway, and most of the men had fled. They weren't accustomed to bars either. Pat could tell this by their faces. Their yipping was sanitary and depressingly virginal, though their eyes were expectant, like vacationers waiting for free fireworks.

"Who the hell are these clunks?" he asked Bill.

"God," he answered, in black holiness. "Manager told me to serve nothin' long's they're here."

"Are they teachers?"

"Good guess. Eastern Conference of Teachers of Speech. They're stayin' here. Couple of hundred."

"Well, there's that one in the yellow."

"Yeah, I seen her before, I was lookin' at 'er. Don't seem to be enjoyin' her table none."

"Speech teacher, huh? Wish that little canary bird would come over here and give *me* a lesson."

The girl in yellow was quite pretty, as the men had noticed. She was tan, and, though alert-looking, was only half listening to the chatter at her table. She turned at Pat's laughter and looked over at the bar. Then she got up, took her bag, and went off to the ladies' room.

"Gimme another shot, Bill," he said, laying down a five-dollar bill.

Bill poured, then rang up for the drinks.

"What's the news on the whale?"

Pat had forgotten the whale.

"Real good," he said quickly, then darted a glance out the window. It was not there.

"Too bad about the police," Bill said.

"We'll fix that easy," he said, wondering what they had done.

"There's a flenser comes in here for a drink every afternoon. He'll be real interested."

"A flenser? What the hell is a flenser?"

"He'd be real useful to you, way I see it. He's a whale cutter. You know, on a whaling ship. The fellow that carves it up so they can boil it down."

"Oh yeah. He sure would be useful to us." Pat's sense of caution awoke once more. He'd hoped to sell a few stock certificates on the basis of gathering interest and the actual presence of the whale when the drinking got going. But with an expert on the way, maybe it was time to move.

"Probably make a pretty good estimate. Like how much oil she was good for. Think so?" Because he always had escape planned, Pat could always appear calm.

"Yeah, you bet. He sure would," Pat said in eager agreement. "When's he due here? What's his name? We could cut him in."

"He's a Norwegian fellow from Brielle. The real thing. Arms like timbers. Here every day when he ain't at sea."

"That's great, Bill. We could really use this guy. Talk about it soon's I get back." He winked and cocked his head toward the ladies' room where the girl in the yellow had disappeared.

"Going to welcome Miss Canary to Atlantic City." He picked up his laundry package. "Give her a little hospitality from the Acme Laundry."

He intercepted Miss Canary when she came out of the ladies' room into the dark little hall it gave on. There was a set of penny scales standing by the wall. She was primping there in the mirror.

"Madame," said Patrick in his best voice and with exaggerated politeness. "You have certain contours that suggest you belong to the female sex." He took off his hat and bowed.

"Do I?" She laughed lightly. "Can you tell from there?"

"I can indeed. And a civilized regionalism to your speech that strikes my ears as Venango County, Pennsylvania."

She stopped patting her hair, stepped down off the scales, and looked full at him.

"You're way off about Venango."

"But you're a girl, aren't you? I'm right about that? And a speech teacher?" He drew a shade closer. "Don't go back to that damn convention. Have a happy lunch with an Irish minstrel. Have a drink with him. Out of sight of your principal. You're in the vacation spot of the continent."

His voice fell and he peeked out toward the bar. "They can't serve you a drink in there. But look——" He opened the box. "Now,

wouldn't you enjoy an innocent drink with your new-found friend
Patrick Farrier?"

The girl blushed slightly. Adventure came into her eyes.

"Yes, I'd love it. But where? How?"

"Well, not here." He covered the box again. "Could we slip up to
your room?" He saw her quick doubt. "Or take our chances in the
main dining room. Get there before the rest of your friends."

"They're all going to the Lobster Pot."

"Serves 'em right. Just want you to have a good time, Miss Honey-
and-Gold-and-Yellow Aster. You'd probably say no if I suggest my
own suite at the Breakers."

"Wouldn't there be a risk involved?"

"Yes, there would. Tell you what. Take you to a real cute little
place here. Not touristy at all. I *can't* believe you're a schoolteacher."
They were in motion now. "What's your name?"

"Charlotte."

"We'll have a good-luck, get-acquainted drink in your room before
lunch. What's your room number, Charlotte?" He could sense her
coming hesitancy on revealing it, and went right on, dismissing her
fear with a reassuring gesture: "We'll leave the door open, of course.
That's my promise to you." He held up his hand. "We'll have one
or two. No more. *And . . .*" He looked down gently on her upturned
face, trying to dissipate the doubt he could still see in her eyes and
in her twisted but good-natured smile of open suspicion. "If you can
get away this evening, or even a part of it, we'll have dinner in the
Grotto. After that, you can have your choice of the open-air concert
or dancing at the Breakers. Or we can chair down the boardwalk
or see a show. *Irene* is here. And *Gold Diggers*. We could decide
that during dinner. This your first time here?"

"Yes, it is, Pat." She was a little calmer now. She'd been offered
a great deal in a short time. This had never happened to her before.
"Do they call you Pat?"

"They do."

"Pat," she said, as if trying out a word in another language. "How
do you know it so well? Atlantic City?"

"I *have* to come down here. And I have to go to a strange place in western New York called Chautauqua. Several times a summer. I'm in the community-concerts business."

"You *are!*" She was obviously delighted to find him so innocently employed. But then, he spoke well. He was forward but he wasn't fresh, she told herself. And he'd promised to leave the door open. The evening might be quite a thrill. She'd heard of the Grotto.

"You mean you manage some of them? The concerts?"

"Oh no. Not that big. But I have to catch a lot of the new talent. America's soaking up a lot of culture, you know. More than ever since the war. Summer's a busy time for us."

"Gee, what a job!"

"Well, yes. I guess. My own isn't too important. I'm director of a division they call Eastern Auditions. I'm not the big boss. Just one of the field hands really."

"I bet you're bigger than you're saying. You get paid for just listening to people *perform?*"

"Well, pretty nearly that. But I'm supposed to know . . ." Here he laughed with self-reducing lightness, a spontaneous outlay of modesty Charlotte found charming and a little boyish. He got younger as she listened to him. "I've got to know whether they're any good. And just how good. That's what I get paid for."

He had a young spirit all right. And what an exciting way to live! He was a little blotchy and she could smell liquor on him, but she realized that she herself had planned, if they could duck the others, to have a drink with Miss Feigenspahn. So she couldn't hold that against him. Anyhow he was a man and he sure knew his way around this town.

On the way to her room, Patrick saw a coin phone at the corridor's end near a rope coil and a fire ax. He passed the box to Charlotte.

"See if you can get a cork out of one of these, while I ring up and get us a table reservation for tonight. And"—he held up a reminding finger and waggled it puckishly—"leave the door open. I'm nervous around young women. I'm an out-of-town fellow myself."

"You!" She laughed and watched him go down the hall, jouncing along happily and jangling loose change in his pocket. Suddenly he began to whistle in an extraordinary fashion. She had never heard anything like it in her life. It was lofty and ethereal. It had the magic of harmonics and aeolian harps. It held enchantment above anything she had ever heard, preternatural, disquieting, something to follow, perhaps something to wait for in the night.

When she opened the box and started the unfamiliar task of getting a cork out of a whisky bottle, her hands were trembling. She thought a man who could make sounds like that could be a changeling or a visitant, that he had powers not given to others, that she might peer now into the hall and not see him while still hearing the sounds of him.

She went to the door and looked. At the end of the hall, silhouetted against a large bare window, he stood looking out at the bright day, holding the receiver at the end of its cord. Even here, chained to the wall, as it were, he was making little dance steps. And she could hear now, too, his hearty assurance, his direct pronouncing of his own name, his courtesy. He was having a joke with the clerk. If someone had told Charlotte that Patrick had not been talking to anyone at all, she would simply have refused to believe it. When the receiver went back on the hook she went back into her white sunny room.

Here she pulled the shades half down. An invisible plume of delicious air lifted through the room, rustling papers, stirring, tormenting, plucking at her lungs. She drew the air in with a sudden crying sigh. She felt rich and sad and excited.

Where would he take her? She wasn't going to let him touch her but she wished she had put on the pale green underthings she had put in the bag at Wheeling. Supposing he *did* kiss her? And that she liked it? Then supposing it got worse? That he just kept on and on? There'd have to come a time when they had to think of lunch. What should she ask for?

She heard loud talking and a couple of shrill coos from down below. "The girls" were going down the worn seedy path lunging and darting like a swarm of exulting truants. Charlotte felt guilty. She should be with them there. But she felt relieved and exhilarated and choked up with the wonder of the sea and the odd stimulation of the Irishman who had stepped around from behind the scales.

Then he was back in the room, grinning in the doorway, his eyes wide with an expression of prankish capering, of secret accomplishment.

"Wait till you hear the plans for tonight." He beamed.

Coming very close, he took the whisky bottle and twisted out the cork with a strong expert single movement of his thumb and forefinger. Then he poured a shot in each of two glasses that stood on a white napkin on the commode.

Another girl in a hotel room, was the thought that was in his mind, a satisfying thought, pleasantly there and pleasantly showing on his face. Liquor, which always made the pallid Seton paler still, merely made Pat grow pinker.

"To us," he said with a flourish, touching the glasses, and tossed down his drink. Charlotte took hers with caution, with the delight of doing things forbidden. She wondered what the "plans for tonight" might include. The whisky made her feel as if she wanted to do something splendid and refined, something with the full rush of orchestra music cascading down on them; to look well beside him, to have people notice, perhaps a few to wonder who "that couple" was. Between lunch and dinner she could get a fresh marcel. She'd look nice for him. She looked nice right now, she felt.

He poured another drink for himself, but she held her glass back when he extended the bottle.

"You know where we're going? I've got the best table in the Grotto. They call it the 'nook.' Little alcove room for two only. Right over the water. And a good city block from the bass drum. But wait'll you hear about *after* dinner. Caroline Beebe's Little Symphony is here! They're giving a world première of Deems Taylor's 'Through the Looking Glass.'"

He drank eagerly, then looked at her, roostering his head as if about to peck her.

"You know what you look like, Charlotte? This is the honest-to-God truth! You look like one of those little Dutch dolls that were so popular about ten years ago. Couldn't sell 'em. They were just too pretty to be real, prettier than anything that was alive. Nobody would believe them."

He leaned down quickly and kissed her cheek. "I just wanted to be sure."

"Sure? That I wouldn't refuse?"

"No. That you weren't china."

"I'm not china, Pat. Do you really think I'm pretty?"

"You're the face in a million faces, Charlotte! Picked you right out!" His eyes zigzagged about, critically reviewing the place they were in. "I wish we could shut the door. Just for a *second*. I want to kiss you. I feel very bold." There was entreaty in his face. He was closing the door with his foot as he talked. "I never expected anything this thrilling could happen to me in the midst of my daily labor. Drink?"

"Yes. But I have to have some water." Pat got her a glass from the cooler in the hall, shut the door then, and made her another drink.

With the second drink she began talking about school, about her life as a schoolteacher, her plans to take graduate work. Pat suggested her coming to N.Y.U. so he could keep an eye on her. She was interested. She didn't want to stay with Speech. She wasn't going anywhere with Speech except maybe this radio thing people talked about—English was the thing.

He set his glass down, took her two shoulders, then leaned down and whispered in her ear: "Miss Forester, as a lover of good English you will understand my feelings about you." He was very close but he wasn't trying to kiss her.

"I want to split your infinitive with my dangling participle."

This jolted her body. But Pat released her so quickly after saying this frightful thing, she could only feel safe; safe and exquisitely shocked. She felt herself coloring but she didn't turn away. She certainly didn't feel like slapping him, the way she ought. The idea! He said the most monstrous, the most unexpected things! Then she laughed and set her drink down. He turned the key in the door and picked her up.

"Can't we have lunch a little later?" His voice was different now and his hands began to touch her. Soon he was pressing her so hard she could not have said anything. Then he took her hands and guided them down, down. He had opened his trousers. "Charlotte, honey, why don't you take this bull by the horn!"

At four he left her bed. She was a little drunk, very drowsy.

"I'll be back at seven," he whispered.

At seven his train was crossing the Delaware River, and Pat was quarreling with Sam Fisher about the twenty-five dollars he'd been promised when they discussed terms on Daisy Glad's porch.

On the train to Cincinnati, Patrick was drunk and ugly. He ate quickly, spilling food. When he got no money from Fisher he left the diner and began to explore the train.

There were some parachute jumpers on board. They were tanned, garrulous, and untidy. Lest anyone miss their vocation, all were wearing their goggles, tossed up excitingly above their foreheads. Their girls wore beaded scarfs. They were drinking too, bound for Omaha. They were talking about a small chimpanzee. It was in the next car.

Patrick's meal sponged up his afternoon's drinking but by ten, still drinking, he was on the prowl, dangerous and inventive. He didn't know anyone but he very soon introduced all the members of the air circus to the vaudeville performers in the car behind. The chimpanzee—a small but surprisingly powerful four-year-old they called Peony—became a popular attraction where Pat took her. She held up her paw and went wherever she was led, horrifying or delighting the passengers she paused to study, a distraction and sudden terror to the porters who were trying to make up berths.

For costume, Peony wore a parlor maid's apron, tied in the back in a bow. Her owner, Jungle Purdy, was in a crap game in the baggage car.

In the men's smoking room a surprising thing happened. Peony knuckled over to the window sill, picked up a glass of gin, sniffed it, and drank it down. She became quite drunk at once, jumping up and down, showing her white teeth, then backing over to one of the washbasins and somersaulting about.

The men roared and offered her another drink. Then they passed the bottle to Pat, whom they presumed to be the ape's owner and trainer. By eleven they were all staggering. It was suggested they parade the chimpanzee up and down a few aisles, perhaps open a door in the car's vestibule to get the animal some air.

All the men came along to watch and to improvise.

Peony bounded up and down sleeper curtains, nipped up ladders, clung joyously to curtain bars, grinning, rocking, swaying. By and by the men got the idea of stealthily unbuttoning the protective curtain in some of the lower berths and flinging the drunk but willing

animal upon the passengers within. Pat agreed to do the flinging if
they did the unbuttoning.

There was a moment of giggling, of furtive preparation, laughter
smothered by the train's roar, noisy shushings. Then Pat picked up
Peony, the others pulled a curtain apart, and in went Peony with a
friendly squeal and a wild chatter of arboreal neighborliness.

In the lowers there was immediate screaming.

There was an immediate ringing of porters' bells. Inquisitive,
ghastly heads bobbed through slits in the uppers. Men shouted. A
conductor appeared. Pat and Peony and their crapulous crowd fled
each new scene of panic and at once created another in a new car.

Peony helped everywhere, jumping up and down on old men,
embracing drowsy women, throwing their clothes into the aisles, tearing sheets, hair nets, camisoles, often emerging in a hat or leaping
away festooned in suspenders or knitting yarn, dragging kits and cases
that disemboweled themselves and left a wake of cosmetics, brushes,
shaving gear, hairpins, nail buffers, emery boards, dentifrice, and tobacco. Tousled men in towering furies leaped about redundantly.
Hysterical women appeared flinging their arms, shouting instructions
and surmises. A revolver went off. A brakeman appeared with a double handful of lanterns.

Patrick could never remember such a night. The Pennsylvania never
had such a problem.

There was no way to police it, not with sixteen cars to play with.
Card players and late drinkers in the club cars, or those still awake
just reading, took a fast puzzled look at the bounding Peony and,
far from trying to stop anything, joined the chorus and the chase and
brought new notions.

No one agreed about the end of it.

In the hotel lobby in the morning where Fisher's company was
to meet, Peony showed up, still visibly drunk but undefeated, flung
her long arms around Patrick's neck, bounded across the amazed
lobby, and bit the bell captain savagely in the calf. He screamed
and began to bleed.

Police appeared. Fingers pointed to Patrick. He was identified
positively by the railroad conductor. Pat denied positively and
altogether. He blamed the Pennsylvania for allowing the animal to

take over the train. He said he'd tried heroically to catch Peony, and he briefly flashed his New York City Police courtesy card. He was drunk but he was convincing.

Peony began biting the police.

Sam Fisher came into the lobby. His face turned gray. Finally Jungle Purdy appeared, slipped a collar on Peony, and chained her to a sand-pail cuspidor. Purdy kept people off by announcing the animal despised anything in a uniform, that Peony had been cruelly reared by a young trainer who wore nothing but uniforms.

Pat was never sure how long he stayed with Fisher's company. Three weeks? One day in the dressing rooms of the People's Theatre the rumor went around, coming early to Pat, that Fisher was going to abandon them here. Just scoot, and pay no more salaries.

It was believable. And it had happened to them all. Here, after the first two weeks, audiences had not been big although no one in the company felt the show was a flop. Pat brought vitality and unexpected professional *esprit*—even a hardness to the production. His whistling, which he'd agreed to experiment with, had become a big thing in the show and drew good notices. So did his "Jenny Cooler" routine. It was killing his legs and he came off so spent, he had to lie down after every performance. He'd go into Gwennie's room, where the girls had a couch and Gwen would massage his legs and let him sleep and keep the other girls away. Pat had done the exhausting "Jenny Cooler" in every performance. He'd whistled in every show too, and the house wanted more each time. He'd earned his money.

The company agreed to take turns guarding Fisher's door two hours apiece, day and night, to block any getaway attempt.

"It's easier to stay up than to get up," Pat said to Gwennie and the girls. "I'll take the six to eight in the morning."

And he was there exactly at six in the morning, relieving Choppy Handel, the music man. Fisher heard the two talking and came out. Choppy slunk off, hoping his being there would look like a chance meeting with Pat.

Fisher just stood there in his doorway, staring and questioning with his eyes, saying not a word. He was all dressed, his room neat. He set down his suitcase. Pat looked back unabashed, coldly, drunkenly amused. Then with large mocking importance he sat down on the canvas stool that Choppy had brought, and crossed his legs. With a tight Irish smile, he looked up at the manager. It was the smile of the tormentor after the victim is fastened but before the iron.

Fisher knew the look.

"I'll make the deal with you," he said, his face pale, his eyes bright. Pat rose. The two men stood in the red shoal of light that glowed there all night, marking an exit.

"Gimme the twenty-five first. That you owe me from Atlantic City."

There was a quick twitch in Fisher's eye corner that suggested he might cut and run for it. Pat moved over and crowded him back ever so little. "The twenty-five," he said cheerfully, holding out his hand. "And two C's for this week. I kept your show goin'. Me and Gwennie. You know that."

Fisher looked back and forth across the spread of the Irishman's shoulders as if reading the tip bar on a set of scales. Pat was in terrible condition, that was easy to see. Older, too. But he'd been strong once, real strong, and there was still some of it in him, maybe a good deal.

Fisher counted out two hundred and twenty-five dollars, picked up his suitcase, snapped the money across, and walked down the hall without looking back.

Pat sat down on the stool again. He could kill the two hours till eight o'clock, give over his spot to whoever came to relieve him, pretend Fisher was still inside (he reasoned he could prove it by Choppy), and take his own time about leaving. Maybe he'd go back and bounce Gwennie once more, maybe take her along with him if she had her fare. In bed Gwennie was a biter and a thrasher. If she wasn't sleepy. And she was careful about her language when she was around educated people or people she didn't know. You could take her places. She'd even been married a couple of times. She was married right now, he thought. And she bought her things at Arnold Constable when she could.

All at once he felt weak and homesick and a little frightened. He knew he was a born blackbirder, as dirty as Fisher: that he'd settle for his own cut any time, no matter who else got gypped. He'd get his. He was no welsher but everywhere else he was a real run-out. He was a rat and a bait stealer. He smiled insecurely and slowly got up.

Pat felt he had forever been trying to get comfortable on a slope. He wished he could lay down his life where it was level. Just once.

Daylight was somehow finding its way to the corridor.

He wished he were back in New York, cadging off his mother, insulting his old man, sponging meals or going without, picking up a girl or a ticket or a box-office job for a short run, promoting a ride to Belmont, going up to Thum's for some pool, over to Stillman's to watch Siki or Slattery or Berlenbach.

He wished his brother was all right. To hell with his mother and father. Old crocks, nearly spent.

Thoughts of his mother always stirred him and made him twitchy, his tired-out heroic little mother, thirty years on dope and ten years off it now on nothing but Irish nerve (the best that was Irish was in her for sure) and those everlasting nuns that kept visiting and praying and bringing things and clicking their damn beads and mailing prayers and pictures of saints and that horrible picture of Christ's feet—just the feet—with Mary below, looking up. Nuns coming across the street, eternally it seemed, like those pictures of the Germans coming up out of their trenches in the Argonne. After hours of perpetual adoration in their own church across the street, they'd come into the side entrance of the Byzantium, come upstairs, and start saving his mother and having tea.

But they cured her!

By God if they didn't, the nuns and the prayers and his mother's nerve. Never Pat or the old man or the doctors. And his mother knew that Pat had kept the dreadful secret. They were the only two who realized the satanic subtlety of heroin. They were the two who knew the others did not and could not.

And this was the bond between them.

He got up from the stool and began to walk. On his way to his own room to drink some more, Pat thought of his father's despair, his looking at, wincing away from, his wife's desolating addiction. Pat thought of Seton's horror of it, Seton's embarrassment about their mother, his sense of family disgrace, if he were to find out. Seton's hands would go atremble whenever the matter came up, though he'd seen not a damn bit of it. No matter what the family problems were, Seton would be afraid of only one thing: that someone *would* find

out! Seton would never think his mother might not live through it,
whatever the source of her torment.

Over this one thing Pat hated his brother. But only this.

Pat thought of himself now in the whole sad ugliness of it, the only
one near the wretched woman who could *feel* her agony, the only
one to connive and steal and forage and lie and take chances to bring
her the innocent envelope. Often he tucked the decks in cheap
bouquets of sidewalk roses. Often he left them in his hatband and
left his hat behind. Or sent dope to her in a new pair of hose or
tucked into the toe of a repaired shoe. Once, even, in a box that held
a silver chaplet, the chaplet she could never touch again because it
was so covered with her guilt, so pricked with it.

The old man knew she got it but he never knew how, by God!

Bring her the secret, take her down from this Cross, bring her the
drug that let her live for a moment, for a night, without pain, without
her insides screaming like a child on fire.

Christ, the places he'd been for her!

And she knew!

And the sordid knowledge of these vile expeditions, the vicious
people he'd had to go to, vicious even to Pat, who knew vice as he
knew pin boys, the slipping about in the dark, the being gay when
you were terrified, this was an agony that lay on her conscience, as
piercing and as tearing as the unspeakable craving itself. The humiliation she inflicted upon her older son, the humiliation he showed no
outside trace of; and the tearing up of her nerve-ends that she inflicted
upon herself. These were the black arms of the Cross upon which his
mother was nailed. And he, too, had been crucified there beside her,
a thirsting thief.

Poor woman! Poor creature! Poor old wasteland with the bony
hands and the broken heart.

With the gratitude of release, her Irish humor had come back a
little. That was one agony that was over years ago, thank Jesus!

Thank you, Jesus!

He drank eagerly from the bottle, exhaling and hawking the fire
out of his throat.

He thought of his mother's crucifixion, of her eventual descent
from the Cross and the scarred and twisted heroism that lay there in

those hands when they opened a book or reached for the candy jar.

Patrick could be tender about such memories, when he had enough whisky. His hatred increased for his father. And Seton was yellow. Worse than that, Seton was a girl, not a man. He'd be an old woman soon.

Pat always began to love his mother and to hate his father and his brother when he drank enough, for then his mind always went back to this same horror.

Death itself could be nothing now.

Everything we do, he mused—sitting there by the window—good or bad, we just do it for a time. It all goes away. Christ Himself only hung on the Roman spikes for a short time as time goes—six hours or so—not all those centuries people had been weeping for, weeping to get Him down, to comfort His hands and feet and the spear jab in His side. Hell with that! It wasn't as if they never got Him down at all, was it? Christ, no! What the hell is all this Catholic weeping?

But pictures of the crucifixion stood right there in his mind as he drank. His heart pounded, his hands sweated.

He drank from the bottle again. He better get going.

He looked at himself in the mirror, combed his hair, washed his face, pulled his tie straight. He began to feel good about the two hundred and twenty-five. That was pretty good money. Maybe he'd wake up Gwennie and ask her to marry him. She'd like that. But suppose she said yes? Suppose he was wrong about her having a husband?

It was terrifying! Man of his age! But she sure was cute with a silver-headed walking stick and a silk hat cocked over her saucy eye. Exactly right with the knees too. If she only didn't have the goddamn appendicitis scar—that rip clear across her belly. Goddamn fool doctor, it took Gwennie right out of the front line!

This morning was the first morning he could remember when he felt he'd go crazy if he couldn't get a drink. What was happening to him? Was he getting into the trap that caught Seton? That he couldn't quite quit when he wanted to? Couldn't stop when he started? Or was it the kind of stuff you were getting?

He better look into this. He poured out a tumblerful and swallowed half in two gulps. It bounced, then came right up again. He had to rush to the basin. Once in a show in Detroit a trombonist told him to shake pepper in the whisky to keep it down. Pepper would keep it down for you, even if your stomach tried to reject it. "Paralyzes your guts and you can't vomit if you try."

Patrick ran down the stairs into the empty dining room and snatched up a glass pepper shaker. A bus boy stared at him.

Back in his room the pepper let him hold the whisky. His stomach reached up to grab it. His gasping eased off. Standing by the bureau, holding the bottle in one hand, a glass in the other, he drank a pint, wondering in luxurious and time-slowing unconcern what city he was in, what day it was. Sometimes he could tell where he'd been the night before by looking at the match covers in his pockets.

On the street he bought a newspaper. He was in Cincinnati. It was Thursday. It meant nothing to him but it was comforting. It cleared up the mystery if there was any.

Carrying his bottle in a hotel towel, he walked into the center of the city and got on the Interurban for Covington, Kentucky, across the river. In the rear seat of the car he drank from time to time, looking out at the brilliant reflection of morning sun that shot back into the car from the flecked surface of the Ohio. It was too bright. He looked away quickly. It was an open car and it smelled sweet outside.

Thoughts of childhood came into his mind. He remembered the time when his house was quarantined, when he was a boy of ten or eleven, when his cousin Rhoda, seventeen that summer, had come down with scarlet fever; when she was delirious and only a few hours (as it turned out) from death. Everyone had fled the house to get doctors. He couldn't remember whether Seton was even born then. But he remembered stealing into Rhoda's hot room and raising her sheet, then lifting up her white nightgown and just staring and staring; and pinning the weak ray of a flashlight between her legs, marveling and wondering, his own skin seeming to get as hot as hers, his own body surging with a fever as real and burning.

It was his first sight of a woman, of her "place," her secret. He had wondered about it for such a long time. He remembered confessing this sin to a priest in his freshman year at Fordham seven or eight years later. He remembered confessing it once again when going past

St. Cecilia's, stony with liquor, when actually on his way to a Luxor steam box right next door to the church on Forty-sixth Street.

For some reason this was the only thing in his life for which he really wished to be forgiven.

In the swift car he spilled some liquor on his trousers, looked down, brushed it off, and realized he needed a shoeshine. He always liked to have a shine and a good haircut and a shave. These were first.

He got off the car, began walking again. He went into the men's room of a railroad hotel near the Interurban terminal in Covington, put a nickel in a pay-toilet slot, shut the door, sat down to drink as he pleased, and went to sleep there.

When he woke up he did not know where he was or what time it was. He looked into a stack of papers on a news rack. It was no use, he couldn't read while he was in motion. But he could tell he did not look well any more. People began to look at him and then pull over to the other side of the walk.

He knew now he was visibly drunk. He did not like to be drunk in a strange place. Especially he did not like to be drunk in a strange place in the daylight.

He sat down on a bench in the square and wiped his face with the hotel towel. A policeman passed and paused and looked him over. Pat stopped drying and looked back coldly, not caring. Here he finished the whisky. He felt thirsty for water, but he felt all right, even peaceful. He wished someone nice would come by and strike up a conversation, or propose a project of some sort. He felt very competent, very sure, very open to interesting suggestions.

Children played in the grass behind the war monument, an impromptu game full of laughing and pointing. Each time they ran past the public fountain they squirted water, then they howled and hooted. The sight of the water brought Patrick to his feet.

He walked over, steady enough after a few uncertain steps, and paused by the fountain, bowing slightly for a middle-aged woman who had also come to drink. She laid down a black net shopping bag in the grass and nodded to Pat for his little courtesy. When she arose after drinking, he nodded back.

She was a nice woman. A *nice polite good Christian* woman, he told himself. She was taking home the groceries to take care of her *fine husband* and rear her children. His mind invested her with virtues she may or may not have had, and his liquor italicized them as they tumbled about in the idle tracery and the irresponsible trickery of his recitations.

She saw him studying her, smiled shyly, and picked up her bag.

"Very dangerous, ma'am. Water, I mean." Pat offered this conversationally, leaning down himself over the rim.

"Dangerous? Plain water? How can it be dangerous?" She laughed.

Pat looked up, shook his head in mysterious earnestness. Then, looking at her formally, and in a tone of pulpit solemnity, he delivered four surprising words:

"Fish f—k in it."

When he straightened up from his own drinking she was gone. He felt very lonely. He felt as if he wanted to kiss somebody. Or be invited somewhere for the weekend. Or play Santy Claus. He usually played Santy Claus in the middle of July in Freeport, Long Island, for the great colony of vaudeville people who summered there and who traditionally had their Christmas in midsummer. He always whistled at these parties. And he always wowed them.

He couldn't think right now where he'd left his Santy Claus suit.

"The Great Atlantic and Pacific Tea Company," he read aloud, saying the words ornately to match their crimson ostentation on the store front. Then he repeated the same much louder, as if announcing arrivals at a royal blow-out. In front of the A & P a car was parked, a Dodge touring car, its motor running.

Pat hated the Dodge shift, the perversity of the Dodge management that would do the whole thing backward just to be different, but he got in the front seat anyway, engaged and shifted and drove away.

He drove back over the bridge into Ohio. A few miles north of Cincinnati a man sold him some raw liquor in a dry-goods store, but he wouldn't let Pat take a drink there, not even in the back of his store. So he had to drink in the car.

Somehow he would have to get a better supply. Maybe in Columbus. He was going the right way for Columbus. He wondered rationally about gas. He could still smile, still nod, still walk. But he couldn't say anything as complicated as a whole sentence. They'd know. His tongue had begun to curl over on its side, the hinge of his jaw to freeze. He wouldn't be able to say "See how much she'll take" when he got to a garage. He'd just flash ten fingers. Or seven. Or whatever he thought.

He found a garage right away and got a man to measure the tank with a dip stick. It looked like an unpainted ruler. He just pointed, not even getting out of the seat.

He tried to remember where he'd left his Panama hat. There was a big gout of grease on his right knee. His nails were vile. He needed to get back to the Luxor Hotel. It beckoned to him like harbor lights on your own shore. He began to whimper for its comforts, for the restorative powers of its tropical therapies, the masculinizing sense of its simplicity, its monkish bareness. In just one day or just one night at the Luxor with nothing supporting your body but a spread of canvas over a two-pound cot, you could be slick by morning.

Pat's mind pleasurably juggled these benefits. Easy, one hand. What the place was for. Fix you up after a rough couple of days. Boys carrying a little too much and not eating. Tidy up. Clean up. Clear the smoke out. Put a shine back on your soul. Get your smile out of hock. Get your knees back, and a good breath. Sweat out half the poison, piss out the rest. Doze back to docile living. Calm the nerves. Show up on the street again with an honest appetite for the Automat.

Where he'd go.

Show globes, red and blue and starboard green, were lighting up in phantom drugstores through all the little towns and hamlets. He ought to eat. First he'd take one more snap of the dragon spit that old man sold him in the dry-goods store. Then he'd find a diner or a dog wagon. A real nice clean joint with a sliding door and a good sting of onions. Get to Columbus. Get the hell to Columbus. Get a drink in Columbus. Plenty of money. Plenty to make it from there. If he was too drunk in Columbus to pick up a friend, he could buy a girl, buy a couple if he wanted to stay. But I got to hang onto my money. Disappeared fast when you were on one. Especially if you couldn't get off. Even alone when you didn't have to watch or keep awake or count your money or add up a check or call for a manager. Disappeared anyhow. Somehow. Him and money, good friends but never went around together very long.

"I'll keep this car to Columbus, then turn it in for a new one!"
He roared this jest aloud, banging the steering gear in delight.

"But God, how I have to pee! Have to water my snake! I have to
pee like ten men!" He wheeled into a dim garage on the fringe of a
town. A man was washing the front and hood of a shiny Cunningham.
He was pinching the frayed end of a garden hose to control the power
of the spurt. Another man was wiping down the rear of the car with
a chamois. Soapy water ran down a central drain in the middle of
the garage dirt floor. Pat unbuttoned his trousers and sent a stream
down with it.

"Hey!" screamed the man with the chamois, springing over.

"Whassa matter?" Pat replied. "All going the same place."

The wet chamois whistled before it slapped him, then landed like
a whip. Pat ran out and drove off, angered, bewildered, anxious to
hurt, to fly, to break something. He'd never fight in a garage, wrenches
around and all. Two to one anyhow. But what a hell of a thing to do!
When a guy was just watering his snake! What a hell of a thing!

Trolley rails served to guide him north. He drove with the gun-
sight vision of a concentrating drunk. He straddled the Interurban
tracks for mile after mile. Moons and wheels and globes of light
would form and move in and out of the dark. Villages spun past his
senses, coming to life in his ears like a sudden train roar in a tunnel. He
opened the cutout, then reached over and fumbled for the whisky. He
found it wedged in the cushion, uncorked it with his teeth, tilted his
head back, sucked down the hot wash of its searing ferment. He
blinked his eyes. Then he couldn't find the cork. He groped about with
his right hand, steering with his left. He came suddenly into a large
town. He relaxed pressure on the accelerator, closed the cutout while
advancing the spark on the wheel so she wouldn't stall when he
slowed her down far enough to let him cork his bottle and coast
through town.

He was braking gently to forty when a horse and buggy left its
hitch at the curb and went up on the crown of the road right ahead.
Right where his own radiator was aiming. He could see a coal-oil
lamp swinging dimly on her springs. He braked hard, cut sharply
behind the buggy, grazing its skinny wheel. Then the Dodge crashed
with authority into a wooden light pole at the edge of the sidewalk.

He was in the very center of town, in front of a motion-picture theater.

There was a crash of glass as the shock toppled the globe from the light pole. Pat's head bobbed down hard into the steering post. Absurdly the horn sounded. His stomach rammed into the rim of the wheel. Nausea flickered in his throat.

He remained conscious. He became suddenly sober, entirely so. His whisky was all over the front seat, all over his clothes. He opened the door and stepped out into the street. Beneath his feet he felt the strength of smooth macadam. It reassured him. He could smell Tarvia and hot rubber. Blood, too, faintly. The hot rubber and the Tarvia were city smells and he felt safe.

All about was a great silence. People stared with a persistent dream-like unresponsiveness. He felt as though if he were to grab them, they'd shrink out of his clutch, that they were making no sound because they really weren't there at all; that he wasn't either. People were coming out of the theater. "*Joan the Woman,* with Geraldine Farrar." It seemed quite natural, for he knew Geraldine, and Lou Tellegen, her no-good husband, too. Geraldine was one of the great ones. And Lou her no-good goddamn husband, a real bum. A worse bum than Pat himself, if possible.

Joan the Woman. It was hanging right there on a big banner under the dinky marquee, and a man with a sprocketed stick, halfway up a ladder, was about to take out some dead bulbs. He'd stopped there, hearing the crash, to look at the ruined Dodge.

There was a narrow black alley beside the theater. Pat held his belly, his arms locked. He stood there a moment in the street, half bent and hugging himself like a chilled bather. He had to vomit. He didn't want to be seen. He ran into the alley, into the dark, and let it go. Twice. His head reeled and his belly churned and twisted over.

Convulsions sent him bending again, but he was empty. He gasped for air and straightened up. He had no handkerchief. Blood dripped off his chin.

He stepped into the embarrassing brightness of the sidewalk.

"Don't walk! Don't move around!"

It was a man in a derby that shouted this. He wadded up a raincoat and put it right down on the sidewalk. People helped Pat to lie down.

He could see and hear. He felt nothing. He just felt cheerful and relaxed and loving and pure. He didn't move. A man leaned down and wiped his face.

"Got an ambulance coming," he said with tender concern, patting his shoulder, feeling his head. Then he shook out a fresh handkerchief and wiped Pat's mouth and chin.

"Thank you. I'm all right."

Pat could hear the foot bell of the ambulance a long way off.

"Were you alone?"

"Was he alone?"

"Did you see anyone?"

"He's bleeding."

"You're bleeding."

"He just missed Hathaway's horse."

"Too bad he missed Hathaway."

A little girl of nine, crowding sideways against her mother, looked down in fearful gravity. She was carrying a roll of funny papers and her sweaty little hands had begun to erase the long neck of Happy Hooligan. Pat couldn't understand why he noticed these things. Should he tell the little girl? She was wearing a tiny locket.

He thought of a girl named Miriam. She had an Italian last name, Aiello maybe. Back in school. Back in New London when he was a boy. He thought how Miriam would never play with the others, how she always ate her lunch alone. No one ever knew what she had. She was dark and beautiful and she was always looking away. Outside of New London and outside her family's house, in the high uncut grass of the yard, there was an old sleigh with its shafts up. Its bells, though brown with rust and as dead-looking as rotten apples, were still able to chink and tinkle in the wind. The smaller ones at the end could still ring anyhow. But there was something the matter with Miriam. They said she was embarrassed all her life, all her school life, over the "For Sale" sign sticking in the ground in front of the sleigh. All she ever wanted her father to do was to drag the sleigh into the barn the same as the others had. But he never would. So one summer when she was fourteen she'd run away. They tried to find her but they never did.

The ambulance was a big Peerless, with a round brass gong on her side panel. Pat said he could walk but they wouldn't allow this. They slid him in. He closed his eyes and reached out for the straps.

He saw them swinging there.

He felt the ambulance move, felt its power and mercy.

He opened his eyes again. He could smell ether.

He was in the hospital now.

Washing over his body like a tide of hot oil a consuming maniacal need for a drink of alcohol engaged all his senses. With sudden brief clarity he thought, this is the way Seton must feel when *he* needs a drink. He realized he was lying on a rolling stretcher. He did not remember being rolled in on it. He felt no pain, only the terrible disabling desire for more liquor. Any liquor. He would kill for it. The thought sickened him but he began to move and to search.

He sat up. He swung his legs over the padded side. There were no voices anywhere. People passed in the corridor outside, but no one came in. Somewhere he could hear the squash and squeak of the rubber heels of a heavy nurse. The steps were going away, not coming. His sense of danger became an animal sense, as did his sense of need: gross but dependable, alive, protopathic, and of deadly concern. Instinct directed his movements now. He could smell alcohol but he could see no bottles.

The pail?

He walked over to the porcelain draining board and looked in the pail. It was full of surgical instruments, still bloody after use. They were waiting for the sterilizer. The alcohol in the pail had the pinkish color of faded firecrackers. Its surface was choked with instruments, poking up their heads and handles like the spars and masts of little ships sunk in shallow water.

Alcohol fumes rose and stung his eyes and nostrils. With a greedy gasp, half a sob, his eyes streaming, he lifted the pail and drank off a pint. As he was still holding the pail for another toss, his glance jumped to the door. A nurse stood there. She sprang at him. The pail fell to the floor with a felted jangle.

When the alcohol hit his stomach Patrick looked at the nurse with eyes that had ceased to see, eyes that looked like glass grapes, their vitrified pulps popping out from pressures behind.

Interns ran in. A colored man stood with a mop, unable to use it.

Pat had bloody alcohol all over his shirt. His stomach felt lit up.
Tongues of fire pierced his outer skin. He felt like a man flung into
the firebox of an engine.

It was such a burning, he wondered insanely why he couldn't *hear*
it.

He flung his arms at the faucets of the sink but couldn't spin the
water on. Two men grabbed him. He was back on the stretcher. He
could hear the men grunting. But Pat was instantly back on his feet,
raging for water, screaming now.

Then a soft blackness enveloped him.

Later there was a dripping going on about him, close to him. It
sounded to be under him. The room was dark but not pitch dark.
In a tilted chair near the door a man dozed.

In the half-dark Pat could see tubes leading down from cans above,
and into two points in his legs near his knees. He could feel dull
aches in each knee, aches that grew as he breathed and that seemed
to be alive and breathing apart from his own body.

His thirst was wild and he stirred to sit up and see. It aroused the
man in the doorway.

"Don't get rough, mister. Just stay as you are."

What an odd thing to urge on me, Pat felt. Who's rough? I'm not
rough, I'm delightful.

And the voice again: "You can't lick it. Just take it."

Lick what? Those bastards in the garage? Lick who?

"I wanna drink. Drink o' water. Water," he pleaded.

"You're getting it, mister. Just as fast as they think you should."

The man was above him now. His knuckles tapped a can suspended
over Pat's head.

Pat saw it was a policeman. He could remember but one thing
after the garage: the lights of little towns. Was he on a train now?
He listened. Did he have a date? Was he due to go somewhere? He
could hear humming and clicking.

Looking at the ceiling but not at the man, Pat said the next thing
like a little prayer, as if the words should start with "Dear Jesus" or
"Please, God":

"Give me a drink and let me go."

"You're not going anywhere."

"Drink water."

"Just don't try to move around. You're getting good treatment. More'n you'd get at the Columbus pen."

Columbus?

God! How? He took a deep breath. His arms felt cramped and crowded. They felt mummified. He tried to stretch them out, but his elbows felt bound to his ribs. Then another wash of terror, another burst of sweat at the hairline. He could feel sweat jump from his insteps and from the back of his knees. He was too horrified to ask what bound him.

But he knew he was in a strait jacket.

Weakly he began to sob. The officer stood over him a moment, looking down.

"We'd like the car license. We'd like your name and address." He said this with a kind of patient earnestness. "We couldn't find a wallet. Did you have a wallet?"

Christ! he thought. I had money!

That meant it was gone, then. If there'd been any left, it was gone.

"Yes, yes," Pat said, his assents mechanical as his mind tried to turn on the situation, tried not to be caught.

"Can't you take these off?" he asked, his eyes begging.

"When the doctors come."

There was a silence. The man moved away.

"Do you want a priest?"

"Am I dying?"

"You can have a priest. You sort of burned out your insides."

"How? Was I in a fire?" He could remember little. He could only feel thirst now and a helpless humiliating sense of being tied up.

"Man, you were in a good one."

"Where? I don't remember."

"We called 'em up at Weber and Heilbroner. Where you got the suit. But they didn't know nothin'. Didn't know who you were. You want to tell us your name, mister?"

"Ferguson."

He knew someone named Ferguson. He knew Elsie Ferguson.

A doctor came in, glanced at the policeman, dismissed him with a short pleasant nod, turned on a light at the bedside table, and looked at the rigging of the jars and the placement of the needles before looking at Pat. There was a nurse behind. She had a tray, which she set down. She had a laundry-fresh smell about her and cool air followed her when she moved.

She held up his head and gave him a pill and a half glass of water to wash it down.

"More," he said. "More."

"More later," she said.

He didn't want to talk. He had been in jams but not big jams. This time he feared there was something on him. Something big.

The room was still again. A clock struck. It chimed first, then struck. It struck eleven times. It was eleven at night. What night? Jesus! Again! All over again! He better get a paper. He better not ask. People didn't understand when you didn't know where you were.

Then he realized they were untying the ends of the strait jacket, the nurse holding him while the doctor worked.

When the canvas was finally unwrapped, cool air passed across his skin like a caress. He wanted to thank someone. He wanted to thank God but he didn't know how. His skin was bare. His arms stayed up, crossed, as they had been while he was so tightly bound. How long was that? His hands were puffed. He smelled like Lysol and witch hazel and fresh sweat.

The nurse began to open his arms, pulling them out. She was careful of them as she might be with the uncut leaves of a book. The doctor spoke to her, then went out of the room. Pat grew quiet within himself as he sat up in bed. The nurse kept unfolding his arms, pumping them slightly, then passing a strong dry hand up and down the inside of each arm, from wrist to armpit. He felt drowsy and suspended. He felt as if all his pains belonged to somebody else, or that they were momentarily given to others to bear; that they were somehow separated from him physically and placed nearby where he could look at them from time to time. He kept feeling them, yet kept feeling that they weren't quite his. Each time he sought to disown them, or to relax in the safety of their transfer to a place apart, they came back. The pains were like birds wheeling around and around a chimney, wheeling off, then all showing up again, all at once and together. He could hear the whir of their return, the fearful competent flutter of their landing, feel them as they re-entered his body, feel their savage slow pecking through his vitals, their concentration upon it, feel them eating there.

They were in no hurry to devour him in just this one visit.

If he knew birds.

He thought he was being punished for stealing in on his cousin Rhoda when she was dying and taking that long, forbidden look at her between her legs.

"Mary! Full of grace—Hail, Mary!"

"Do you want anything?" the nurse asked clearly.

"Water."

"No water. You're taking it all the time." She touched the rubber tubing. Then she asked: "Do you want a priest?"

Someone must have stolen the wallet and kept it. He had no money. That was terrible. But then, he had no identity either. Was it lucky? Was it why they asked? Because they didn't know? He wished he knew where he was, who these people were. But he didn't ask. Some city instinct told him not to. Anyhow he couldn't think of what hotel he was staying at just now in New York. So he had no address. Name, Ferguson. Address . . .

His mind moved down to his diaphragm. He forgot his problem. The pain ran right over it.

"I don't want to be a bother," he said softly to the nurse. She stopped her motions a moment and had leaned over quite close. His words did not sound like his own. Nor could he tell whether he was giving a responsive answer, not knowing who was with him, what they had asked, nor indeed whether he had been asked anything at all.

He shut his eyes. Once, later, he heard an ambulance arrive, heard its bell, the coughing of the motor as it stopped, then the slide and creak of the stretcher. Voices, too, in the dark. It seemed familiar to him, merciful, well regulated. Someone was in charge of something. That was always a comfort. He must be right over the ambulance entrance, the emergency entrance.

He lay thinking, periodically in pain; then in unexpected moments of release his thoughts cleared. A streetcar passed, grinding loud around a curve. Its headlight, blue and chiefly bright, flashed through his room. Blue lights were the Interurbans. Local trolleys were always yellow, all over the U.S. Why was that?

With the roving beam of the Interurban sweeping the room like the fan from a lighthouse, he could see his clothes hanging in a closet close to his bed. How long had they been there? Had he? Had a nurse undressed him? That was a bit the wrong way around, was it not? And a pleasant absurd picture of himself being slipped out of his trousers and stripped clean by a nurse illuminated his mind in the dark.

Then he thought of the blue light again, of his clothes, of the policeman who had come in. He must be right *on* the Interurban. *Some* line, anyhow.

Suddenly he had to see what he had in his clothes, what clues they would yield, what others who had searched them first had found there. He sat up slowly, peering into the darkness at his doorway like a man on patrol trying to make form out of the formless. His heart kicked over. All he wanted to do now was to ransack his own clothes, see where he was. He wanted to see if he could stand. Most of all, he knew, he wanted to get out, get out, get away.

He pushed the sheet away from his knees and immediately felt the needles squirm and go into new tissue. It was more a bruising sensation then a pricking one. He pulled away the adhesive tape, then pulled out the needles, letting them fall where they might on each side of his bed. With his hands pressing on the mattress, he twisted his buttocks on the bed and slid his feet over and down. His knees ached. He realized he had to have water or he couldn't go far or move much. His was a thirst most awful, and his eyes groped in a senseless hope there might be some in his room. But there was neither pitcher nor glass nor faucet.

He felt at once for his wallet. It was gone. His hands became more active and useful, slipping down quickly in their desperation into his trousers pockets. He felt a few bills in one pocket but it was too dark to read their value.

He got dressed, groaning lightly, aspirating, and holding his air in whenever he had to lean forward. He discarded his socks and garters and slipped his shoes onto his bare feet, not bothering with the laces.

He stepped softly to the door. He made a quick silent survey of what was on either side of him—his steely eyes darting back and forth the way Seton's always did on the street. Close by, to his right, was a screen door, with a pale blossom of light drifting beyond. The other way, at the extreme end, was a desk, unattended, and a shaded bulb.

He slipped toward the screen door, passed a tiny alcove where mops were drying upside down on their handles, stuck his head under the faucet at the porcelain sink and sucked in the water till he felt his lungs burst for air. The water was warm and delicious and inexhaustible. He drank again, then straightened up and went through the screen door and down a short flight of cement steps, holding a railing there, and through the cut grass of a big flat yard, ignoring paths and heading toward the light he'd seen. He could smell hydrangeas.

Soon he stopped to lean against a tree, to breathe, to try to think. He reached down and rubbed his knees where the needles had been. They itched and stung like ant bites. He wished he could find a street lamp or a drinking fountain or a newsstand. It was quiet everywhere. He did not feel frightened, and the pain, when it hit him, hit so hard he had to stop. But always it went away again, or dropped its level. He did not know much about pain. He'd had little.

An automobile honked at him and passed on. It was a Chandler, a Chandler touring. He could tell by the shape of the window in her rear. He thought of autos then. His mind stayed actively with autos as some subception sought to rise and break the surface. A Dodge! He'd been somewhere in a Dodge. He could smell it, its gasoline and its leather and the hot stench of its floor boards. His feet still stung from the heat of them. Then the picture sank back, waterlogged in a black bayou of crepuscular fragments and shadows that moved on just before he could make them out.

But it cheered him, this positive remembrance of the Dodge. At least he knew he was not unconscious; at least he knew he was not dreaming.

He crossed another street, and again heard the sound of a tower clock. Four bongs this time. Under an arc light some men slept, backs pressed against a low wall of stone. Each man had a dinner pail close to him, each seemed feebly to be hugging his own. They had

heavy work shoes. Pat walked over to wake them and ask them where
he could get water.

From behind a dark church the Interurban came, its wheels complaining again. One of the men got right up. He turned around and
tossed some water into his face and shook it off. The men had been
resting and sleeping against the horse trough. Patrick lurched up to
the trough, parting water with his hands as he buried his head in it.
He was still drinking, with gasps of pleasure and relief between each
plunging down of his head, when the blue headlight turned on them
all. The men got up, straggling and stretching, one or two turning
to watch the man drink where the horses drank.

Then they all got in the big car. It was nearly empty. A few men
slept by the open windows. Patrick gripped the backs of seats, slid
down carefully by himself, slid over close to the open window, put
his head against the cool bars, and slept.

Someone was shaking him, not hard.

"You getting off at Springfield?"

Patrick did not hear but he nodded.

"Pay your fare."

He felt in his trousers. He had three dollars and six cents. He paid
his fare, forty cents, got off and stumbled into the depot. There
were people about now, not many, but they had a morning look.
Some of the men had collars. They looked at him queerly.

The soda fountain was not open but he caught a sight of himself
in the mirror behind its counter. His suit was ruined. It looked like
blood all over his coat. He took it off and folded it carefully and
combed his hair with his fingers. He felt he could not walk across the
main waiting room of the depot.

He put a penny in a gum box and got two chicklets. It hurt the
muscles of his jaw to grind them up but they began to take his breath
away and to give him something to think about. He thought also
that chewing would give him a more natural look, as if he were not
concerned with himself.

He had to find a place to lie down, a place where it was safe.
Springfield what? Springfield, Massachusetts? Springfield, Missouri?
What the hell Springfield?

A man at the Western Union banged open a couple of rolls of

bound coins and began shaking silver into the open drawer of the cash register. Patrick could remember the motion from somewhere. From his mother shaking coffee from a bag into a percolator when he was a kid in New London?

"I want to—wire New York—for some money."

Patrick felt the swift eye, the flash inventory.

"I know, I'll pay," he whispered weakly.

The man slid him a blank across the counter. Then he looked at Patrick more carefully. He saw the broken face, caught a whiff of hospital disinfectant. He saw the eyes, the pitiful eyes that looked like peeled grapes. He saw the shirt.

"There's a seat inside here. Where ladies can sit down to write out their messages. You want to use it?"

Patrick nodded, stepped around the little barrier, and went in. He picked up a chained pencil. He found he could not write longhand. He had to print.

A burst of hopelessness showered over him. He thought of his forty years, the crazy times, of this time now, of the pain going with it. He wished he were dead. It shouldn't take too much more, not now. Maybe just one or two more would do it.

With great concentration he began to print simple letters. He had never done much for anyone. Neither had he ever before asked Seton for help.

9

FAR DOWN THE BEACH JILL SAW A MAN WALKING, HIS head bent forward, through the sand. He was too far away for her to determine whether he might be carrying mail. She knew that, even when drinking, Seton was a faithful correspondent. If it were the mail, she could add a paragraph to the letter in her lap.

The tide had begun to turn. There were pools of shallow water for Sean to splash in. She looked again at the approaching man. It was not Jimmy the Tattoo. It was the movement of someone she had not before seen. But he had the cap of the Coast Guard.

Mail always excited her. The man had a canvas bag flung across one shoulder.

"I'm Lieutenant Munoz," the man said easily. "Hear you had some trouble getting your pump going." There was an easy strength to him, and a kind reserve.

Jill jumped up then.

"Oh, that's a help! A real help! Do you think you can make it go?"

"I can look at her anyhow. Here's your mail, Mrs.—Farrier."

"Thank you. Thank you very much. Would you take these? When you go back?"

"Sure, ma'am. But I'll see to the pump first. I'll pick 'em up on the way back."

"Would you like me to show you where it is?"

"Oh no, ma'am. You sun yourself and play with the boy. Is the pump in the kitchen?"

"No. The boat room. It's great big—kind of empty—where the lifeboats used to be."

"Yes, ma'am. I'll recognize the boat room."

She felt foolish, except that his smile was friendly. He was tan enough to be a sailor but he had the look of a man who wore glasses when he read. And he took good care of his hands.

"How come your husband couldn't fix it?" he asked unexpectedly, half turning. "They tell me he was in the Black Gang."

Jill remembered the expression. It meant the engine-room crew of a cargo vessel.

"Yes. Yes, he was." This world was unfamiliar to her, but her loyalty to Seton produced the sentence that seemed to satisfy the lieutenant's question. "He was an oiler and wiper. He had nothing to do with pumps."

Munoz went away then, smiling the pleasantly tolerant smile of a patient man being told things he knew better than the teller; and holding back a little.

It would be an event of interest and relief to them all if the lieutenant *did* get the pump to going—a big item to be able to write to Seton.

She wanted Sean to be occupied happily while she read. She picked up his pail and shovel, took him by the hand, and they marched down the beach a few yards, Sean trying to whistle. At the first small pair of pools the receding tide had stranded, Jill stopped, dug a shallow trench, and handed the shovel to Sean. She picked up a bleached stick and dragged it across the surface of the sand, furrowing it deeply and indicating the line for his own digging. When he found that the water followed his efforts, filling the channels as he made them, his self-absorption became that of his father. Jill went back to the post and opened the letter. This time there was only one, but it throbbed with news. He needed her and missed her. There was money in the bank. Jill was to come soon and bring their boy. Pat was still missing. Rehearsals hadn't started but readings were scheduled. His name kept appearing in the theater news. Life began to glow again, at least for Jill. His horror of cities seemed to build with every visit. She pitied him and read his concluding disturbed page with great tenderness:

Maybe I'm afraid of New York this time! Maybe that's it. Maybe I've been hiding in Village back alleys. In saloons and ships! Maybe I'm afraid to come out, and dread having to (if this is what is going to happen this time). Maybe I'm partly woman. I don't feel manly now. I feel it's ages since I've seen you. I'm so hungry for you! And I can't write in cities. I just can't!

Kiss Sean for me. You're quite wrong! I do love him. Just can't show it. Wish I could grow to his manliness. Feel detached from all living. On the way to nothing but more silence. Hung on a closet hook in the unbearable late-summer chills of New York. How I loathe it! Every foot! Every hotel! Every person on the street! Every theatre! I need you so badly, darling. Oh, Jill, Jill—in these dirty coils and tunnels how can I ever write a line! Someday I'll slam the door on this rotten city. I'll take their dirty money and

*fly back to you—forever to you, only you! Forever you! For-
give my tears, my horrid horrible moods.*

*How I hate it. New York is a whore! Broadway is her
disease! I am drinking too much. Help me, mercy of God!
How I love you!*

Seton

Her eyes stung. How he could wrench her! How she wanted to help!
But how? How?

She heard the flywheel of the pump being spun, kicking to start.
It coughed hard twice, then made a grab for life and started to go.
She could hear the lieutenant's experiments and tinkerings and the
engine's response to each. She looked over at Sean. "Oh, he does
love you! He does! He does!"

Sean's listening face and his larkish look, his mouth-open wonder,
his grave study of twigs and periwinkles, his starfish fingers dripping
sand, his slow-gathering smile of total trust, his return to the vast
problem of his tiny trenches, his repose in the safety she meant to
him, his joyous gurgles, his earnest protest—it all stabbed her. But if
Seton loved him, if he really loved——

Now Sean had his back to her again, his whole attention held by
a hole full of water. For an instant it held all the world for her too,
all of it but one, and she wrote with great speed and feeling:

*Oh, Seton, whatever may be wrong with the days right now,
our life is rich, our boy is healthy and beautiful and alive—
you are strong and useful and alive! You are going to have
all the things you have sought so long. Every one! And whatever you wish of me will be here—whenever you come back
to it. I can face any difficulty so long as I can have my two
men, so long as they want their mother, their wife, their
hired girl, their cook, laundress, and lover. Give my love to
your mother. I am overwhelmed with joy to be coming! Good
luck with all your plans! I say prayers for you every day,
every night. Maybe the bender was good for you but I
know you're glad it's over. If you never find your way to God,
you will find peace just seeking Him—in the kindness (and*

*the time) you can find to give to some other. I love you,
my own husband. I can love no other!*

Jill thought of New York now. She was determined, on the beach
that afternoon in the solitary sun, with her boy engrossed, her house
in order, but her mind shaken with the great doubt about her husband,
that she would seek help for him, that she would ask some doctor—
perhaps one of the new psychiatrists she from time to time read
about—ask him to help her understand who her husband was, not
only for herself in how to live with him, but for him too, mostly for
him—that he might know and see his fears, know enough to live
with them, whatever they were.

Once she had written him—it was four years ago when his play
Harbor had been seen in New Haven and they had had a separation
as baffling and unsatisfactory as the present one—she had written
the sentence: "It is not my plan to grow up 'wistful.' I want life *here*."
Seton had wired on receipt of the letter, accusing her of warning
him about something. Her wire back had been just as direct: "Yes,
it is a warning." And that directness had kept things clear for them
both for a long time. It was the best year they had had. Sean had
been conceived.

When she heard the soft shuffle of sand and realized the lieutenant
had returned, the sound of footsteps was a relief.

"The engine's all right now, ma'am. New, you know. I'll show
you how to throw the flywheel."

Jill got up.

"I'm ever so grateful." Then she scribbled two words on the flap
of the envelope: "Pump fixed!"

The lieutenant showed her the hidden secrets of the engine, slowed
it down for her, stopped it, started it again. It was not complicated.
He was patient with her, showing her over and over the few things
that had to be done to start and regulate the engine. His own
motions were sure and slow.

"Your boy has a fever, ma'am," the lieutenant said quietly.

The word always frightened Jill. She touched Sean's cheek, then
his forehead. Then she picked him up and held him.

"He was all right. Only a few minutes ago. He was cool when he came down from his nap."

"Start real fast with kids sometimes. Go right down again, of course. Could I do anything more, ma'am?"

"No. Thank you. But if I needed anything, could I come down to the station? I'm alone—my husband, he'll be back soon. But if my boy——"

"Easier than coming all the way down, why don't you just hoist a shirt on the flagpole? Halyards are still good."

"But could you see it? So far off?"

"Oh yes, ma'am. Quite easy, with glasses. I'll look over this way—time to time. Good-by, ma'am. Good-by, sonny."

He put his cap on and went on out of the boat room and down the beach. Jill's feelings went with him. At least he was not Jimmy the Tattoo. At least he was a man who was not looking.

10

WHILE SETON SAT NEAR THE BACK OF THE THEATER, alone as always and slouched down deep in the rough covering of the seat, his play's director, Charlie Westover, stood quietly in the center aisle ten feet from the apron and told the cast—speaking clearly and without hurry to them across the empty pit—what the play was about. Assembled before him under the wretched gloom of a work light, the cast stood as if drying out after shipwreck.

Seton peeked up at them now, mystified at the durable phenomenon a rehearsing cast always presented to his eye. Through the years it was an odd moment. Nothing ever looked right in rehearsal, actors and actresses least of all; the very same actors who, with a show just over, might look intelligent, might look alert anyhow; these same actors had then moved with a stride and a pride and a sure sense of objective. Now they hung about, shuffling and shiftless in the half-

—and say impromptu—a thought so relevant! Seton realized that for himself it would take him, the writer, half a morning to phrase the same thought in such a paragraph.

These are good thoughts, felt Seton. This is a good man. His mind began to join that of his director, just a little to envy it.

"As an actress," Charlie continued, "you will have no trouble projecting the idea of your destructiveness. The idea that emotionally whatever you eat, you engulf. But your characterization must carry much more than this, something quite terrifying in its subtlety: you are not aware of your system of motivations. You do not realize you operate out of a complex set of fears. If you were to see yourself in the action of some other, what you saw would be abhorrent to you. You are therefore as trapped as any of the others. If your audience is to hate you for the enormity of your acquisitiveness, they are given glimpses of your own self-doubt and so can temper your own misery, which is total before the play ends, with snatches of begrudging pity. They know the bite you have taken is so big it will choke you. But they must get to know this a little at a time."

"Good, good," thought Seton. "He's really on it. As good as Arleigh said."

There were a few more sentences: "There is hope and there is purpose and there is careful planning—but don't endeavor to bring a noble touch to the interpretation of who you are or what propels you. It is a play without nobility of thought or motive. This is deliberate avoidance, not oversight. This is a play out of the depth of the heart, out of the dark of the belly, unillumined by any bright arcadings of the human spirit or any brave reaches of the mind. So don't play it out of your head. Play it out of here."

He ground his fingers into his abdomen and wrenched at the muscles there. He looked as if he might tear his shirt.

"Take your positions now."

There was a stirring on the stage, a short slight hesitancy, then a settling down of movement, a setting up of tension that was quick and alive. The faces of the actors became faces of other people, their own personalities stoppered, their gaits altered, their posture and attitude transformed.

The tight speech of New England, gnarled and spare and stingy-sounding, mean-spirited and querulous, spread out into the seats like the quack and yarring of an angry barnyard.

Westover had set this feeling for it in the long readings the week before. Seton leaned forward, listening for false notes in its carping ruralism. He was a New Englander himself.

After a few moments he crept forward from his seat in the back to Charlie Westover's row and whispered:

"The stage is too dark."

"Yes," Charlie agreed, turning. "Borders!" he roared. At once the borders were turned on and an illusion of daytime fell over the stage.

"Sorry, cast. Take it without a break to the entrance of Emily. Take it from: 'You will never get it out of me. Nor out of the ground.'" The entrance was made again, the cue given, the line repeated. It didn't satisfy Charlie. "No. No!" he shouted with energy. "Come in sooner! Move faster! *Walk* faster!" He grinned and poked his finger at her. "You're hoist of your own retard!"

The cast loved the impromptu witticism, but Seton scowled. He was suspicious of laughter at rehearsal.

Charlie remained quietly in the center aisle, watching and listening, turning his head away from the action in order to hear only, turning back, jotting notes in his own shorthand.

He had no script. Seton suddenly realized something astonishing. *His director had memorized the entire play.*

Seton had never heard of such a thing. He felt more than flattered, he felt secure and uplifted. But this feeling was immediately destroyed when he thought of the stark (gratuitous?) sentence his director had used in his prefatory remarks to the cast: "This is a play without nobility of thought or motive."

The hell it was! Charlie would have a lot of explaining to do. And he better be careful never to say such a thing—nor to imply such—again. Not before the company. Was he trying to put Seton in his place?

Five-Below crept out of the dark and whispered to Seton:

"Mr. Brayce says to remind you the newspaper fellows will be in the manager's office at one."

"I told Mr. Brayce I wouldn't see them."

Five-Below, peering and furtive and in a half squat like a lemur on a bough, knew his friend had never said this to Brayce, that it was just Seton's way of taking care of things he didn't like. "Yes, I know. Shall I remind him you won't see them?"

"Yes, remind him. Tell Brayce to see them himself. Or have Mr. Westover do it. Or cancel it. I'm not a public curiosity. I'm a writer. Why do they want anything now? We're just starting!"

"Well, maybe they want to know about the play," Five-Below offered with dissolving clarity. His reasoning had the directness and economy of a child's. He never saw anything but the main point.

Five-Below went off in the dark, up the stairs to the balcony where Arleigh Brayce was sitting in the front row. Electricians were adjusting clamps to a bank of light. Arleigh was sipping coffee, at rest, patient, alert. His white hair shone like phosphorous in the gloom.

"He won't talk to the fellows from the newspapers."

"All right," said Arleigh without turning.

"Shall I call them up and tell 'em not to bother to come?"

"No, don't do that. They're all over the city. No way to get at them now."

Arleigh decided to corner Seton and force him to face the press. They'd be easy men to be with; Arleigh knew them all. Newspapers never sent critics on errands of this sort. It was always the youngish knockabout reporters who came, all of them with special favorites of their own, most of them with writing aspirations, many with real theater savvy and sharp judgments.

Arleigh knew that once Seton was over the shock of being trapped, he would very soon begin to enjoy himself.

In his mind Arleigh decided the meeting should happen on the stage itself, when the cast broke for lunch. He had a couple of bottles of Old Grandad in the office. He'd put it out on a prop table, get Seton talking about the novel set that was being assembled in a Tenth Avenue loft. He was sure Seton's abnormal self-consciousness would fall away. With this set it was going to be possible for an audience to see independent but related actions at the same time.

An entire façade for the farmhouse was neatly separated into four quadrants of the same size. These quadrants were actually sliding panels which, when closed, looked as bleak as any other New England exterior but when pulled apart and shown to the audience section by section, room by room, and mood by gathering mood, seemed to dissect the architecture and the lives of the occupants just as unsparingly as Seton had uncovered the cold greed that destroyed his characters.

Robert Barry Devereaux, whom Brayce had brought in to design the set, adapted for the special needs of Seton's action a plan he'd seen in Germany the year the war ended.

Arleigh doubted if he could get Seton to talk to the newspaper men about his play. He even doubted the sense of trying. He was such a bad talker when compelled to talk, he might botch his own opportunity. But he knew Seton would open up if they got him going on the Devereaux set. He got up then and went looking for Five-Below and found him smoking on the stairway between floors.

"Tell Jim—he's the assistant stage manager, the fellow with the glass eye—to put the model of the set in the wings. It's in the office now. And tell him to get new batteries for it so we can light it up."

That would take care of the main problem: getting Seton relaxed enough to talk without fear.

Arleigh now reasoned that since Seton probably felt he had already got rid of the newspaper interview and would show some kind of hostility, even panic, if he saw he'd failed, he had better make Seton's physical escape impossible. He knew that Seton could turn and run; that he would probably do so if he saw people bearing down on him.

Arleigh struck on the idea of having the stage door painted. This would seem to make legitimate its being briefly barred from use. Quietly but at once he ordered it locked, ordered the painting started, had the carpenter put horses around it and hang up a "WET" sign.

Then he crept back to his seat in the balcony and watched, and waited calmly for one o'clock.

Charlie Westover was punctual with the break. The stage cleared. The borders dimmed and went out. The basketed work light went on. Conversations and snatches of laughter, of examination and surprise hellos, passed through the air. A piano tuner came into the pit. A fracture of discordant octaves stole up out of the dust and the dark.

"They're in the lobby!" It was Five-Below.

Arleigh saw Seton walk down the aisle to Charlie, two tall men, their heads close together. Seton was gesturing, his teeth showing. He was disagreeing about something. Then he saw a stagehand bring the set model to the very center of the stage and put it on the prompter's table.

This was going to be all right.

He heard the newspapermen laugh at something and hurried down to meet them.

"Has he got the biggest thing Broadway ever saw?" asked one of them at once.

"Why don't you ask him yourself?" Arleigh answered, shaking hands. "I'm Brayce, the producer. Hello, Eddy, hello, Don."

There were casual greetings, a few introductions.

"You fellows like a drink?" Arleigh asked.

There was an electric response to this. Arleigh turned to Five-Below. "There's a small cabinet, a wall cabinet, above my desk. Bring the bottle on stage."

Five-Below drifted off but he saw that Seton had turned, that he had guessed at the situation, and that he was walking away toward the stage.

"Where's Seton?" Arleigh asked, bringing up the others.

"He'll be right back," Charlie said. "Bathroom. Hello, fellows. I'm a little sweaty. But we got a great play. No doubt of it. And I don't say great unless I mean it. There's no Belascos around this company."

"I thought we'd go up on the stage, Charlie, and sit around and have a drink. Thought they'd like to have a close look at the Devereaux set. The model, I mean."

"Sure."

In the wings the electrician paid no attention to Seton as he went up the ladder to the light bridge. He assumed it was his assistant. They were the only two allowed on the bridge.

When Seton saw the men moving down on him he ran for the stage door. He found it locked and got paint all over his hands. He turned like a pursued criminal and went up the light-bridge ladder as though he were coming up out of an engine room of a torpedoed freighter. He ran across the bridge, his jaw set, his eyes flinty, his

body crouched. He would be dangerous to meet. He leaped from the
end of the bridge to the narrow vertical ladder that disappeared in
the darkness of the flies. Tiny gasps were coming from his mouth,
little grunts as he forced greater speed from his legs. He heard his
shirt tear. Change fell from a pocket and bounced musically far
below. He never looked down. He kept looking up, up at the forest of
ropes, catwalks, hanging backdrops, cykes and scrims. He kept hating
Arleigh for springing this trap, and exulting in his own strength and
ingenuity for being able to escape it.

He ran across the narrow catwalk at the very top of the flies to the
tiny ladder leading to the trap door that gave out on the roof. If this
was shut? If this was *shut?*

He lowered his head ready to buck, and with his shoulders and the
back of his head and neck he charged up into it with enough force
to shatter a bathroom door. The trap gave easily and he went spurting
right through the aperture into blinding sun and a suffocating sensation of heat and melting tar paper.

In the glare he covered his eyes for an instant and sucked in the
air. Then he looked down into the black hole and fitted the cover
back on the small square he'd plunged through.

He had no idea where he was except on top of a theater. He was
trembling, but he could feel a wild inner exhilaration too. He had a
feeling of physical conquest and revenge, of beating an enemy, out-
scheming a rival, and turning a hostile force all the way back on itself.

He cupped his eyes and viewed his situation. He was on an exact
level with the building across the street, south of him. It was the Edge-
ley Hotel, eight stories high. East of him was open air, for the theater
stood on a corner. He walked across the hot gravel of the roof
to a brick wall on the west side. Two steel rungs, set into the
wall, enabled him to get up and look over and beyond. Here the
theater building was contiguous to a nondescript building of some
sort, an apartment perhaps, for clotheslines were stretched across one
end. An intense, florid, old woman was beating a carpet strip with
a broom handle. She looked up when she saw his head and shoulders
appear suddenly over the wall. And she looked ferocious.

"Don't you come over *here!*" she shouted, red and sweating. "Don't
you *dare!*" But he jumped over and down and ran past her. "You get

off my roof, you cat burglar!" she screamed, chasing him with her stick. Then she shouted down a covered stairway.

"Fritz! Fritz! Call the police!" She was out of sight now, down the stairs. But Seton had jumped to the next building, another theater judging by the boxlike projection coming out of its flat roof. On the opposite side of this roof, still running west, he found the top of a ladder of an outside fire escape but he spurned its use, for fear the woman beating the carpet could make her own way to the street before he could.

It horrified him to think of being taken publicly, people staring, police waiting below.

Goddamn this city and all the people in it!

Stretched out on an army blanket and a thin blue pad was a young lady in a bathing suit, taking the sun. She looked up startled, with resentful inquiry and sullen challenge. Beyond her was a tin door close by an open skylight. She saw he was breathing hard and she sat up quickly, pulling in her knees and stiffening her back.

"The stairs," he gasped, beseeching. Blindly she pointed toward the tin door beyond the cluster of chimney pots. He ran to it, jerked it open, and began feeling his way down the dark stairs. They kept going around and around a central shaft. Halfway down he realized the shaft contained an ancient elevator, for the shadow of its ascending car passed him like something huge and determined and underwater.

He could see a little better now. Some doors had signs: CELLO LESSONS. RUBBER STAMPS. HEMSTITCHING. DOLLY DRESSES. A man with his coat over his arm fumbled with a string of keys and looked at him vacantly, working a toothpick across his mouth with his tongue and lips. Seton thought he was trying to smile, then the man belched loudly and went on fussing with the door.

The last flight of stairs took Seton into a cool tiled entrance hall, past the brass fitting of the elevator door. A colored porter in a tilted chair leaned against the back wall, his eyes closed. Seton heard a wagon pass, then went into the street and began walking south. He wanted to hurry, but even more he wanted to duck in somewhere and become invisible, with a sandwich, or a paper. He hungered for safety. He thought of his wife. Small sobs caught his throat and tightened it and died there.

At last he saw the Astor Hotel. He went into the side entrance on Forty-fifth Street, rushed across the lobby to the newspaper stand, bought a paper, and went up the stairs to the balcony and sat down in a black leather sofa. He was sweating and shaken and spent. Tears flooded his eyes now and he wept quietly into his handkerchief.

He wished some miracle would bring news of Patrick, good news of him. If Patrick was in a jam, Seton could help. He could even send money. For the first time he could send a little money.

Traffic sounded far away. People disappeared. His pulse quieted. But he knew he would not go back to rehearsal, not that day.

He began to think of Holly and the nights they had had.

He decided to go to his brother's room to bathe, put on a fresh shirt and stop by the Far Cathay to see if Holly was there. Or maybe by now Jill had written.

He wanted a drink.

He leaped up. Then forced himself to look calm. People. Posters in the Astor lobby announced that Madge Kennedy was back on Broadway after a three years' absence. *Ladies' Night* was a smash.

The Lou Tellegen-Geraldine Farrar quarrel was on the street as an extra.

But it all depressed Seton. Sandwich men, with cards sticking out of their heads like people from Oz, loped by under signs for *Rollo's Wild Oat*, and Fred Stone's *Tip Top*. Even *Liliom* was being promised again.

How vile it all was, vile, glassy, meretricious!

Was *he* the only man in the world who knew what a theater was *for?*

What junk! What a dump! What a jungle! What apes and adders! No wonder I drink so! It wasn't a city at all! It was a tunnel under a ruin, a crypt under a dead cathedral. It was a civilization drowned and left to land crabs. A sideshow with nothing but trained fleas!

At Seventh and Forty-third a Salvation Army lassie held out a tambourine. The quiet smile in her kind eyes tightened in alarm when she saw the soul-sickness and the terror and the agony that was passing her corner then.

She had a wild desire, a flaming female desire, to follow him, to take him by the arm, to feed him.

Seton went back to his brother's hotel room, pulled the shades down, and took his clothes off. He drank a tumbler of liquor, then went into the bathroom and began running water into the tub.

The image of Holly lying there in that same tub half asleep and himself coming in to her more than half drunk, brought her freshly and excitingly into his mind again. He should have tried to reach her —just drop in on her as if he were passing by and wanted to say hello—when he left the Astor.

He knew if he had by chance collided with Holly, or overtaken her on the street somewhere, or really gone right by her window and seen her, he would have been overjoyed. With Holly you didn't have to be afraid of anything. Now, thinking of her, of the time of day, of the half-terrifying, half-absurd flight he'd taken over the dirty West Side roofs, of the probability she wouldn't be able to leave her work anyhow, he turned off the water, stirred the tub with his hand, stepped in, slunk down, leaned back, and hooked a long bony foot over each edge.

It never occurred to him that Holly was a living replica of his own wife, companionable and believing, not expecting much, gentle, understanding, amused, waiting, protective, generous in her thoughts of others. He had not noticed she had the same body, too, and, as far as he knew her now, she had the same needs and sexual responses, the same hunger for quietness, for kindness, for joining to some other person and sharing her experience there.

A twinge of guilt which he refused to call guilt went through his chest. He tried to think that the times he had taken Holly had been an accommodation to her more than they had been any planned seeking of his own; that it was more than anything a response to the quietness of her, to the still charm of her, to her unasking acceptance of him that had been there from the first moment, even though it was a moment of tumult in a hurdy-gurdy block-party atmosphere, jammed against a waltz marathon.

In this miasma he had found a serene woman. And she had found a troubled man. He sought to set it this way, a woman's way—it seemed so much easier and nicer—putting to one side their rapturous interlockings and his own troats and croakings and spent gasping, the final exhausted uncurling of his own hand. Forget this.

Forget this?

He wanted to do what he wanted to do and do it without the world's comment, with no signal hung from the yards of conscience.

He could almost achieve this, the nonchalant occasionalism of urbane love-making. At least he could almost achieve the manner in which he had always supposed history's sophisticates took their women: bit them a little, then spat them out. Yet something heavy stayed on to load his mind.

He was tormented by the situation he had left in the theater. (Had he been seen, escaping into the flies? Or had he fooled them all and left them stunned and chastised? Who was foolish?)

He was tormented by being away from the silence of Cape Cod, by being flung out upon the risk and sprawl of a city he hated, and separated from the impregnable safety of his work shack.

Mostly he was tormented by thoughts of Jill. He could never quite achieve the casual look, the impersonal throw-away. It made the pricking lighter to think with what devotion Holly held him. (*There* was a woman who really thought he was special!) And it excited him to think of the wild coming to him when her shyness had flown.

It made it lighter but it did not make it less.

Why should he suffer so? This little thing with Holly—my God!—it was less than a peccadillo right now. How could anyone——? For that matter, with Jill so far away and no one about her on the whole Atlantic shore, no one but dangerous men perpetually available, how could he know that Jill was not being unfaithful to *him* day and night right this minute? That she hadn't started the instant the sand wagon—a month or two before—had careened over the last dune? How could any man tell anything about his own wife when he was away from her?

Sexual adventures never hurt the men anyhow.

Come to think of it, he'd never known a man who didn't like Jill. And she was a great, if easy, kidder besides. There on the sand, their boy sleeping, the Coast Guard passing periodically, was there a woman alive whose quick calculation wouldn't assess the physical safety of an amour, even a continuous string of them, under conditions so perfect?

He began to feel sicker in the suspicion of his wife than he did in the dampening fact of his own infidelity. His was invisible, a city thing, fortuitous, spur-of-the-moment, perhaps already all over, while hers, in its fearful isolation, if it were to erupt or if it were already doing so, might destroy all his work, all his hope; might spread over the whole of Cape Cod, reach the Boston papers, bring shame and ruin upon him; then, last and worst of all, provoke the sneer of unspoken ridicule. And do all this when he was about to step through the doorway into his own future.

Under the special circumstances of their own remoteness at the Cape, Jill's misconduct could take on the classic lines and the cemetery permanence of a Hawthorne story. He began to suspect this was exactly what was happening. All women had a power beyond their knowledge; had sudden endings of long controls. There were even women who would murder for sex. He *knew*. Some of them were even in his own plays. They'd all sign waivers to propriety, jeopardize their honor, toss away the restraint of custom and discretion, or, if really caught in these clutches, betray the sanctity of the most holy vows. Holly, herself, was an example: so lewd in her love-making, so willing to be more so if he would lead her there, that Seton could not reconcile the still, shy creature in the cubbyhole of a travel office with the carnal activity she brought to his bed. In her hurry to be altogether possessed and possessing, she tore things.

It was something to marvel at. Seton knew he would not be able to describe even to a willing listener the total transformation of personality that overtook Holly when alone with him—describe it in a way to make it believed. It was too extreme. It was an experience in absolute venery, blinding and emptying, and unstopped by fear, embarrassment, or distortions of face and look.

Yet Holly was extraordinarily shy.

Seton suddenly became certain that his wife was carrying on with the Coast Guard.

He got out of the tub and, without drying, hurried over to the bare table and began writing her his fears.

He set his face severely and severely began:

Jill:

My life here has been too rough and demanding for you
to add to the burdens I carry. You must surely know that I
do it for you before I do it for myself. Even before I do it for
the theatre.

Reading between the lines of your letters to me, it is
evident that I am not long out of sight before the help and
strength of some other man—any other man—replaces me.
Your determination (I can see it in no other light) to rid
yourself of me financially and emotionally—even though you
might flatly deny even to yourself (and of course you would
deny it to me) that such plans were darkly forming in the
back yard of your mind—becomes clearer and takes on
greater substance with every letter.

When I am not with you, you should live your life exactly
as if you were being watched all the time. As you are! And
not by any beneficent heavenly father standing over our
house, keeping danger away from the doors. You are being
watched, or how else would I know what you are up to?
We've had a great many sudden, protracted separations.
We'll have others. By now you should have learned to accom-
modate yourself to their discipline.

You should never drink a drop when I am not there. You
should never see or speak to any man. None except Terry.
He's too old to matter much for one thing, he knows his place
for another, and he has enough instinctive gratitude to me
never to imperil his situation. He was a good deal of a something in Ireland, I can tell you, and was personally acquainted
with the Haymarket martyrs. If he is a bit of a bore to you,
you should find the grace to put up with it. You would be
glad of such hospitality—scanty though it is—if your two
circumstances were reversed.

My own professional contribution to the good of this
world (and I realize it is nothing you care one whit about)
has taken my mind and spirit—and of late, this weary body
also—to some dark places. There are great things stirring
and I am doing some of the stirring myself. I must feel free

*to go on with it. No matter what. Your private life, when I
am not about, should be the very mirror and the mold of
New England propriety and convention, odious though these
words may sound to you.*

*Everything is coming to a boil, some good, some disreputa-
ble. Carlo Tresca has taken over where Joe Ettor was crucified
by the goddamn mill owners (I refer to the Lawrence and
Paterson strikes)—Joe was condemned with no more of a
hearing than they've given Sacco and Vanzetti in the Brain-
tree shooting. I tell you if a God-fearing, noble-minded,
self-declared Anarchist can't enjoy the same protections that
we daily hand out to a Republican or a Democrat, then the
U. S. Constitution has lost its use and meaning—a scrap of
paper. You should have heard Elizabeth Gurley Flynn in
Webster Hall last night! Too bad she's a woman, and most
unfortunate she's the homeliest woman ever to be seen on
this earth (though maybe this works to her advantage, at
least not against it, since no one realizes or thinks of her as
a woman). In any event, she speaks with overwhelming
force. She's speaking tonight in Union Square in behalf of
the strikers who have walked out of the Mesabi Iron Range.
I may go. It depends. (They are calling her "Gurley" now—
I'm sure the "Elizabeth" keeps people away who ought to be
exposed to her fire and heated by it. We're too complacent.)
I've been asked to speak at the Jack Reed ("Ten Days That
Shook the World") memorial, and I may do so, but will
have to see.*

*I talked to Emma Goldman earlier in the week and she
told me of her long interviews with Trotsky—she's been
lecturing at Cooper Union—and there seems no doubt that
Capitalism, as we know it, is doomed. In fact, self-doomed.
Too much for too few. Too little for too many.*

*Labor is the strength of this nation, Capitalism its cancer.
I've nearly completed the scenario for a long play I've had
in mind for many months now. Pennsylvania coal miners,
Negroes, Polacks, kids. You've no idea what's going on
(we've both been too much out of touch—there's so much*

to write about and think about!). Floyd Dell took me to a party off Sheridan Square a few nights ago (I was asked to recite "The Hound of Heaven"—I think it went well—I never do such a thing but I had a couple of drinks) where there was a big room full of people who are doing big things in this old town. Brave things. Things to think about. Max Eastman was there, and Merrill Rogers—all of them intimately connected with (alas, suspended!) THE MASSES. Arturo Giovannitti, a very fierce and imposing fellow, terribly alive, recited the poem that made him famous—about the Northwest Wobbly, Frank Little, who was executed by an armed mob (hanged under a trestle). Very stirring. A huge nobleman of a Negro was there too—Paul Robeson. He sang a lot of spirituals (a good many more than I needed to hear), but it turned out he has been to see everything I have had produced in the Village, and it suddenly occurred to me, though he has never been on the stage as an actor (he's been on the concert stage and has the most commanding presence of any person I ever met, except Mortimer Flowers), he would make an ideal "Baby," the giant gentle gang boss at the anthracite mine head. I'd never thought of Baby as a Negro but a Negro will only make it the more moving.

This man has unbelievable strength. He has a degree of some sort, and speaks Russian. He creates quite a flurry, even among (or especially among) the white girls (which I could do without). But there's "a new world a-comin'," with big changes.

Glad you sold your little story to Biograph. You know full well there is money in our account. I can look the old world right in the eye and tell it to go to hell and don't you ever forget it.

The theatre, which you may someday understand better than you do right now, is a tongue-wagging, rumor-mongering, tale-bearing mash of old hens, all pecking each other's pin feathers when they aren't pecking each other's eyes. When I cannot be on the Cape to protect the good name of Farrier, you must do it. Your motion-picture excitements seem insane and impractical and out of character. Look what it's doing to Wally Reid, what has happened to Art Accord, to Barbara LaMarr, William Desmond Taylor! Do you want to be a flapper? Do you want to know people like Fatty Arbuckle?

That is Hollywood for you! But that is your choice.

I leave you now with that thought.

Rehearsals are leaving me exhausted. I doubt if this is of much interest to you. And for God's sake, stop shouting about money! Brayce has just mailed me another thousand, so relax, trim your canvas, and take care of your own side of the contract. I'm concerned with the unhappiness of the world, and you blather about a pump and a drummer and a dunning drugstore keeper! I'm sorry I'm such a bore! Seton.

The wall phone rang with sudden impudence. Seton's posterior, damp and bare, clung to the artificial leather of the chair he had been sitting on. He walked over to the phone, patting at his behind as if tidying a skirt.

Patrick?

"There's a telegram for you, Mr. Farrier. Shall I read it or send it up?"

"Read it! For God's sakes!" Seton's heart jumped. So did his voice.

"Show closed last week. Been in hospital. Bill paid but need immediately return fare New York care of this Western Union office. Am very weak. Pat."

Seton's hands were trembling. He didn't know what to ask first.

"Where's the wire from?"

There was a short pause, while the clerk apparently looked back at the telegram to see.

"Isn't it on there? You must know where the wire *came* from?"

"Yes, sir. From Springfield. Springfield, Ohio."

"Well, look up the fare and send it. Right away."

"We can't put such a charge on your bill, Mr. Farrier. It's a house rule."

"*But I want my brother to get the money and get it right now!*"

"You'll have to bring it in cash, sir."

Seton slammed the receiver back on its hook and began leaping about, looking for his clothes.

Seton never carried any money on his person. But he had a large amount of cash taped to the underneath side of the top of the bureau. He detached this, slammed the drawer, and ran down the corridor toward the elevators, buttoning his trousers with one hand, working into his coat with the other.

11

IN THE AUSTERE ATMOSPHERE OF HARD REHEARSAL both Arleigh Brayce and Charles Westover had the poised attention and continuous absorption of professional men of the theater. They talked in the present tense. Between themselves, they talked in short sentences. To the spoken needs of others they were approachable, quickly responsive to any question. There was a healthy haecceity about them, a here-and-now look, an on-the-spot readiness. They were present, composed, available.

It was not that way with Seton.

Of course, as with the others, he was present, yet in this very presence there was something fugitive. Withdrawn, too; recalcitrant, often hostile. He mumbled a good deal.

It was not a group undertaking to Seton.

At the sound of other's conversations, his eyes would blaze with odd suspicion, hating the talkers even before identifying them. Those who knew him well knew that in his whole life he almost never laughed (Arleigh had benevolently warned the cast not to worry about it); he didn't laugh when others did, though the provocation and the place were perfect. But in the theater laughter was a sacrilege so black offenders never offended twice. Laughter had one meaning—frivolity.

Midway through the weeks of rehearsal, gloom settled whenever

Seton entered. The cast got so they could tell—waiting in the wings
for a cue or just watching the work of the others—when he was there,
even where he was seated. They could sense it just by the action of
others. There was a sudden tensing-up of their movements. Masters
of voice control lost this control for an instant when they knew Farrier
was there. They had to stop and find it again. They admired him,
and they admired what he had done. But they feared him too, the
flashing look of him, the smoldering savagery, the unwinking eye.
Many of the actors quietly admitted they dreaded him; dreaded his
being there, dreaded his bass gutturals, his fearsome nervousness, his
appalling shortness of temper. He puzzled the actresses, never once
addressing a single one of them. When the fluid quick-minded Westover crossed him, Farrier trembled, never standing up to the cross;
just resenting it, pushing it back, fuming, hurt, dismayed. He had
the look of a man who was sure he was in the midst of a conspiracy;
that those about him were about to spring on him, pummel him, pull
him down, insult his work, change it.

To himself, as to the company, Seton was the only one in the
theater who mattered. All others, every one of them, came to feel
servile instead of subordinate. It wasn't that he treated them with
scorn. They admitted that he did not do this. It wasn't any show of
active contempt, not even a tangible insinuation of contempt. It was
more disembodied than that.

He treated them as if they weren't there.

After weeks of daily contact he often called actors by wrong names.
It was a sham ignorance, for in his letters to Jill, or in his talks with
the producing unit, he knew every member minutely.

He had another depreciating device: he would indicate whom he
meant (speaking with Westover) by a pleasant enough but crush-
ingly impersonal pointing-out of that person with his bony finger.

They all talked of this in their ways. Westover felt it was spoiled-
child cruelty. As the show's director, he had work to do. He cut right
through Seton's moods, paying them no attention. He'd worked in
troubled atmospheres before. He expected talented people to be queer,
nasty. But Arleigh, in his concern for Seton's inability to relate to
others, saw something worse than cruelty, something more wasteful

than immaturity. He saw the beginnings of disease. Seton needed psychiatric help.

His anxiety over his brother's misadventure was an abnormal anxiety in itself—abnormal, because for Patrick's way of living there was nothing new to it. Mostly Arleigh worried about Seton's effect on the cast.

When they had to seek it at all, actors now began to seek Seton's attention with fear.

On the street the cast would nod, but no actor ever joined him, no actor ever hurried to overtake him. None ever thought to. Once in a while he'd be seen going off in the dark, Five-Below shuffling behind.

It was even worse with actresses. With them especially he was distant and formal and austere. They did not know whether they were looked upon as whores or goddesses. (Charlie lightly urged them not to poke into it closely.) When rehearsal circumstances required an actress to be in his presence, to be physically close to him; or on one of those rare occasions—there were three of them—when he went to the apron of the stage to speak a paragraph himself (these were never understood, even when jotted down by the assistant stage manager and studied later), Seton threw up a partition of courtliness so spurious and absurd it was laughed about in the dressing rooms. With a pulling-back of his head, with an inflection of voice that almost said aloud, "Listen carefully so I am not put to this irritation a second time," he would bow, hold them briefly with the glow of his dark and burning eyes, speak gently, then ever so slightly bow once more, dismissing them.

It was cavalier, it was crazy. It was laughable. But it kept the women off. It was effective.

The cast had its own views about the play's author. Arleigh heard them talking all the time, talking about Seton:

"Four times I invite him to the Lambs. The Lambs! With his own father's portrait hanging right there in the billiard room! He's a boor and a bore!" (This was in the men's room, from an actor playing one of the farmers.)

There were a quantity of others, new each day. "He's not cold—he's suffering" (Understudy—girl). "He looks like a drug user"

(Understudy's friend). "He's trying to find his way back to the Church" (Wardrobe). "It's an act" (Grip). "He never did anything but shovel cow manure on a cattle boat" (Best boy).

Arleigh and Charlie Westover were talking over these things in the tiny office next to the box office of the Morosco.

"How did you do with the cuts, Charlie?"

"I took an hour and twelve minutes out of his play." Charlie didn't look easy about it.

"God!" Arleigh was impressed. He felt uneasy too. "How?"

"I haven't made them. I've just marked them."

"He'll probably argue every comma with you. He's not a pro really. In one way."

"What way is that, Arleigh?" Charlie put his feet up on the desk and stretched back.

"No one can teach him anything."

"Well, maybe. In one way he doesn't need any. He's written a magnificent play. It's going to be talked about for a hundred years. So is Seton. But I've studied the play just as hard as he has. And I know it better. Quite aside from all its creaking and groaning, and the goddamn old lady saying the same thing eighteen different times and damn near the same way every time, we got four hours and forty minutes of show, counting intermissions. We got a cast that has to go right back into their own shows as soon as they're done with our matinee. So"—here Charlie took his feet down and leaned over toward the desk—"if we play this show the way Seton wrote it, everybody is going to miss their entrances for *Defense*. Or else go on with no make-up."

Arleigh grinned. It was true enough. It was going to be physically impossible to do both.

"I'm serious."

"So am I," Arleigh agreed. "We can use that argument to force him to take your cuts."

"We can try."

"Let's see the cuts."

Charlie handed over his script. Arleigh put on his glasses, set the script in his lap, and began paging. There were hundreds of marginal brackets, and slashing arrows to show cuts, blends, and a few repositions.

"Where's the third act?" Arleigh asked.

"I took it out."

Arleigh looked over then, closing the script but keeping a finger tucked in. Instead of saying: "*I took it out,*" Charlie might have said: "*I just killed your children*"—Arleigh had that look on his face.

"I spent the whole night on this job, Arleigh. The whole past month besides. Ever since Atlantic City." He got up and walked over to the dirty window and looked out at the ash barrels in the court. "I got the suspicion about this last week. Last night I read the play, standing up, as if it was a *new* play consisting of Acts One, Two and Four. It is a much stronger play." He kept sitting down, then getting right up again. "There is no development whatever in Act Three that we don't have in Act Two. And Act Four brings to final resolution everything Seton Farrier is trying to say. But brings it in *an hour too late!* He's said it all in two acts. He didn't write Act Three for any structural necessity. Or any plot content. Or any character build. He wrote it because he couldn't get the hell off his theme! He wrote it because he's a spoiled goddamn son of a bitch that loves to bawl in his own beer!" He beat the words out, banging his hand on a coat tree.

Arleigh knew all this.

"How much of this are you going to tell him?" he asked quietly.

"I'm going to put it right at him. Right here in this office. Right now." Then he grinned. "If you'll let me."

"Nothing would relieve me more than to have an errand somewhere else the minute Seton appears." He grinned back at the exuberance and the brave willingness of the younger man. Charlie would do anything he thought was right, if it would bring out a better play. He knew more than their authors, every time. And Arleigh knew more about audiences. Their strength was as much in these two great skills as in their special integrities.

"But I'm not going to run out on you, Charlie. If he starts to geyser, somebody ought to be standing around holding the rubbers."

Outside the office, and sounding as if it came from the theater itself, there was a loud strange crash. Both thought of a surprise accident to the set but neither could think of a prop that was vulnerable. They rushed out.

The Great Bear Spring Water man had dropped a twenty-gallon bottle, heaving it up into its rack. Water was all over the back of the theater, blackening the red carpet near the lobby.

Seton came in then. When he saw the two he stopped dead, and so did they. He'd been drinking. He was pale and tense, and his hands had a tremble that was visible from many feet. His tie was pulled to one side. His hat looked insecure and sad.

"Good morning, Seton," Arleigh said.

"You're up to something," he said back, at once suspicious.

"Charlie has some suggestions for cutting the play, Seton. Good ones. We want to go over them with you."

"We're way over," Charlie added. "You knew that, though."

Seton looked back at them, then asked coldly, "How much time have you saved yourselves?"

"Seventy-two minutes," Charlie said, just a little tense but steady enough; a reply that had no kidding about it, no apology, no surprise and no "hope-you-don't-mind-too-much" smile in face or voice.

Seton looked at Arleigh then, not at Charlie. He looked at Arleigh as if the producer had just betrayed him after a lifetime of trust, a look that was hard for Arleigh to return, for in the expression about the eyes and temples there was a man who was beleaguered, piteous, fraying; the face of a man under the lash. His face broke up like a mined hillside.

It was real and searing. No actor alive could have done it. A shiver went down Arleigh's legs.

"At least look at them," he said, taking Seton by the elbow. It was like touching a child. "Let's at least run over them in the office."

Seton was never one who could dominate. But he could domineer. In the office he pulled off his tie and dropped his hat to the floor.

"You've been conspiring behind my back!" he shot at them, his pupils turning to pinpoints of fury. "You began this goddamn conspiracy right after rehearsals began! *You drove me out of this theater!*"

"Sit down and shut up!" Charlie shouted, shoving him into a chair. "You're a suspicious, stingy-minded son of a bitch that doesn't

know when you got the right people around you. And if you want us
to quit this show right now, it's fine with me!"

But Seton's fury was for Arleigh Brayce.

"You're a male whore! You're an idiot manager, Mr. Brayce! Why
my goddamn father can stand you I'll never know. I'm the dramatist
here, not you. It's my play and I'll fight for it. I'll fight anybody!"

"I don't want to fight you, Seton," the older man answered
quietly. "Or fight anybody. We've done too much work to quit now.
So has the cast, God bless it. You'll never get a better. And you better
think that over when you go back to your hotel to tell your family
what a son of a bitch old Arleigh Brayce has become. You can't hurt
me, Seton. And you can't scare me. But I can do *you* a little good.
So can Charlie. Your play's too long and that's that. And we're going
to cut it and that's that. Or *you're* going to cut it."

Seton got up slowly, then slowly leaned over, his knees quite stiff,
and picked up his hat from the floor. Arleigh took advantage of the
pause.

"I know what the public will take, Seton. I know how much. And I
know where."

"I've got two plays running in the Village right now," Seton
answered evenly, "and I know what I'm trying to do in the theater.
So do my friends down there. What I'm trying to do isn't what *you're*
trying to do. It never will be. Not remotely."

"I'm trying to make some money for you, Seton." He knew this
was tactically wrong as soon as he said it, but he was glad it had
come out, and come out so flat.

"Money! That's what I thought from the start! All you think about.
I'm not in the banking business. I write for the *theater*. If I have to
starve in it, I'm prepared to do *that*! I'm close to it now. I've never
been anything but close to starving."

"Oh, for God's sake, Seton, be reasonable! Sit down again. At
least let's go *over* what Charlie's done! I want the same thing for you
that you want for yourself. Only I know how to get it for you and
you don't and that's God's truth if I ever pronounced it."

But Seton remained standing, though he did not start for the door.
Arleigh rushed on.

"I know the Village better than you think. I was doing shows in it long before you ever knew it was there. I did a Moeller play there just last year. I did *Footloose*——"

"A ghastly play," Seton sassed.

"Maybe so. That isn't the point. I believe fine acting can save poor plays and make them pay."

He could see by Seton's eyes that the young playwright was taking a false inference from this, so he held him quiet until he got his point over by lifting up his hand and making a shushing gesture with the palm. "Not much of a play but it had some exciting people in it— Elizabeth Risdon, Emily Stevens, and Tallulah Bankhead. It got some good things going. And I'm *not* talking about putting a bad play over on the public by artifice. I'm talking about what goes on in the commercial theater *if you want to be heard in it!* Believe me, Seton, I respect what you've done. But believe me, you've done too much and you've got to let us help."

Seton looked at the men. Charlie's back was turned. His neck was still red, he was still dangerous, still deeply outraged to find that Seton thought no one had ever done any work but himself. It was a good thing for Seton that Charlie was keeping his back to the whole encounter, Arleigh felt. It was a good thing for those fine contours. Arleigh could see them bloody.

"You don't know how much the public will take of *my* stuff, Mr. Brayce." (Seton is now calling me "Mr. Brayce"!) "And I'll tell you this right now. For you too, Mr. Westover." Charlie half turned, fearing to turn fully lest he might spring and strangle the playwright.

Arleigh knew something was coming now, something that was going to change everything, something final, irrevocable, perhaps fatal.

"They'll take the whole of it. Or they'll get none of it."

Seton was very quiet when he said that, quiet and white. Only his hands trembled. The celebrated boom was still there in the voice and it was rich in feeling again, its control returned. "The *world* can see what I'm writing, if you apes are afraid of my work. I've got a publisher. Maybe you know. Vivian Sable. *He's* not afraid. He's going to print me. It doesn't matter a damn to me what you think. There'll be more than one arbiter about who I am and what I'm saying and whether it has meaning or not. If this isn't your world, for God's sakes get out of it! You're killing the best workmen in it!" He straightened his hat awkwardly. He was not used to hats, to city clothes. "Leeches! Boneheads! Loonies!"

He felt better, he'd got rid of something.

"I've made the compromises. You haven't! I'm secure where my work is known. I respect what they do to it downtown. For the paltry privilege of seeing it performed across the street from the Astor Hotel I'll not have it badgered and pulled apart and rehearsed in the middle of the night by actors worn out when they get here! And I'll *never* go through another one of these flare-ups! To hell with these goddamn money quarrels. *I* can find a producer that isn't a pig! Why don't you just produce what's written and leave us writers alone!"

There was a hot silence. Then the icy calm of Arleigh and his incontrovertible sense:

"We're not talking about money. We're talking about a *four-hour play*." It was almost a whisper but it carried a force that shocked.

Charlie, who hadn't turned, still kept his back persistently to the conflagration. But when he spoke, he sounded like a man under torture:

"You are not in the presence of two men trying to defeat you, Farrier. You are in the presence of two men trying to *honor* you. If you don't know that, maybe *you're* the pig, not Mr. Brayce. In any case, you're rude and stupid, and you're pretty drunk and babyish. As far as I'm concerned, you're just a number."

Arleigh wanted to get quickly away from this calculated insult, deserved though it was. More than anything he wanted to keep alive what they still had, if it was still there. His instinct flashed to him: "Say something Seton can demolish. Save his face." And he heard his own voice:

"I had a weak play with a cute title and a neat if minute idea. The play was called *A Young Man's Fancy*. It was about a department-store dummy. I put Merivale in it, with Jeanne Eagels. I had a weak comedy called *On the Hiring-Line*. I put Laura Hope Crews in it. They made a lot of money. Right here. Right out of this dirty little office. You've done something a lot better. Better than either;

better than both together. Maybe something great, certainly something that *could* be great. I've assembled some of New York's finest actors for you. They've been hard to get. You know that and you know why. And you also know you've got too much on your canvas."

Seton pulled up and away from it.

"It is generous of you to point out you prefer what I have done to something that is noteworthy for being so bad." He seemed to grow taller and more assured as his sarcasms flowed. "Perhaps you and Westover can pluck this turkey and pepper it and drop in a couple of dumplings and make it smell the way everything else has to smell on Forty-fifth Street. Maybe someday if I shave carefully you'll let me meet Laurette Taylor."

Reaching down from his tremulous dignity, he derricked the door open.

Street sounds sifted in. Without looking back into the small office, he said: "There'll be no cutting that I don't make. Not now, not later. If you wish me here for the rest of rehearsals, I'll come. If you don't, I'll stay away. If conditions are impossible—if the play is dead right now—then the play is dead. And you killed it. Not me!"

He looked back at them, squinting, satanic, strangely lecherous. "In any case, goddamn you both. And goddamn you forever!"

He didn't close the door. And he went out the other way, into the theater itself.

In front of the Great Bear water cooler Seton stopped dead. His face and body seemed to rest; to take on a monkish cast of impersonal meditation.

For this moment Seton might have been praying before a shrine.

Then he raised his arms and with a mighty heave sent the huge bottle crashing down a second time onto the rich carpet of the Morosco.

Presently they could hear the clicking of his heels—unhurried in their Gargantuan impudence—on the cool mosaic of the lobby, see his long shadow drift past its east wall.

Then that too was gone, sucked into the sidewalk hum of the Forties.

After a long silence and a quiet sigh, Charlie turned.

"The fellow's quite an advanced p—k, isn't he?" For them

both, it was the right expression for that moment. It broke the tension. But there was no way either man could know that Seton was going crazy, waiting for Pat to come back.

To the shocking indelicacies of Charles Westover, Arleigh Brayce said nothing. The words comforted him. He even enjoyed—for the moment it lingered—the moral truancy of endorsing from another what he himself could not utter.

But Arleigh was not going to condemn.

Now he put his feet up on the chewed desk and leaned back.

"Every good experience I ever had in the theater, whether New York or Dublin or Berlin, required some sudden adjustment to something unexpected," he said. The adjustment usually was not easy, he added, for the unexpected was usually ugly. Betrayal, or trashy behavior, was its commonest form.

Here it was again—the son of the oldest friend he ever had, the son of the finest actor, save Booth, the American theater had ever produced; a son who in the midst of his powers was ruinously bull-headed, craven in his vanity, ungracious, myopic, earnestly weak, and sadly, irretrievably wrong.

"I do truly believe that there are some psychiatric illuminations to his conceit, Charlie. Perhaps verging on the psychotic. He truly *is* a man who does not give a good goddamn. We hear about it. In the theater we often see a close relative. But this is the real thing, Charlie. This is pure quill."

"Pure quill" was a Prohibition term meaning uncut whisky. Charlie admired the neat use of it here.

"Seton is a man who lives altogether for Seton. And I bet you everything I own that he'll live scared the rest of his life and die lonesome."

"I hope so," Charlie said reverently. "For all I care, he can not only die lonesome, he can live lonesome. He can begin now."

But Arleigh might not have heard, for his next sentence was a continuation of his earlier thought: "On the other hand, maybe he cares more than all of us."

Charlie himself began to move around a little, touching chair backs, tapping things on the walls, pictures of some of the horrid thieves that had managed the Morosco at various times, pictures of grinning actresses with wild flourishes of penmanship unreadable against their deadly backgrounds.

He was pleased to find himself still living after the paralyzing shock of Seton, after his cowardly and autocratic defection.

Seton was vicious. Charlie was glad it was over. That he'd never have to see him again was relief.

"He called us quite a lot of things, Arleigh. I don't remember even raising my voice."

"He's not like other people."

"He's not like a person," the director amended. "He isn't a person."

"Yes. That's why we'll always have to make allowances."

"What do you mean by that? Allowances for what? We're through. We never have to see this Irish p—k again."

Arleigh got up then.

"Yes, we do. We're going to do the play."

There was a spastic twitching in Charlie's face, and his eyes fired up.

"How *can* we?"

Then some of the magnanimity and some of the greatness too, perhaps, came out of the old producer.

"I notice the playscript is gone. Yours. I didn't see him pick it up. But it went out of this office with him."

"What of it?"

"He took *yours.* I think that means he's going to study it. If he doesn't go home to sulk and start to drink."

"Even if he does?"

"And I think he expects us to go ahead with the work. I'd also think his own screaming will come back to his own ears and embarrass him. Maybe he'll even cut the show himself. When he sees what you've done. He's got to respect that, even if he'll never say so."

There was something that wasn't coming out for the satisfaction of Charlie Westover. Arleigh could see him struggling to get it out:

"But don't you want to kill him?"

"Of course. But let's leave that for Woollcott or Broun. Right now, let's forget it all. Let's go outside and do some work."

The director seized Arleigh by the forearm.

"*Why* are you going on with this?"

"Because I believe he has written a new and thrilling piece of work. And I am in that business."

"Well, I'm not! Not with this scrawny Fafnir! I can go back to the Threshold Players. Clare Tree Major is cuckoo for me."

He grinned in a sort of hideous joylessness. He meant what he was saying. Arleigh knew it.

"You've got a contract with me, Charlie."

"You wouldn't hold me!" Charlie was begging. "This man-woman-pansy-thinking able-bodied bilge pumper has cut off my balls! I *can't* direct his play! All of a sudden I hate everything he is and does! I'll violate his women. I'll goose his hero in the death scene. I'll float across the set with Maude Adams. I'll tip over the Great Bear water can again and I'll bring the Great Bear to help."

He pulled his coat off the handle of the steel cabinet and slung it over his shoulder.

"I never quit a show in my life, Arleigh. I've been fired but I've never quit. I think you're the finest fellow I ever met in the theater, and I'm quitting you. But I'm not letting you down as much as that mumbling Hibernian trackwalker has let *us* down! And with the cast you got! Mother of God! Mother of Ireland! If he was only a good Catholic. I'd force him to commit suicide. That way he'd burn forever."

"Well, he won't commit suicide. He's too good a sobber."

Charlie strolled over to the desk and hoisted his foot up. "Why don't you let Arthur Hopkins take it from here? He's back. I just saw him. Or that Brock Pemberton? He's starting to go. He's *crowded* with talent."

"Yeah, I might," Arleigh conceded vaguely. "Arthur's good. We work together pretty well." Then Arleigh looked full at Charles West-over, and with disarming kindness told him something he didn't know. "Arthur, you know, respects Seton Farrier nearly as much as you do, Charlie." He shrugged. "Of course, I doubt if he will ever go to the trouble actually to *memorize* a fine playscript the way you did. But he's got some pretty good plans."

"Plans for what?"

"To produce his next play."

"But you must be wrong! I just saw him. Whaddya mean, plan to produce it? *I* read his play. Christ, I read 'em all! You *know* that!"

"Yes, I know that. I gave them to you."

"Sure. Sure. So what's all this? *Hopkins* isn't discovering Farrier! *You* are!"

"Perhaps. That's not what I'm after. I just want him to have his chance. Under conditions that will get him notices. However, I'm not alone. Neither is Hopkins. Hopkins has bought the second play. Belasco has bought the third. The fourth—I understand it's being bought tonight by Isadora Duncan's little brother in the bathrobe and the sandals."

"You're kidding." It was a voice full of a dreadful disbelief.

"I'm not kidding. I admired Seton's defense of his own work. *He* thinks he's right. So if I want another of Seton's plays—and I do—I can have it, but it'll have to be *Oasis* and I'll have to go through this again. And I'm ready to."

"*Oasis?* The sanitarium show?"

Arleigh nodded.

"Maybe they never met him," Charlie suggested, shaken. "Hopkins and the rest."

"I would doubt that. Farrier has taken Rafferty as his agent. He hates people, to be sure, but he didn't take along his agent to do his fighting. I'd think another thing, too."

"What, Arleigh?"

"That everything Farrier writes gets produced just the way he wants it. The hell with producers. The hell with directors."

"To hell with Belasco?"

"It may never happen with Belasco. And Seton may be lucky if it doesn't. The Belasco genius, boiled down to commercial sediment, is his unerring taste. Belasco has unerring bad taste. How can he fail in New York? But Hopkins——"

Subtly but quickly his manner changed. There was something dark and terrifying—something of almost deranging sadness—that Arleigh had never told Charles Westover. In fact, he had never told anyone. Nor had he ever planned to.

"Charlie," he said, his voice odd, his head averted, "what do you know about morphine addiction?"

Charlie's head whirled around. Arleigh was expressionless. He was tapping together a small stack of letters. Then he ran a rubber band around them and tucked the little bundle in his pocket.

"I know it kills people," he said shortly. "What has that got to do with today?"

"When Patrick Farrier was born Molly, his mother, was full of morphine. Hotel doctors those days spooned it out to women in labor. She became an addict. She didn't know it. Few do. But when Seton was born—exactly ten years later—she was in the trap. She was a daily user. She was under morphine when he was born. I was in the room. Have you ever seen drugs taken away from a drug user?"

"No. Did they do that to her?"

"They did it to Seton."

"To *Seton!*"

Arleigh now placed his hand on Charlie's shoulder and shook him gently. Arleigh was not one to go about touching people. But now he was looking hard and cold into Charlie's eyes. He had the look of a desperate man about to do a desperate thing.

"*Seton came into this world screaming for morphine!* Inside her belly, Seton unborn was a dope fiend." Now his eyes glistened. Charlie had never seen this man so nearly out of control. "The only comfort Seton got was his mother's breast. And do you know why? Because her *milk* was full of morphine too. Now, can you bear to think what *weaning* would be like?"

Charlie gulped, then shook his head hard. It was half a shudder.

Arleigh's words were racing now. "It isn't you and I and the rest of the theater that have to put up with Seton. It's Seton puts up with *us*. How he lives, I don't know. What agonies he's stared into, I don't know. How he'll end, I don't know either. But *he's* the big one. We're lucky to be around in the days he happens to be going through. There won't be too many of them."

He turned away from his director and went over quietly to the coat tree.

"Where are you going, Arleigh?"

"I'm going over and try to sign *Oasis*. Then I'm going to get a new director for this show." He put on his Panama hat—Arleigh wore beautiful clothes—adjusted the tilt of it, and started for the door. Without looking back he said:

"I wish you'd stay with the production one more day, Charles." (Never before had he called him Charles. It had never been anything but Charlie.) "At least give me *that* much time to turn around. We open a week from tonight. You realize that."

He went out. He walked straight. His eye and his mind, and the forward lean of his body, seemed intent on next things. Charles West-over watched him walk west toward Broadway. He looked very distinguished, very capable. Passing him on the street now it would not have been possible, Charlie felt, to believe the torment and the compassion and the cool core of integrity that accompanied his gait. He wore his age like a campaign ribbon. It was no wonder that women were still looking at him, women of thirty and thirty-five. It was easy to believe he'd had four marriages, even that he might have a fifth.

The slashing, unnerving disclosure that Arleigh had just brought him, the unexpected horror of it, now began to send down the forks of its torture into Charlie's own feelings. In sudden shame and sorrow, he sat down in the dirty little chair by Arleigh's desk and quietly wept there. He threw his coat on the floor and blew his nose.

He thought of the gay nights he'd had in the Farriers' suite in the Byzantium. It was hard to believe what he'd just heard. Of course Charlie had heard rumors about Molly. The theater was full of rumors. But there could be no doubt of her health today.

Whatever the truth of Molly's history, she showed in neither face nor manner any of the scars or any of the hell of memory. But what she *felt*? Or left on the nerve ends of her son?

The director went into the tiny lavatory, washed his face, blew his nose again, combed his hair. All of a sudden he loved Seton. All of a sudden he would give up his life for Seton. He understood entirely how it had been possible for Arleigh to take so much. The talent itself should be enough. But a talent that had been turning so long on these slow fires—not even to know who had set them, who fueled them now, or by whose hand the spit revolved

—Charlie shuddered again. He pushed open the swinging door into the theater and went to the apron.

"We'll do the second scene of the third act again," he said sternly, tossing his coat away. "Turn on the borders, Harold."

Outside on the street Arleigh wasn't making his way to sign *Oasis*. He needed a little calming down for himself. He dropped into the Rivoli to see *Wings*.

Part Three

12

SETON, WHO LOVED THE HEAT, WALKED SLOWLY
back to the hotel, letting the sun bake him, staying away from shade.
He realized he had on a becoming mournful look and this suited
him, but there was cheer inside. He'd licked everybody, even old
Arleigh.

At the hotel he slipped out of his clothes and wrote a letter to Jill:

Own Darling:

*Forgive my ill temper (my last letter). I wish you could
have torn it up without seeing it. My life is nothing but
delay, suspense, disappointment, betrayal, grubbing about
alone, looking through dirty hotel windows at this vile and
idiot city (Ye Gods! the subways!), paved with chewing
gum, populated with sadistic vocabularies and weak stomachs, smelly rooms, dead faces—(all but Jennifer Bigelow—
she's aglow, at least, and she is going to be great! Well, that's
something, God bless her!).*

*Well, by God, if we aren't going to the worst city in
America to "try out." Newark, New Jersey! I raised such
hell about that rackety muck-hole that I won my only point
so far. No, take it back. I won one the other day, quite a big
one for me. You'll be amused. They thought they knew all
the tricks. And they do. But when they ganged up on me and
had me cornered (yes, there is no other way—the Press, the
Almighty, August Press was actually mounting the stage*

to shake a statement loose from me—God! why do we insist
that writers are talkers? Writers are the most inarticulate
of men). Well, Brayce thought he had me. He'd rigged the
whole thing. And there I was, trapped on my own stage.
Well, old dear, you'd have been proud of your bony husband!
If the only thing I ever learned at sea was to climb a rat-
line or the Black Gang ladder, I learned that well. I went
sailing into the flies like Maude Adams in "Peter Pan"!
They're still talking about it!

I've been drinking a little beer with Five-Below but that
is about all. Didn't get to the Jack Reed Memorial. In fact,
forgot all about it. I've never made a public speech and I
vowed to myself, coming back from the 7th Regiment
Armory, I would never in my life get up in front of people
and say anything! Never. I have been much calmer in my
mind ever since! Isn't that strange?

Two very pleasant things (one a delight, the other an overwhelming relief)! First, your food package! It came! And
all fresh! Just delicious. Thank you, dear Jill.

The other: I got a wire from Pat! God! Finally! Of course
he needed money. Always does (though up to now he's had
better sense than to ask me for any). I wired him enough to
come home on. So that is one suspense that is now over,
thank God. Or soon to be.

I'll feel easier when I know he's actually on his way to New
York, though it would be more like him just to walk in unannounced. I do confess I wish he were here right now. I feel
as though I've had an operation with no anesthetic. Perhaps
if I didn't worry about others so much—you included—I
wouldn't drink so much. I don't like to drink. At least I don't
believe I do. It locks the world out just a little, and allows
me to feel safer. You've no idea—the terrors of being alone.
It is worst of all when one is surrounded with people.

You'll like Pat, Jill. Everyone does. Real sad about him.
You know, once he actually bought a diamond ring. Fell
in love. Nice girl (so he said). But the next morning, the very
next morning! couldn't even remember her name! Or where

*she lived! And he gave the ring to the hat-check girl at the
Martinique. He's the damnedest!*

*I'm assuming you're all right for money or you'd mention
it. All my love, Seton.*

He licked the flap of the envelope, looking out the window into
the dreary back yard of mid-Manhattan, a tangle of squeaking pulleys,
leaning poles, and disinherited underdrawers crucified above the
weeds and milk bottles, slack in forbidden sun.

He sighed at the wretchedness of all he saw and felt. If Jill were
only with him now! How he loved her! He knew if he could only
see her he would feel at peace.

He went down to the main lobby. There were several letters from
Jill. Seton rejoiced at the sight of them. There were other communi-
cations, and a few letters that had a look, an outer look anyhow,
of importance, two of them with embossed flaps. Important-looking
mail always made him feel more complete.

He went into the coffee shop, ordered a tongue sandwich and
milk, and began to read.

Dearest Seton:

*I get tossed this way and that by your letters. Some days
all things seem well with you, then in your next letter all
things sound as if they have been desperate and not worth
any effort at all.*

*Sean has been quite ill. I haven't written, as I did not want
you to worry. He is all right. A sudden fever and a wild
throat infection that had me terrified. Here again Lt. Munoz
was fine, taking the Coast Guard truck over the dunes to get
Dr. Williamson in the night. Lt. Munoz gave me three lanterns, two reds and a white, and showed me how to string
them on the rope of the flagpole. And he gave me a little
written-out code, with the lights in various relations to each
other having various meanings. Quite ingenious but quite
simple. I'll write tomorrow. More about Sean. All my love.*

Jill.

Loving Husband,

They thought Sean had a quinsy, the worst kind of sore throat there is. Perhaps he did. I had to get him to the Truro hospital finally, and stayed there, or in a house nearby, not wanting him to be both sick and alone in a place he never saw. He was so brave you would have been proud of his being your son. Do send him a card, or a simple puzzle, or a water pistol, or a small toy or picture book of some kind. It is true he doesn't know you are his father.

I ordered more kerosene. You haven't sent me any money, dear, none at all. And when I called the bank they had not received any deposit from you. It is truly quite awful of you, when in almost every letter you either ignore everything about money, or merely say that things are going to be "all right." Things are just not all right, but quite embarrassing. Mr. Conklin was very cool with me at the drugstore. I must tell you that the doctors here have insisted that Sean have his tonsils out just as soon as the present infection clears up and the boy's natural strength and health return to him. They also feel that there is only one doctor for this operation, that he's in New York, and that is Dr. Celce. Especially good with children—relieving the "after fear." More later. Much love.

Sweet husband:

I am bringing Sean to New York for this though I don't know the date. I thought I'd ask your mother, when the time got close, if she would have the hotel management provide a small bed for our room.

I love you so. I pray for you and your success. I pray to St. Thérèse about your drinking and your tensions.

I put a small jar of Horlick's Malted Milk in the new food package.

My beloved husband, think of me just before you go to sleep. A long kiss to remember Jill.

Before looking at his other mail, Seton got up, walked across the lobby to the package room. There, sure enough, was the neat bundle from his wife, insured and securely tied. She had even paraffined the ends to keep the food fresh. Seton carried the package back to his table, rested his elbow on it while he read his other mail, and poked about for his sandwich and his milk.

There was a letter from the secretary of the Authors League inviting him to join its membership.

There was an odd letter from the New York Emergency Committee for General Amnesty, a group determined to free all political prisoners. It thanked Seton for his "devotion" to their cause because of his one-act play about a coal miner and informed Seton they were including his name on their official stationery as one of the committee's sponsors.

There was a letter from Yale, from William Lyon Phelps.

Dear Mr. Farrier:
Would it be possible for you to be the guest of honor and speak at a small banquet of the Yale Literary Magazine in New Haven on the evening of Tuesday, November 20?

He read no further.

The thought of speaking terrified him so he could not finish his sandwich. With trembling hands he tucked the letter into his coat pocket. He would try to answer it. *Why*, in the world of sense, did the very best people make the very worst mistake in assuming that writers were speakers!

He slopped his coffee, thinking about it, then dumped the spill-over from his saucer back into his cup and read the next, a short but flattering letter from St. John Ervine.

Seton glowed and preened, looking clear across the coffee shop at his reflection in the mirror on the opposite wall. He wished he were seated nearer, so he could study his own subtleties of expression as reveries of greatness twirled about on the stage of his mind and fancy.

There was a letter from *Seven Arts*. This could be very exciting. He'd sent them his only story, "Eternity."

Dear Mr. Farrier,

Your story is a fine document. Though we feel there are areas of excess writing; though we feel too that the postscript concerning the legacy weakens the poignancy of your tragedy by introducing an unrelated and facetious . . ."

Why, for Christ's sakes! Who the hell do these *Seven Arts* jugs think they are?

The actress Bertha Gorgas had written, urging Seton to try to be in New York sometime before her departure for Europe. She suggested he write a play for her for next season.

Actresses! Ye Gods! Seton's mouth curled. "Please write me a play for next season. Please arrange to be in New York when I may be there!"

The *nerve* of people! The immeasurable vanity of all these Thespian flapheads, these wheezy wigs!

His day was ruined!

A delightful letter from Hesperus Ward changed his whole chemistry.

Seton had written the actor-playwright, suggesting he play the lead in *Treasure* and had sent a typescript of the play to him, asking what he thought of the character Captain Whitney of the bark *Cereus*.

Dear Farrier,

No, I'm not so tough as the Tillie Starbuck *any more but I can still reeve a new becket in a wooden deck bucket. And the house numbers on my place here in Camden were the draft numerals railed to the sternpost of the* Star of Iceland. *You'd feel at home here, Farrier. Come Thursday if you can. Captain Blair (Belle of Oregon) is here just now.*

It was Blair persuaded me we should take charge of the Spanish-American War (you never saw such beautiful women as Cuba has!), which I did all alone as Blair fell with fever day we landed. I was wounded, decorated (for not one damn thing, I swear!). I got drunk, drew my pay, shipped to China. Went through the Boxer Rebellion. Tell you about that later, but we were really fighting to stay in the opium trade! Got a Chinese arrow across my shoulder blades. Fell in love with a Chinese girl. Took ship (the schooner Shasta*) and took the girl. No money. Sailed deck passage. The* Shasta *missed the light at Guardafui and her bottom was holed out on the rocks. I never saw the Chinese girl again.*

We fought Somalis. Strange picturesque fellows. Red-headed, you know, yet black as oil barrels. I opened a casino in Biloxi. Got arrested. Joined the Boers. Blew up 9 of Kitchener's blockhouses. This was after Ladysmith and Mafeking, mind you. (To this day, there's no satisfaction like a fight with an Englishman!)

Shipped on the Jasper Hicks, *Alaska Packers. Went through one "Bristol Bay" season. You could make $4,000 in 18 days if you could stand up to it. Some did. With only 3 breaks for sleeping. I was tough but I was 30. But I made $3,100 at that. Men are too soft now.*

I'll be proud to appear in Treasure. *Great story! I've sailed everything your skipper has. Went direct to the theatre from the sea. Don't know which I love more. How we ever survived the fights! I've left knuckle skin and bone chips from Fairhaven to Kobe! I know it's the same thing with you.*

It's great to read something about the sea by a man that's been there, I can tell you. We'll talk all night. The bell-rope on my porch is the whistle landyard from the Vega. *She struck Duncan Rock off Cape Flattery. And there's a framed leaf from the log of the* Beatrice, *largest of the French full-riggers. She grounded north of Columbia River, January weather. Her mizzenmast, embedded in the cargo (cement), is still standing. Over the mantel I've a fine model of the* Prosper. *Remember the name? Shanghai to Puget Sound—31 days! I berthed on 'em all, Farrier. Been aboard everything from sandbagger sloops to colliers.*

The house is big and cool, and close to the water. Write or wire. There's no phone. But there's a barrel of whiskey. You've given me a tremendous thrill with Treasure. *Let's do it!*

Cordially and respectfully,
Hesperus Ward

The letter seemed to cling to his skin. It sent a multitude of feelings, all jarring against each other, through his body.

It *was* true, what the actor had written him, that they were cut from the same timber.

Seton got up from his table, feeling manly, lost in thought, clutching the rest of his mail, shaking, exhilarated, confused, choked up with such sweepings of the past, with such fears and fidgets and frustrations for his present play that all he could think to do now was to get upstairs, close his door, lock out the world, and fish out the last of the alcohol he'd brought from the Cape.

He wished for Jill.

He wished there were no problems. He wished he had a tremendous success behind him, just one, but one so lasting in prestige, so rich in financial return that he would never again have a worry of any kind.

In his room he began to weep as he poured out the liquor. He looked in the mirror at his streaked face, watching the tears gather and spill down. Once again the biting wash of diluted alcohol stung him and braced him and seemed to bring him together.

He wrote Jill. His letter burned with his sudden intense and saddening assurance of his need for her, an assurance that reversed his written feelings of only a few days before when he had reviled her for what he suspected were lurid indiscretions on the Cape.

Now he wanted to withdraw the accusation, to annul it, to blame the story on others. If he could have intercepted the letter, he would have.

He was proud she'd sold a story to *Smart Set*, proud and strangely agitated. She could get her things done without agonizing over them. He couldn't.

Remorse came lightning fast as his mind moved back to the violence that had gone into those sentences. He shook with shame.

Was he crazy?

He tried hard to get at his own inexplicable sobbing, at the reason for the disintegrating talks he had with Jill whenever they had the slightest disagreement. He even had a flash of insight regarding his own impotence upon the instant of those separations; his inability to cope with anything when alone.

He became lost and childish the moment he left the tiny world of the shack, the beach, and the breast of his wife.

His daily, orderly, tireless output did not interest him. In fact, it was not even noted in his own mind. It was what one did; what one had to do.

Writing was lonely. What of it?

But why was *life* so lonely, so dreary, so set about with terrors?

He thought of Hesperus Ward in the surf off the coast of Somaliland. He thought of Hesperus Ward ducking and dodging in the swish of arrows in the crazy fighting with the Boxer Chinese. Seton was flattered to be considered the same sort of swashbuckling romantic that the actor-playwright so notoriously was—friend of captains in any port, joyous Pacific roustabout. How could the man get it all done! How could he move so fast! And turn out one hit after another! Fame. Power. Hilarity. Girls. Fights. Color. Even the U. S. Cavalry! And this is what Ward really thinks I am too!

If he only knew!

Why couldn't *he* do anything that others admired? Things *they* couldn't do? It was some comfort that others couldn't do as many push-ups. Or swim as well. But who knew about any of this?

Seton searched in himself for the courage coldly to turn over the truth and look at it. He was frightened all the way through about everything. He even cringed, today, at the very memory of South America fifteen years before. Today he could admit he never would have gone at all if his father hadn't staked him; if others, familiar with the country, hadn't been there to receive him. The romantic story the world was told was not *really* the reason for his going. Those who knew he was away thought he was prospecting for gold. But who knew the truth—that he'd run away from a marriage he didn't want? From a son he never intended to claim? That he had not the least notion of the whereabouts of either one now and no desire to learn?

He simply could not endure being on hand when his child was born. The mere idea of fatherhood was annihilating!

The only thing he could ever finish was his work. From everything else in the world he ran. He didn't know why. Before running away from marriage, he'd run away from college. Except to write, he'd never done anything but run. It was his tragedy never to see his strength; it was his blindness to see strength in others that was not strength at all but exuberance only. He *had* the strength of the true artist. It came from the torture of solitude. And exile was the price of it. Seton paid it. But he did not understand that that was what he was doing.

Now in these mighty tortures to tell the truth, to find the truth and face it—the image of his son whom he had never seen floated past him like some distant swimmer. At these times Seton would scan the horizon of his mind to see if the young swimmer might be in trouble of some kind, as Jill from time to time implied; to see if he, the father, should not perhaps row out and inspect the situation. Yet each time he debated these paternal excursions, he pulled back, reminding himself of the extraordinary adaptability of the young, their remarkable strength. Of *course* the boy was all right! If he weren't, Seton would be bound to hear about it. Hear it from the boy's own mother.

Idea of bringing the boy back! Stupid idiot woman notion of Jill's! She had a son of her own! *Their* own! Let her take care of *that* one. The other one—they called him Derek—bound to be all right. Kids grow up. One way or another they grow up. Even if he could some-day afford——

He began thinking about Hesperus Ward again. He could see Hesperus Ward stride into the saloons of San Francisco, see him leaning into the fire of San Juan, into the icy breakers of the Alaskan coast, into the sweating shimmer of oriental ports, the tinkling *cantinas* of Havana. Everywhere Seton could see men stop their talk, look up quick and startled, nudge the man next him: "There he is! He's the one!"

They'd say it softly. Into the sudden silence he would stride, a fine strong rhythm running down the side of his legs, a smile just leaving his mouth corner. Even the girls at the bar, Spanish mouths on Island faces, the sideways look, the flowers; delicious thighs retreating, the sloe-eyed soft-sounding passionate invitation of Caribbean girls, the backward glance, the latticed boudoir, the whisper and the sigh and the faraway music . . .

Yes! Yes! To live, to *be* like Hesperus Ward! To fight and to come back victor!

But with the wild pages before him, Seton was once more compelled to take a furtive over-the-shoulder look at his own past.

He remembered a horrible moment in a Barclay Street saloon called the Taffrail when a bum had crowded him, slopped his drink, challenged him, knocked him over a table. Patrick, not Seton, had stood up to it and taken an Irish beating all alone, while Seton stared from a corner, whimpering, outraged, so weak with terror he couldn't breathe. Seton, who had been adopted by the Hudson Dusters, who had friends in Hell's Kitchen, who was sought after by shipmates real, self-styled, or imaginary.

("You got yourself in the wrong saloon, kiddo." That was all that Pat ever said of the incident. Was it warning? Or was it scorn? Did his brother think Seton was a physical coward, one who hung around tough places to take on a toughness he didn't have?)

There were many things Seton could not bear to look into. Little by little he had learned how to plate himself in these dismissals. Yet inside he knew he was as timid as a thrush. And he knew he'd sailed the world trying to hide this fear. Ships had about them a sense of massive protectiveness. And they all carried a master and a navigator and a man at the wheel, someone to cook, someone to go on watch; someone in charge, that was the thing.

The irony of Hesperus Ward's letter was that Ward really thought of Seton as being just like Ward himself; that Ward thought Seton was as bold and resourceful as any other modern *voyageur*.

The actor's turbulent letter seemed to say that Seton, too, could have survived the Chinese arrows or the charge up San Juan Hill, or even shipwreck, if he'd chosen these.

Oh, God! God! If he only could!

The glow faded, the glow of being honored for things one had not done, of being respected for qualities belonging to others.

He was alone again, disjoined from the people of earth; unrelated, self-exiled. It was a matter of manhood. He knew he had none, as others had it, and he did not know where to go or how to seek. It was a pity he could not take heart in the knowledge that the work he had put together could not be assembled by any living artist. It was a greater pity that he who was endowed beyond all others could not separate, in his definitions, the image of manliness from the sound of brawling.

He wrote again to Jill, this time complaining of insomnia, palpitations, shortness of breath, thyroid insufficiency, and the hotel's carelessness with his laundry. He was thankful Jill had got the engine going and that there was a flow of water running through the house. He was glad she'd sold a story to H. L. Mencken. He was sorry Sean's health had "kicked up a bit" but assured her it was probably a summer cold the boy would throw off in a few days.

> *Keep writing* (he urged her). *I can't understand why there should be any trouble about money. I'm sure I asked the bank here to send a draft to Provincetown.*
>
> *The suspense of waiting for the curtain to rise (which I won't see) is getting me down. They're trying to cut the heart out of my play. They'll have to cut out my heart first! Love. Your fading Seton.*

He addressed the envelope carefully, writing in a larger script than he used for his own work, took the letter into the hall, rang for the elevator, and handed it to the boy to drop in the lobby.

Having got rid of the letter he was immediately impatient for an answer to it. It was that way with all things, with the money he'd wired his brother. Why hadn't he heard? Thoughts of Patrick and his escapades crowded now into Seton's memory. There were a few that were worse than shocking, criminal really, things that people didn't know and never would. One was the practical joke Patrick had played on a good-looking lady lecturer in a hotel in Bridgeport the year before. Her name was Tanager Bolt. They'd been drinking, drinking hard, then right in the middle of the night Patrick had shaken her awake, scolded her for snoring, pushed her out of bed, and forced her, stark naked, into the hall and locked the door on her. Out there in the hall she'd begged and beaten on the door. A hotel detective had come finally, then town police. When Patrick at last had opened his door, he'd denied he knew the girl, that he'd ever had any woman in that or any other hotel room and invited them to inspect the place. They had done so but had found nothing, for Pat had thrown all the girl's things into the street!

They'd had a good laugh—he and Patrick—at the novel predicament of the girl, but Seton thought of the new shame his family would have to face if this horrid mess had ever got into the papers. For a disgrace to get into the papers was Seton's greatest living terror.

Patrick just didn't give a damn about anything.

He'd even told Jill, with Seton right there and unable to shut him up, of a homosexual experience he'd had on an all-night drunk in a hotel in a town in one of the Dakotas, and of the beating he'd given the man—twenty years older than himself—the very instant it was over.

Seton had been horrified at the telling. Sometimes he saw Lucifer in his brother; a man so bold he'd send the Devil spinning his first day in Hell!

Pat had the physique of Carpentier—the luck of a two-headed quarter. So what was all this malarkey about a hospital?

It was good to know Patrick would be home. It would relieve Mother. Once back in New York, he'd calm right down.

Once home, Mother would take care. The rhythm was the same with all these rebounds of Patrick's. To be sure, they were slowing down, but this would be like all the others—everybody finally adjusted to everybody else's "way."

Soon he knew he was telling himself a lie. He realized his brother, whom he loved beyond all others in the world, was in trouble. Deep trouble. Then the shivering thought struck him: *he might be dying!* Though Patrick had been a taker from the start—a bald-faced moocher, if one were to be blunt—he'd never in his life sent a wire like that one.

Why the hell hadn't he wired earlier? At the start of the trouble, not the end of it? Seton shook with extreme irritation. Why wasn't Patrick a famous lawyer by now, instead of the constant problem he'd become?

What's the matter with us all? Why did the old man quit at the pinnacle? Why didn't he stay up there once he got there?

Why can't we be like other people?

A long muffled sigh came out of him. Thank God, thank God, this time he himself had come out of his own long bender. Damn lucky too. With this pile of work. Lucky to be sober when the wire was phoned up. Maybe Jill is right. Maybe I hate liquor. Maybe I crawl into a bottle to hide. Jill is praying for me. Every day. Praying for God to tell me that I won't be giving up anything, just getting rid of something, if I quit.

Oh, dear God, how do you do that! Everything is easy when you're not afraid. I'll ask Pat. He's not afraid.

Once Seton had seen Jill kneeling. Whenever she prayed she looked up, as if trying to see the face of God.

Dear Jill. Dear, dear Jill. Why can't you be here now?

He slapped his arms hard against his flanks and looked back at the desk where all the torment of his work lay. He put his hand to his mouth, thinking of the mighty labor he'd given it, the work it still required, fighting the dread of beginning. Then he moved toward it. And in that movement was the exact difference between these gifted brothers: Patrick the esker, his sandy margins wearing away a little more each time the waters rose; Seton the monadnock, gloomy and remote—beyond touch or comfort—impervious to erosion, impermeable: Seton the rock.

He did not know this. He knew only that there was work here, his work, that it had to be got through, that he knew how to do it, that *only* he knew how to do it, and that all other concerns—his poverty, his wife's complaints, his rejection of his son Derek, his neglect of Sean, his resentment of his parents, his terror about Patrick—all these were merely interruptive, distracting, and brief.

Nothing mattered but the theater.

Now, wearily, he went back to the manuscript he'd taken from the Morosco office many days before and began to study the work that Westover had done on the cuts. Each time he forced his mind to look at the mind of Westover, new illuminations came. In a few seconds he was wholly engrossed.

For two days more he never left his room. He lived on the sandwiches Jill had mailed. Once he sent out for apples and cheese. He lived on coffee sent up by a makeshift room service. As for the liquor right there in his room, he drank not a drop nor thought of it. He sent corrections to the theater by bellhop. Westover had certainly done some work. And some thinking. The more he studied the man's work, the better he felt. Better not be so rough on Westover. Might use him again, this comes out all right. Knew the theater cold.

The wall phone rang suddenly. His hands shook. His heart jumped.

Seton walked over stiffly, trying to hurry. All his muscles rebelled, they'd been cribbed under the desk so long.

It was Arleigh.

"Are you sick, Seton?" Arleigh sounded cross.

"No. I'm working." His answer was just as cross.

"You've had long enough. You get over to the theater in one hour or I'm dismissing the cast and canceling the production."

He hung up.

"God*damn* you!" Seton screamed at the dead phone. But the sound of authority always made him jump. He always resented it but somehow it always made him feel better controlled, just a little safer.

Muttering, he reached for his trousers. But his heart was racing. He could feel a throb in his temples. He was altogether alive. And he'd done the work.

13

JILL'S MIND MOVED BACK AND FORTH FROM PAST days with Seton to the present excitement of right now in New York; the excitement of walking down Fifth Avenue with the adventuresome Sean, stalk-eyed, every tentacle out, every cup open. He was seeing it all for the first time.

The moment just ahead, of surrendering him to a surgeon and to the silence of a great hospital, she dreaded. But she hid the fear she felt. She was grateful for the city's distractions.

Sean walked beside his mother, a little independent of her, taking charge of all he saw—people, corner police, store windows, the rumble of buses banging by on their solid hard-rubber tires, bright women under gay parasols on the green decks. In the air were police whistles.

At every intersection there was a policeman to raise an arm slowly, majestically, to stop traffic, to escort women at crossings, to give precedence to an occasional horse over the ubiquity of trucks and touring cars. Once, to his unbearable delight, all activity was waved to the curb in order to let New York's fire engines roar by.

Sean looked at the garish glory of it all with continuous turnings of his head, trying to keep track of its continuous motion. As the intensity of its splendor began little by little to subside, his sense of proprietorship began to rise. Very soon he owned all that he saw. Now he'd glance quickly at his mother from time to time, as if to offer her shares of it, or to point out some unfolding fascination before it disappeared. Then his eyes would dart back into the sunlit treasure of it all, receiving impressions he'd never lose.

Others noticed Sean: bus conductors collecting dimes in their little belled coin takers, lady shoppers with bags and boxes from Best and Arnold Constable. Twice men stopped and squatted down, looking right at the boy, who looked right back; then up to the bright beauty of the boy's mother with a slight apologizing embarrassment of their own, wanting to know her too, no doubt, yet wanting to extend this moment of charm, of positive, unexpected happiness.

With great inner pride, with a glow of surprise, Jill realized their son Sean was a crowd stopper, that strangers just had to talk to him, to touch him, to exchange something. His sailor hat announced the S. S. *RELIANCE* was in harbor, a ship of no designated flag or tonnage but of obviously swashbuckling complement, for streaking right across Sean's middy blouse was a four-inch cutlass. He was ready for the boarding. Was New York ready for him was the question.

In the stationery store at Madison Avenue and Fifty-first Street Jill bought her son a kaleidoscope, then took him on over to Park and Fiftieth to the office of Dr. Celce. It was one of his operating rules that parents be separated from his young patients at this moment, not to be rejoined until after surgery. In the office she delivered Sean to a middle-aged nurse, starched and bosomy, easy smiling.

"I'll see you tomorrow, Sean. I'll bring your daddy, too."

Now she kissed him. He looked at her, puzzled at the retreat. But the nurse, quick to the problem, was already showing him new wonders in the kaleidoscope.

Jill hurried back to St. Patrick's now. She went in the side entrance, between the Lady Chapel and the main altar, and for a long time knelt at the feet of St. Thérèse.

Outside she walked through the perennial knot of cronish pigeon feeders who seemed to live in the shade of the downtown side of the cathedral, then walked quickly into Saks. She needed underwear, new handkerchiefs, and a few new dresses. Cotton would do.

Jill went first to the handkerchief counter. Next to her, at "Gloves," one of the polite clerks, with several samples of washable kid spread out before a lady customer, was having a difficult time. The customer was a flaming person, copper-haired, reddening in a clutch of fury that seemed to build as Jill watched it.

With a mighty sweep from the customer's hand, all the gloves and boxes went tumbling. Some fell behind the counter, some on the main floor. People stared and stopped moving.

The customer—she was very well dressed, very New York, elegant even—next snatched the saleslady's order book from her hands, ran her eye down the pencilings listed there, then flung the book into the stack of boxes in front of the counter. Its leaves fluttered, its carbons tangled up in a sad snarl.

"You horrible old idiot! I'll bring the manager over myself!"

Shoppers were flustered. The red woman strode away, colliding with others.

"What a horrid person," Jill said at once. The saleslady was a woman nearly sixty. "How *can* anyone be so rude!" Jill retrieved the book for her. "I'll stay right here and speak to the manager myself," Jill offered.

"No, please. It would be better not. We know her. She scares the younger sales girls, but she doesn't scare me."

"Really? Well, I think you were wonderful not to lose your temper."

The saleslady, still straightening out the pages of her book, now leaned across the counter separating her from Jill, lowered her voice in confidence, and with a tempering sympathy of her own she said:

"The woman has a terrible problem of her own. She has to go to one of those new psychiatrists that tries to help you out. You know. When you can't solve your own problem."

"Oh, that's too bad. I mean, that she takes it out on others." Jill waited a moment, intrigued. She hoped she'd hear what the problem was. It was obvious it could have nothing to do with money, or clothes, or style. Nor beauty either, for she was noticeably, even vividly, beautiful. What other problems were there? Jill could not resist the question:

"What *is* her problem?"

"Her legs. You saw that."

"I didn't notice."

"She gets photographed all the time, but it has to be from here up." The saleslady indicated with a gesture.

"Photographed? You mean she's a society woman?"

"No. Not society. I don't even think she's a married woman. She lectures. What about, I don't know. I guess you'd just say she's well known. That she's a well-known successful woman."

She shrugged and smiled and straightened the boxes in her counter. "But if you got piano legs, what can a doctor do? Even one of those——" Here the lady stroked an imaginary short beard. "She has to wear black hose, summer and winter. Long skirts, too, whatever the styles are doing."

They laughed together at this disclosure. It was the worst possible year for long skirts. How would a man feel, Jill wondered, seeing the face first, and being caught up in the breeze of manner, in the strong sweep of this unusual personality, then looking down at the legs? Jill had beautiful legs. She was lucky about this and she knew it.

She had a protective desire to linger at some nearby counter and inspect this tawny termagant when she came back. She wanted to see what techniques could hide such a blemish. Then she was suddenly ashamed of her motives, said good-by to the undisturbed saleslady, and quickly finished her shopping.

She had one more errand. Jill had such narrow feet—quintuple-A —that she had to go to a special store on Fourteenth Street. This would be near the Byzantium. She'd wear her new shoes. She wanted to look just right for the Farriers. She wanted to look just right for Seton.

She walked out of Saks, crossed Fifth Avenue, and took the downtown Number 4 bus.

Soon she was at the fringe of the Village. The early days with

Seton came back now. Her mind jumped back and forth between her anxiety over Sean (Will Seton think I did this the right way?) and the glad days of first love before and after marriage.

The Village days when she herself was having so much fun, with money coming in (not much) for the pulp stories she wrote, a four-hundred-dollar advance on a half-written novel, and Seton always broke and dreary and fretting and irresistible—those days, and nights, all seemed lovely now, for he was wholly hers then, wholly, joyfully absorbed.

She stepped off the bus and began walking. Now she remembered a raw cold evening, dangerous ice on the sidewalks. She remembered standing right here on this crazy little patch of real estate—a tiny triangular island just off Seventh—that included a few feet of Fourth Street and an unlikely four-story building that seemed to stand athwart the whole river of traffic. It was right here that Seton had pointed with great seriousness to the second floor. In the snow and the cold he'd stopped Jill and held her by the elbow. What a bleak little building it was! You couldn't tell whether it was a small factory —the Village was full of them—or a dwelling.

"My machine gun will be right there. The second window."

He showed her which window was for Terry, which for Jack Reed.

"This is where it'll be. Where we'll meet 'em." Seton had said it with a most awful seriousness, a kind of dreadfulness. "Not too many of us needed, either."

"This is where you meet who?" she asked. And Seton had hesitated, not wanting to be too specific.

"This is where the Revolution is going to start," he announced with a tone of impatient grandeur.

"What revolution, Seton?"

"The workers'. The workers'."

Standing there in the safety of the snow and the pleasant ding of trolleys, Seton had seemed quite invincible. He could be altogether convincing. The plan therefore seemed good enough to Jill, especially for a revolution that would never come. Anyhow, all she wanted to do was marry this dark man with the dark purposes.

Jill could never be clear about Seton's revolution. Some in Greenwich Village even seemed to know when it would occur and who would benefit. She presumed it had something to do with Russia—everything seemed to—and that the 1917 uprising that had forever lifted the proletariat to where it should have been before the Czars would now come to New York and lift up Seton's acquaintances to positions that were beyond them. Being a writer, she was more noticing than most women. The men who did all the talking were never the men who had come back from France. The men who did the talking were invariably the men who hadn't made it (Seton's "nerves" had kept him out of uniform), men too young or too spindly, men rejected at Dix or Yaphank or Anniston as being unable to take the shock of combat.

Loyal to him, and loving him (if dubious of his plan and his gun ports), she had had to confess that Seton was one of the Village multitude unable to fight. At a tremendous party one night on Patchin Place, he'd fled the room when the group broke into war songs. The whole thing was silly. But it was disquieting too, for Seton was over thirty. Sometimes Jill privately felt that the young men were just talking, not really planning. She did not believe that there was a cache of arms accumulating under Webster Hall, though Seton did, or said he did. And she knew, once they began to break out the weapons, Seton wouldn't be able to assemble a machine gun if he had all day and a diagram. He was just no good with his hands. She knew this, but what was more important by far—what she knew and kept to herself—was that Seton knew it too. It was close to the center of his insecurity. Indeed it partly explained the odd frenzy of his exercise, a little-boy determination to measure up, to belong to the adult world about him.

To be so much a man and not to know it; to be so much an artist and not to rejoice in it—each time Jill thought of this; each time she sought in her mind to compose or reduce the unnecessary agonies that went with her husband everywhere, she had to blink back the mists that began to gather in her eyes. His suffering was breaking her heart.

She would love him forever, no matter what came to them. And be there forever to fill his need, no matter what its nature or amount. If his work must at times tear her up, let it flourish even so out of the tortures it might cost her. Let her find the resource to recover, the forbearance to keep still, the heart to smile, the maturity to wait for his own growth to find its painful way; for his own flowers, no matter how dark, to open in their own time and reach for the sun.

Big things were near. She knew it.

Patrick had returned, so Seton had written Jill. But there was a slight guardedness—an equivocation really—about his coming. At least as to Seton's report of it. "Act as if you don't even know he's been away. He's had a hell of a time. The folks don't know. And they aren't to know."

Had he perhaps been briefly in jail? Surely, by the way he lived, he'd walked close to the shadows of more than one!

Well, Seton should know better than to worry about Jill.

She slipped into the store on the Broadway diagonal south of Union Square and bought her new shoes. They were blue, to match her hat and her summer scarf.

"Shall we send the shoes you're wearing?"

"No, thank you. I'll carry them."

On her way to meet his parents, looking smart, feeling confident in something new, she realized some of her problem could be found in their own two different attitudes—hers and Seton's—about writing. Of the two, she had been the more successful in the beginning. She had been at once more practical and more coldly seeking in her whole view of the craft. She wrote for a living and she made a living at it. But in the Village it turned out to be quite a rare thing—a writer who wrote. Most of the writers in Greenwich Village never wrote anything at all. The sculptors seldom sculptured anything. They would appear in their smocks in Village speak-easies and Cordial Shops, fundless, chattery, looking for food or girls, for excuses not to work, cadging drinks.

She passed the defeated place where Seton had taken her one night to hear the Great Debate between Scott Nearing and Clarence Darrow on the burning subject: "*Is the Human Race Worth Working for?*" Afterward there was all-night talk in some forgotten garret that housed an herb seller, a man who ground nutshells, a woman who dyed table linens, and a violent man who had just written a book on coincidences that had never quite happened and about how these would have reshaped history had they just managed to occur instead of just managing to miss, and how they would reshape his life if somebody would publish them.

Thinking back now, Jill recalled all her first impressions. She loved Seton for the private reasons women love men: in her case because Seton was lean, deliriously mixed up, and going through a prolonged mourning over catastrophes that had not happened. Too, he kept telling her he needed her. She wanted to believe it. So she did. Other women before her had done the same. There was something else: because, in a hive of drones, he was a man who worked every day and night and worked to the point of collapse, she could bring him respect and a sympathy and the beginnings of a real understanding. Jill was simple. She wrote for editors. She wrote to make money. She wrote for definable markets, for stated fees, for describable readers, for deadlines. Checks came in. After the age of twenty she'd never written home for a cent.

But Seton wrote because he was on fire.

It would be different now, for herself and Seton. After all the years of trying, the years of skimping, after weeks of checkered separation, this time there was a real chance that Seton's labors would pay him off, that what they had so richly earned they would now begin to receive; that his play would pull everything together for them both, and that the full flow of new plays, already finished, would soon find productions.

At the Byzantium she looked at her reflection in the glass of the revolving door, touched her hat, and went through the lobby to the elevators.

She could hear music.

14

THE FARRIER SUITE IN THE BYZANTIUM HOTEL HAD A cheerful shabbiness, shabby not from neglect but from too much use. There was laughter in the living room. There were far too many people. Jill looked over the group with a swift shyness. She'd seen this congestion before in these same rooms, but it excited her all over again. The theater world was special. By sight she identified six or eight stage celebrities right away. Seton was helpless in such moments, slow in introductions, unable to think quickly of names of people he had known since his childhood.

Mrs. Farrier kissed Jill's cheek, then took a good look at her and hugged her as if she were a child of her own.

"We've got a crib for Sean, you know. And permission to dry his diapers on the roof."

"Oh, but he's all grown-up. He's a little man."

"It's a shame about the operation. Is it tomorrow?"

"It is right now."

"I suppose he's scared to death."

"He knows something's up. But he's not showing his fear."

Then she saw her father-in-law. Though she'd not seen him in nearly three years, it was quite possible to believe Dermod Mac-Murrough Farrier was America's greatest living actor. He had the look of it. He had a wonderful head, Jill thought it a bold head, and a great love of being alive. He was noticeable wherever he stood, luminous when he moved.

Mrs. Farrier passed Jill a plate of mints—candy was everywhere.

"Kiss your daughter, Dermod."

Now her husband's father looked down at her a long time, smiling, his eyes glowing in a sudden threat of tears. He said nothing at all, just patting her two elbows, then patting her shoulders.

"My dear girl," he said. "Dear, dear girl. What a time you've had! Is the little one going to be all right?"

"Oh yes. We've a fine surgeon. Mayfield Celce. The best there is."

"You don't weigh enough, daughter. Molly," he said quickly to his wife, "you must see to this. Porridge in the morning now. And bacon."

"It's the Clann Phaidin, we are here, Gillian, even if you're of English descent." She smiled at her daughter-in-law and spoke in Gaelic. "*No blaithche buige, an arain eorna an bhrachain seagail.*"

The old actor laughed at his wife's accent, then translated: " 'Yellow buttermilk, rye porridge, and barley bread.' 'Twas a noble family—the Donegals—that fed many poor people in the famine, my own parents, God rest them, among the multitude of unfortunates."

(Jill heard it as "unfartunates.") In a few seconds she lost the feeling of ever having been far from them.

"But *you* don't remember the Irish famine, Father?"

"Indeed I do, daughter. I saw it and I suffered in it. It's deep on us all. Like a scar."

"Like a blessing," his wife corrected.

"Aye, to some." He broke into a song, still clinging to Jill's arms as if she might flee. The voice rose in a sudden wail, a cry in a rain cloud, a prayer in a wet cemetery:

> "*Ma taim-se fial agus mo lamg d' sine*
> *Beidh lion an fhollamhuithe 'g coir na h-oidhche.*"

Jill shook her head. The old gentleman smiled down.

" 'If I have riches and give them away—if I open my hand—before the night comes, my hand will be filled again.' "

He nipped her cheek lightly. "We'll fatten you, daughter. Mother and I."

He put a drink in her hand, then passed her through the choked room, pronouncing names clearly, leaning down to hear everything she said or asked. The room was a tumult of Irishmen.

Dermod would break off suddenly and say something quick, just to her.

"He's a black-tempered man but he's good to you, I hope. I pray to God. Is it the truth?"

Jill realized the old man meant Seton.

"He's good to me, Father." She looked up seriously, without smiling. "We've had trouble. But we'll come out of it."

Then very quick, with a compelling squeeze of her biceps: "He never hurt you, did he? With his hand?"

He had a *claddagh* ring that some of the Irish wore for good luck. Jill remembered that her own mother's Irish gardener had worn the same ring.

Arleigh Brayce came over. Without being told, Jill knew who he was by the attitude of the two men to each other. And she realized she had seen Arleigh's picture on the theater page of the New York papers many times.

Arleigh was holding a glass of Apollinaris Water.

"This is Jill herself, Arleigh." He bowed to Jill then. "I will leave you with your husband's producer."

"How does it look?" she asked at once. "Or is it bad luck to inquire?"

He leaned over so his words wouldn't drift away in the noise around them.

"We've had a hell of a time with your husband. And he's had a hell of a time with us. Only three days ago he finally made some of the cuts we wanted. I'm no believer in the so-called sensitivity of the artist. Your husband is a piece of flint! But I think we *both* won. It's a great piece of work, Mrs. Farrier. Jill. If it doesn't come off the way I think, it's no one's fault that's worked on it."

"I'm glad to hear *you* say this."

"Doesn't Seton say anything?"

"Nothing that tells me how it's going."

"Well, you'll know just as soon as we do."

"What do you mean?"

"You're here for the opening matinee, aren't you?"

"No. Seton never allows that."

Arleigh's face tightened with astonishment.

"You mean you're here in New York and you're not coming to your husband's play?"

"Well, Mr. Brayce, I'm not going to make anything of it," she told him frankly. "It's the way he always is about this. And he has his

own answer: 'I've never seen one of my *own* openings.' It's hard to
say anything after that."

"I'm very sorry, Jill. Very, very sorry."

"No, don't be sorry." She told him of the emergency that had
brought her to New York with Sean. His tonsillectomy was scheduled
for the same day; she couldn't leave him.

Arleigh Brayce found a seat for Jill near the window that looked
down into Twenty-eighth Street and over the roofs of St. Leo's Church,
the place where young nuns maintained a perpetual adoration, where
the dreadful secret of Mrs. Farrier had been opened out, where it
had been miraculously relieved. Perhaps the priest in the room right
now was the Father Ducey who had built the church. No, he looked
too young, she judged, as she glanced across the loud room. She'd
meet him soon. She'd find out. She'd make a contact here. She'd
find some help for Seton too, somehow. She was determined to save
her marriage. She was determined her son would have a father. She
was determined to be frank to any intelligence that would return it.

All at once she decided to ask Arleigh Brayce if he knew anything
of the first marriage and the whereabouts of *that* son. Her instinct
told her that this was dangerous but that Arleigh was safe. And she
felt an inner positiveness, irrational in later review, that she would
know her own husband in an area where she now knew him not
at all if she could first of all find, then somehow become acquainted
with, her husband's other son.

Arleigh kept coming back to her, each time with another friend
of the Farrier family, a judge, a Tammany sachem, theatrical greats
of days past. He brought over Avery Hopwood. Then he introduced
a bent pixy with an ear trumpet who could remember when Wanamaker was A. T. Stewart's Thread & Needle Shop and New York's
biggest store.

Jill had a sense of old people but of old people who were bright
and happy and accomplished and at ease; a generation that looked
well back into the century already past and looked upon it with love,
even with longing.

Something was going on in the room. Soon she isolated it. It was
the magic of her host, Dermod, her husband's father. She'd forgotten
the projective power of him. He was everywhere in the room, never

still yet never hurrying. He had a bewildering theatrical heartiness, yet a continuing and genuine concern for all his guests. He was trying to impress no one, but was just vastly alive. He bobbed and weaved about, carrying his crickety cheer everywhere, constantly filling glasses, continuously offering the cake plate.

Once more Jill noted his secret solicitude for his wife Molly. He gave her sly little pats whenever he was near. His deep rich laugh, the quick concealed sweep of the room with his magician's eye— Seton had this habit, too, but used it differently—all of it seemed comforting and familiar. She saw in the old man the same animal responsiveness and well-muscled movement, the same grace still, though by now she knew he must be over eighty. Some of the gestures were mannered but they were nonetheless easy and warm and enveloping. One suspected he could be eloquent. Certainly he was endowed with the magic of presence. He drew and he held. Seton drew without wanting to. Patrick drew, then dropped what he had after taking.

Seton grabbed Jill, picked her up in a strong hug, kissed her, and set her lightly down. Then he was off. A few minutes later she could see him in the bedroom, swarmed over an ottoman. She knew he was getting drunk. It transformed him quickly. He looked like a Harrison Cady insect, his long legs moving like a jackstraws pulled slowly by careful children. Before long he was wearing his drinking look, an expression of mournful but attentive stupidity; the look of a deaf man who has found himself at the wrong funeral but who stays on, willing to grieve while the whisky passed. Who cared whose funeral it was?

The word "funeral" in her mind brought back a sentence of Pat's a long time ago. "Dad's place" (he'd meant this one right here, this hotel suite where the aging Farriers had made their home ever since the actor's retirement in 1915): "it looks like an antique store set up in a Fourth Avenue funeral parlor."

In her effort to brighten it at various times in years past (as accurately as Jill's eyes could take it in), Mrs. Farrier had choked the place with forlorn finery she had picked up in Union Square, in Brasstown on Allen Street, in Sixth Avenue Armenian shops. There were book troughs in all the corners. There were cages of dead trophies, mounds of bound programs, seals, ribbons, plaques. There was a break front full of stuffed but headless costumes from the actor's well-paid but tawdry triumphs in vaudeville years before.

The ostentation of the living room—almost audible—was neutralized by a forgiving inadvertence. "Not a room at all," Jill had told Molly on her first visit. "A whole memory book. A nice one."

Arleigh brought her another drink.

"I want to know," Jill said, lightly touching his sleeve, "if you think I should sometime ask Mrs. Farrier whether I should try to meet my husband's other son. What do you think I should do about that, Mr. Brayce?"

He stood still, holding the drink, looking down. He seemed to be going over her sentence to make sure he had understood it.

"Arleigh," he corrected, before saying anything. "I realize it's more than curiosity," he said after a pause.

"Yes."

"Why do you wish to meet him, Jill?"

"I want to know he's all right."

"You have a lot of troubles now."

She ignored this. "I want everything that touches Seton, and everything that *is* Seton—whether he recognizes it or not—to be properly resolved. Is that foolish?"

"No, ma'am," he said gently, "but it's hard."

"There's the comforting sentence in Spinoza."

"Which one?"

"All things excellent are as difficult as they are rare."

He looked at her so steadily, he might have been trying to guess her weight.

"Yes," he said finally, somewhat to himself. "I think you could meet Seton's boy. It would be a bit of a trip. However . . . Why don't you get the old man alone sometime, Jill? You could have a good talk with him. He's wise. And he's just. Been badly hurt by Patrick." There was a light nod of his head. "Seton too, I'm afraid."

With slow and courtly assurance he picked up her hand and held it, lifted it higher and kissed it, then put it back in her lap.

"Is Patrick coming today?"

"I hope not. The brothers are no good together. I'm glad he was on a tour while we needed so much from your husband."

He set a fresh drink beside her, took the empty glass, and went off.

Ask old Dermod sometime? Ask the old man, when they were alone? When would that be? When could that ever be?

Looking about the room, she wondered why, with such success behind them, the Farriers lived so drably. For twenty seasons of forty weeks there had been nothing but hotels, one day at a time, two days perhaps, never so much as a week. But these dreary journeys had been over now for ten years.

Jill began to reach for a finding that interested her very much indeed; that might be important, once found, in helping her understand her own husband. It was simple. At least it was of simple beginnings and it went through her mind this way: How unprepared these people were for the living they might enjoy now. If the mercy and the resource of the Catholic Church had carried them through catastrophe and grief (besides her morphine history, Mrs. Farrier had lost one of her babies, another boy, after Patrick and before Seton); if their own spirit and their sense of work had carried them through the basic indignity of show business, through the disabling vicissitudes of continuous travel, through everlasting homelessness, upper berths, hotel doctors, greasy breakfasts, corner saloons, money troubles (a trouble show people faced as a daily expectation)—if these had been the conditions of their life; if hardship was something they engulfed without wincing, it was *success* which they could not meet or cope with.

Conditioned to the harsh, accustomed to the crippling, the humiliating, the suspenseful, they could not now accept or use or even joyfully impound the happy results of all the wild vagabondage of days past, of money saved, of comforts earned.

It was this, then, that Jill saw: conditioned to the meager, they couldn't accept the much.

With his powers guttering, it was nonetheless Patrick who could do it, who could accept the circumstance before him; only Patrick the useless who could use it; only Patrick the peripatetic fidget who could relax in it.

How awful! How unjust! How wasting!

A hurrying man, impatient with the jammed rooms, squatted down beside Jill. He suggested a sprinter, quivering at the starting holes, waiting the pistol.

"I'm Charlie Westover. I'm the best director on Broadway. Easily."

Jill had seen pictures of him in *Theatre Arts*. He had the reputation of being a connoisseur of women (whatever that was) and was currently being seen with Tanager Bolt, the most renowned, most photographed "successful woman" of the era, a brand-new type that the postwar emancipation had made possible in New York.

Jill felt his energy, his excitement. What he'd said of himself had no conceit about it. To Jill it was transparent: his flippancy was a cover. There were other talents like his in the Village (though uptown the conceits were real enough). They were serious all the way through but afraid to show it.

More than ever, Jill wanted to see the opening of her husband's play.

"You're coming to it, of course."

She explained about Sean.

Westover said he'd take her to the play himself whenever she could come.

"We've had quite a time with your goddamn husband," he told her cheerfully.

"It's come to the stage where you aren't speaking?"

"Yes. And both of us grateful for it."

"It'll be over soon."

"Not with me."

"What do you mean?"

"I mean we're two people who can't get acquainted. I mean we've all beat this damn thing into something great. It's going to happen. He's famous already."

All the time the director was talking, Jill was watching a woman who had appeared in the bedroom doorway. She must have been there when Jill arrived, for she hadn't passed through the living room. Seton had surrendered his ottoman and was on the floor, looking up, enthralled.

Charlie read Jill's question. He leaned over near her ear.

"She lives on rich old men but she travels with young neurotic successes."

"Has she met my husband before?" Charlie caught the edge of this.

"I hope not. If I liked him, I could spare him a good deal."

"What do you mean?"

"She's a bore. A shuddering bore. But you don't get to that till you're in the trap."

"How is she a bore?" Jill felt this the safer question. Perhaps the "trap" would come out by itself.

Charlie Westover shrugged, not a shrug of dismissal but a shrug reaching up to the shelves of selection. It was a gesture that suggested he could bring down almost anything Jill might care to price or sample.

"Does all her reading on the subways," he said at once. "She's an intellectual clubfoot. But she has vitality. She has self-preservation. She has a fluid wardrobe. And she's the most vivid redhead this town ever had."

"You know her well." Jill said it as a judgment.

"Better than she wishes. But don't think I take her lightly. Or that New York does either. She's a relentless hostess. You're bound to get caught in it." Then he smiled. "Especially if Seton hits."

"Who invited her here? Does she know the Farriers?"

"She knows everybody she wants to. Right now she's here to have a look at the new playwright."

"Really?" She glanced over. "It seems the other way round. And she *is* beautiful. I never saw such hair. Real copper. With that hair it takes courage to wear those colors."

"Nerve. Not courage."

"What would you call those colors? Deep orchid and fire-engine red?"

"Well, that's close. *Vogue* calls it Louis Sherry Lavender and Long-champs Red. There's a sketch by Neysa MacMein."

"What's her name?" Jill was getting a little uneasy. The coppery woman in the red and lavender commanded the ottoman and the cluster of sprawled and seated men with a sort of imperious reversal of the classic Turkish levee. One expected fans and eunuchs and Maxfield Parrish.

"Her real name is Hilda Peterson, but nobody knows that."

"Well, what does she go by?"

"That's the skillful and sinful Tanager Bolt. Would you like to meet her?"

"I can wait. Especially if I'm bound to later."

Tanager seemed to have a way of holding her head very high, lips parted, eyes half closed, the long throat stretched to straining. Charlie Westover told Jill that Tanager had once been told she might have been the very model who sat for Raphael Kirschner's "Opium Smoker."

"That's when she first came up here to New York."

"Where did she come *from?*"

"Ocean City, New Jersey. Her father dredges for scallops."

Jill had a sudden desire to giggle.

"My father is an artist but I don't think I know the 'Opium Smoker.'"

"You can get it in Macy's for a dollar twenty-nine. But only recently. When it first appeared, Anthony Comstock outlawed it. Picture of a nude woman playing with her breasts. The eyes were real sluggish and come-hither. Good commercial eyes. So they got Kirschner to paint out the critical area. All you see now is the neck and the head and the half-shut eyes, and a wisp of smoke."

Charles Westover got up then and bent the kinks out of his knees.

"So that is how Hilda Peterson became Tanager Bolt. And that is about all there is to her," he said.

She looked up quickly at his face. It seemed spread with acid.

"How do you know all this? About the clothes and everything?"

"Because I pay for it. I'm one of her neurotic successes. Or was."

"Whatever it was is all over?"

"Yes. Turned out I wasn't neurotic at all. Just normal. *Deplorably* alive." He crouched down again. "One Sunday we were having breakfast. I told her not to say anything. Just for once. She can dismember you with talk. She talks about the French satirists without ever mentioning their names or their satires. Without ever reading them. Even with a pony. She talks about the eighteenth century without ever saying *whose*."

Charlie's face began working, becoming agitated, frightening, exploding with a strange necessity to jettison a hot cargo, to speak out, perhaps to devastate. Seton had described this quality in letters to her.

"Hell!" he shouted, his voice heating, "*everybody* had an eighteenth century! How could they miss! Even the Fuegians had an eighteenth century!"

Contempt began to curl his words. A disquieting recognition came to Jill: in his mind Charles Westover was lashing Tanager as if he had her tied.

Tanager stood up. She had left the caliphate and made a new entrance under the proscenium arch. Her head was still high, her chin out. Jill felt that Tanager, because of her arched neck, might stumble over something right in front of her.

"Uncommonly dull things come out of her with measured force." Jill realized Charlie's whisky had reached the blood stream but not the brain centers. He intensified his last sentence.

"Uncommonly dull things come out of her with elocutionary precision. They're given the sound of papal bulls. Of proconsular consequence. But the *substance*"—here he exhaled smoke—"of piccalilli!"

He crushed out a cigarette and smiled winningly.

"Actually, Jill, Tanager hasn't got the brains to blow hot soup."

They both laughed. But Jill sensed his flaming hatred of this flamboyant woman.

"Not the brains of a newt really"—he was still at it—"but *brass*——" Here his eyes narrowed with sudden Satanism. "Oh my, Jill, Tanager has the brass of a Madame Blavatsky!"

It came to Jill then that Charlie hated this woman (whatever their relation might be, whatever it might have been in the past) for the ancient reason that men hate women: he was afraid of her. She guessed it was Tanager Bolt who had given the lashing, Charles Westover who'd taken it. When and how didn't matter. He was a cut man.

"She sees me now," he hissed to her, keeping his lips still and his jaws locked as a ventriloquist might. "She pretends to be looking for me but she sees me. Now she's rising—with the serene manner of a spider woman who's just won a dishonest argument!"

Jill thought Charlie was a little crazy. "Look at her!" he was saying. "Look at her now! It's called Land Sighting."

Jill looked directly over then. Tanager had stepped up on the ottoman. She was conning the rooms, her eyes shielded.

"It's part of her repertory of living statues," Charlie interpreted.

"Which one is she being now?" Jill asked.

"De Soto," Charlie guessed. "De Soto astride the Mississippi delta. Or Balboa. She's very democratic about it." He belched delicately. "Isn't it breathless?"

He sounded ill.

Tanager's extravagant cigarette holder shot out toward Charlie, like a baton arousing woodwinds.

"She's arranging to tumble into your husband's arms," he informed her. "She brings something meticulous even to her crudities."

Tanager tottered then, and squealed and fell, a fluttering valentine. Seton could be graceful only when unhurried. Now in this tumbling emergency he seemed a stork, half risen, wings out, and about to try the air. There was a fine joyous colorful fall, a tinkle of bracelets, quick risings and gropings from all the men, brushings, apologies, jiggly solicitudes.

"She has a lorgnette at home," Charlie offered with marvelous irrelevance. Though far from the accident, he leaned over and began brushing his own trousers as if he'd been in the spill with the rest. Still bent over, and working at invisible dust, he finished explaining Tanager to Jill.

"She has a refreshing facility for what you might call the rehearsed impromptu," he told her. "And a rudeness that belongs on canal barges."

Then he kissed her hand quickly and firmly. Jill had known many men in the Village but she had never before met anyone who was so volatile and so substantial both at once.

"Where are you going?" she asked, as he started off.

"I'm taking her home. We're lovers. We're ardent afternoon lovers. Or we were. We're breaking up. It's in all the worst papers."

He twirled his hand and was gone.

Jill watched him saying good-by to Mrs. Farrier, then to the old gentleman. Their heads went back in a final pleasantry. Tanager was imprisoning Seton, saying good-by to no one, unaware she was not alone with him. Or not caring. She crooked her finger to hook Charlie, but he seemed to need no hooking. They went out. Seton stared after, then turned to his father, passing him his empty glass.

Other departures were readying. The room began to breathe, the press of people to thin out, the charge to lose its voltage.

So that was Tanager Bolt. Purple and scarlet, and a swan's throat. Jill had noted she had bad legs, very bad. She felt better. No doubt Tanager would take Charlie's skin off if she'd heard a single phrase of his commentary. Even so, Jill could believe a good half of it, for she'd seen her earlier that day at the glove counter in Saks Fifth Avenue.

Jill walked over and sat down beside her mother-in-law. Here she met Ballston Pilgrim, a young actor.

Mrs. Farrier leaned over to Jill and quickly explained the young man.

"Dermod and I are going to spend the next two months catching up on the theater. Mr. Pilgrim is telling me what to see and what to miss. Now go on, Mr. Pilgrim. The play called *Mirage*. What does Woollcott say to that one?"

"Not much."

"That Woollcott! He doesn't like *anything!* Maybe it was a better play than he said it was. I understand he isn't married. Men like that never know what they've been to. If they want to enjoy the arts, at least they should keep their opinions to themselves."

"But he's a reviewer, Mother," Dermod offered. "It's how he makes his living."

"He should find something better. More suitable. I hope he stays away from Seton. What else, Mr. Pilgrim?"

The actor brightened a little.

"Mr. Woollcott has some pretty good things to say for Francine Larrimore."

"Never heard of her. What's she in?"

"Play called *Nice People*, at the Klaw." He lifted out the fragment and read: "Francine Larrimore does all the things dramatic schools make a special point of correcting. She stands abominably. Her walk is outrageous, her voice has all the dissonance of a jazz band." Here Mrs. Farrier clucked at the world's unkindness. The old lady had far more spirit than Seton had ever implied. Jill was enjoying her. Mr. Pilgrim resumed:

"But she can act with the best of them. She is one of the most talented of the younger American actresses, gifted, skillful, intelligent."

"Well, now! You must take me to this one, Father!"

"Yes, Mother."

Seton looked up bleakly from across the room, came over and sat at Jill's feet. She reached down and touched him and he leaned his head back against her knees.

The priest joined the talk.

"Has anyone seen the St. John Ervine play, *Mixed Marriage?*"

"No, we haven't seen it, Father," Mrs. Farrier turned to him. "Is it something not to miss?"

"Have you a note on that one, Mr. Pilgrim?" the priest asked.

"Only a single line, Father. The *World* says: 'Although it's given a full production, forty minutes would suffice.' "

"What a slander!" Mrs. Farrier was happily shocked at almost everything.

Jill looked down the long clean line of her husband's cheek. The tan had gone. Drinking always made him pale. The hand that held the glass had a slight tremor. The ear was turned to the talk but Seton's mouth seemed shaped and ready to repel what came. She recognized the setting and the mood. His mind was locked off. There'd be no responses.

Jill wanted to disenagage herself and get back to the hospital. She felt guilty over the hours she was away from Sean. Dr. Celce had told her she could do nothing. Laughter behind brought her thoughts quickly into the room again.

"Margaret Wycherly, at the Punch and Judy Theatre," the priest was reporting.

"What's that one about, Father?" (Jill could hear a faint edge of Irish in the "a" of "father.")

"It's about an Irish Protestant boy who starts a riot."

"A Protestant indeed! They're always doing that!" Mrs. Farrier was on it at once. "Now how did he go about that, Father?"

"He marries an Irish Catholic girl." Mrs. Farrier clucked suspiciously here.

"Well, he was lucky to get her! Did he turn Catholic and put his bad ways behind?"

"Indeed he did not!" the priest said firmly. "He never did and the young girl got killed in the riot too!"

"*She* got killed! The Lord's mercy!" With shocked surprise Mrs. Farrier leaned over to the candy jar. "What's at the Hippodrome, Mr. Pilgrim?"

Jill glanced down again. Seton was so still he might be sleeping. Then she saw the slow brushing of his eyelashes. The head turned ever so slightly. There was a downward glance. He saw his glass was empty. He leaned forward slowly from Jill's knees and bonily got up. He was so graceless now it was hard to believe he was such a beautiful swimmer.

Jill was always finding herself in the midst of sudden adjustments: was he sick or healthy, was he good or bad, had he purpose or had he none, did he have more energy than other men or did he force himself to every action? Did he drink to get drunk or did he drink because he couldn't stop?

Who are you, Seton? Who am I? Where are we going?

"May I have another drink, Father?"

There was an instant's pause. All could see that Seton was logy.

"Of course, son. Tip the bottle. Help yourself. Bring it for Arleigh and Father McShane. I know we're not to talk about it and I shan't do so, but good luck to your opening matinee, my boy. I'm proud of ya' and so is your mother."

He lifted his own glass then, saluting his son. Seton stared back, smiled wanly, remotely, as if he had not heard. He turned his back and stalked into the kitchenette. Inside herself Jill shuddered. Was there no grace about him whatever? Or was he deaf? Or perhaps too preoccupied with his own terrors of the days just ahead even to know where he was?

There was a knock at the door. Darkly, Seton went to it, holding a bottle by its bottom.

Patrick stood there, pale but sharp. Seton grinned. He'd expected his brother. He set down the bottle and picked his brother up and held him. Years of understanding passed between them, though not a word was said.

"May I come in?" Patrick asked his mother. He looked somber and appealing.

"Patrick!"

Molly sprang from her chair like a young woman. She was upon him like a young woman, rushing him into the room. No prodigal had ever been so welcome.

Patrick shook hands about, nodding, smiling. He had a Broadway elegance about him, and yellow gloves again, but there was something shaky too. Jill sensed wreckage somewhere.

In the eyes of her mother-in-law there was nothing but relief and joy. In the eyes of Seton a great welcome. In the eyes of Dermod a raw surprise and a raw and open loathing. He seemed to sense it himself and covered it by taking the bottle from Seton and passing it to Arleigh and the Catholic priest.

Suddenly Jill felt the change that was in Patrick. His assurance was gone, so utterly gone it seemed irrecoverable. It seemed as if it never had been there at all. Only his clothes looked new. Pat himself was a walking ruin. A look at Dermod and Jill knew the party would now start to skid.

Mrs. Farrier saw nothing but her son, her first-born.

Pat and Seton exchanged a wink. Jill saw it. The brothers kept track of each other. Always would.

"For weeks and weeks we've heard nothing," the old lady said. There was reproach in her tone but none in her manner, none in the hunger of her look. "Were you on the road? Have you just had a closing?"

"Yes. In Columbus," he said, and he told them enough to make it real.

"But it wasn't a good show. Anyhow I had to attend Seton's opening, no matter what."

"Good for you, Patrick," the priest said. "We'd never know a thing from your brother. It's only through Arleigh I'm getting to the play myself."

Suddenly Arleigh got up, not with hurry but with deliberate purpose, and stood before the two ladies.

"Thank you, Molly. Thank you, dear." He kissed Mrs. Farrier, then leaned down and kissed Jill on the top of her head. The priest was shaking hands with Dermod. Arleigh shook hands quickly with Pat, squeezed Seton's shoulder, took up his hat, and opened the door. The priest followed. Then the young actor, Pilgrim, seeing he was the only outsider, took his leave and hurried after.

Jill thought of the sweet-sour condiments of a Chinese meal, each of the Farriers seeming to be set about the room like dishes of sauce, some pungent, some peppery, all waiting to be sprinkled about and devoured. Seton seemed to be the dish that steamed.

"Come on, have a drink, Pat. What the hell! You're back!" But Pat smiled and shook his head.

"Not if he says no," their mother interposed. "Jill?"

"No, Mother. I won't have any more. And I must get back. Seton, you stay."

"I'll come with you, child," Mrs. Farrier offered.

"No. But come tomorrow perhaps."

Dermod was pouring a drink for Seton.

"I've put you through a great plenty and I've asked for nothing out of it a-tall but that you try to bring a small measure of honor to the name of Farrier. And maybe a bit o' gratitude."

The old man looked hard at Seton, who now sat apart from the other, leaning forward, motionless, perhaps listening, perhaps as remote as the departed guests.

Patrick was safely back. Let the old bastard rail all night!

"Poor people we came here from Ireland and poor we return to God, but there's riches that went into the making of us all. And there's beauty of the land and the names of it and the strong people that lived on it. You call your own boy by the name of Sean. But are you mindful why it's a great name? Do you not know the Rebellion of Shane O'Neill? Or his kinsman Hugh, the Earl of Tyrone? 'Twas him who defied the English and licked them forty times and forty ways and died in Rome, his lands taken and his children slaughtered at Kinsale."

Seton took a long pull. Patrick picked up his mother's hand and smiled queerly at Jill. Dermod never stopped. The boys knew this mood of the father. They retreated into reveries of their own.

"Every drop in the Blackwater, every ripple in the Foyle, every tear in the Mourne, and all the pebbles along their shores have watched the villainies of the English and carried them clear to the oceans. There was never an Irishman that was a coward. But what have you two done with your heritage? Patrick, you're not named for any saint, God knows. 'Twould bring back the snakes! You're named for Patrick Sarsfield. They never licked him, the whole pack of them, and he kept the British blackguards out of Limerick after the Battle of the Boyne and they've not entered the town to this day!"

"What would you like me to do?" Patrick perked up a little. "Join the Sinn Fein?"

"Do? I'd like you to work. That's all. Work!"

"But he's just come *back* from working, Father." Mrs. Farrier knew where this talk could go. It was nothing for Jill to be hearing. It was embarrassing. "And for heaven's sakes, no more talk of the Battle of the Boyne or the Loigaire MacNeills. You'll be talking next about the beauty of the Boggeragh and the Sperrins——"

"Aye, I might so. There's nothin' like it upon the globe."

"Your daughter-in-law is English, Dad. Or partly so. London-born of an English mother. And she's got miseries that's nothing to do with Patrick."

Dermod reassembled himself sternly.

"Saints forgive me, Gillian! You look like morning on the Derg. You look like moonlight on the Ree, you're that pretty to me. I'd forgot wholly you were the enemy! Hand your glass."

Jill smiled and offered it. Seton lurched slightly, in some sardonic amusement of his own, but said nothing. The movement that was so close to breaking the surface had gone down again.

"I don't think you should speak of ingratitude, Father," she said cheerfully. "You know how often Seton and I have asked you to the Cape. We have more than one reason, too."

She took the drink, then rose and stood in front of him.

"No one has ever had a home so beautiful as ours. It's a clean and hospitable house. It's a great big huge friendly house. It's the grandest present anyone has ever given. As your daughter-in-law I thank you both. As the mother of your grandson, I'm proud to be in your family. I assure you, Father, there's no absence of gratitude. On the contrary, we're overflowing with it. Here's your health, sir, and my heart is in it."

She took a sip and kissed the old actor on the cheek. Then she kissed her mother-in-law. Dermod put his head down on Jill's shoulder and a sob shook him.

There were nervous good-bys then. Dermod Farrier blew his nose and sent his wife to the bedroom chiffonier for another handkerchief.

There had been no scene, no fighting. Jill felt relieved. And she felt glad to tell the old gentleman, especially with Seton present, how much the house had meant. She knew that Seton had never said thank you. It was one of those simple things he could not do.

She put on her white cotton gloves and picked up her bag.

"I'll call you tomorrow and let you know the visiting rules," she said to Mrs. Farrier.

Jill could not bear to look at Dermod. The shock of her appreciation, visibly something that had never been shown to him before, was unnerving.

All of a sudden she had a blind, cold hatred, not of Seton but of Seton drinking, and the whole shabby mechanism of his relation to other people.

Then she was immediately ashamed of the chemical violence of her own feeling. She reached out to tuck her arm into her husband's. But he'd tucked his own into Pat's.

"We're going to Barney Gallant's," Seton told her. "Pat and I have a lot to talk over."

In the ornate lobby of the Byzantium, Pat stopped at the tobacco counter for cigarettes. Seton took his wife toward the corner of Fifth Avenue.

"I could kill you for opening your mouth about the house!"

There was no sense in talking now. Calmly she said: "It's a thank-you that's been owing a long time, Seton."

"You're a fool. We'll never get another *thing* out of him."

Jill was shocked. She tried to hold on to her feelings. "What else *can* you want?"

"Want! He's been very close to buying a place in Bermuda."

Did Seton mean, *could* he mean that by thanking Dermod for one house now they might not get a new one later?

Her husband was drunk.

What a bore drunks were! What boors! And how quickly fine feelings could sour. Suddenly she lost control of herself.

"You're drunk." At once she knew better. She'd always known better. She'd never said it before.

He looked at her sideways, in total amazement, then slapped her across the cheek. They were passing the front of the Latham Hotel, adjacent to the one they'd left.

Jill felt nothing. She could hear the report. She could see Seton walking away, walking back toward the marquee of the Byzantium. She could see Patrick stepping down onto the sidewalk from the hotel's lobby. She could see people walking, one or two turning to stare. And she could see, almost to the corner of Twenty-eighth and Madison, a couple of men, one of whom might have been a priest, chatting in front of the steep brown steps that led up to St. Mary Reparatrix.

All this she saw but nothing felt. And this, she realized, was the exact kind of petty violence she had resolved that very day to ignore.

Her pity went to him, not to herself. But something went out with the pity that could not return.

She did not know this then.

Seton never came to the hospital to see his son. Nor did he sleep in the hotel.

Four days after the operation Jill heard a door open at the far end of the corridor. A man came in. With joy, Jill saw it was Arleigh Brayce. Midway he stopped at the desk, asked a question, and proceeded.

"Well, Jill," he said cheerfully. He had a cardboard box that contained a toy biplane.

"I'll hook it up for him. It loops the loop when you swing it back and forth on a stick. The pilot is supposed to be Eddie Rickenbacker."

Jill took the box and thanked him. They were alone in the visitor's nook. Arleigh sat down in a wicker chair and smiled at her.

"Is he all right?"

"He's not scared any more. But his throat hurts. It's a dirty operation."

"It's too bad he had to have it."

"It's over." She said it with relief. "He loves his grandmother. She's been here four times. And Grandfather Dermod!"

His eyes softened. His face relaxed.

Suddenly the black eyebrows arched and Jill felt herself the subject of intense penetration. Dust particles seemed to stand still in the shaft of amber sunlight that slanted down between them. Something deep but immediate was disturbing Arleigh. He leaned back against the creaking wicker, his knees separated, and he laid a wrist on each one, tucking up his trousers with his finger tips.

"I saw Seton strike you."

"Did the priest too?"

"Yes."

"I was afraid you'd seen." She turned away.

"I think he may have some sort of collapse." Arleigh spoke calmly, almost reassuringly. "He hasn't shown up at rehearsal."

"Do you know where he is?" Jill asked. Arleigh could detect no urgency in the question.

"Sort of," he said. "Pat's been on a bender. Your husband bailed him out. Then I saw Tanager Bolt in the Morosco lobby. We haven't seen Seton since."

"You came to tell me something," she said, waiting to hear what it was.

"Yes. I did. I think your husband needs psychiatric help." He looked at her quickly and covertly. He could see no surprise there, and he went on, feeling his way. "He hasn't had a life like other men."

"He hasn't wanted a life like other men, Arleigh." She got up and walked over near him, sticking her finger into the loop of the curtain cord, and swinging it gently as she talked. "I've thought of psychiatry. I thought of it on the beach only a month ago. His running off. The sudden unendurableness of everything. Yet nothing in our life has been unendurable. Not really. Much has been hard. Money. That's been hard. Having no money. But if you have to live without money, we're living in the right place."

He picked up the box that Jill had laid down on the table, opened it carefully, and began to assemble the cardboard airplane.

"You've known my husband longer than I have. What do you think is the matter with him?"

Arleigh lifted out a wing and tucked it into a fixed slot in the fuselage.

"I don't think Seton ever quite tells the truth about anything. I don't think he ever has."

"Why doesn't he?" Jill asked.

"I don't think he can."

He set the propeller against its tiny glass bearing, spun the blade by a snap of his nail, then made airplane sounds, circling the plane about his head. Looking too serious to be silly, he placed the toy back on the table top. It seemed to have passed its trials.

"I think he ought to see a doctor named Mortimer Flowers. But I think you ought to see him first."

"Do you think we could see him together? You and I?"

"Of course." Here Arleigh tucked the end of the string into the metal ring on the plane's back, held it thoughtfully on the end of its little pole, then made it loop the loop.

"When do you think this should be?"

"Right away. While you're here in New York. He happens to be here himself at the moment. At least I think he is. Usually spends the whole summer at Lake Placid. I saw him having lunch in Maillard's. Suppose I call him."

"Yes, call him." Arleigh handed Jill the airplane for her inspection, but she set it down on the table. "Is there something the matter with Seton that I don't know about?"

He considered a moment how to answer. "I believe it more correct to say that something *happened* to Seton a long time ago that you don't know about."

"Something severe?"

"Something altogether shattering."

Jill winced.

"Shattering to what, Arleigh?"

"To his whole nervous mechanism. I'd be patient with him. No matter what."

"I've tried."

"I know, Jill."

She realized this part of the conversation was closed for the moment. Arleigh wished to protect Jill, forever if possible, from the shocking story of Molly's morphine history. She returned to the more immediate problem of the play that was in rehearsal.

"How is the show going? Has he been pretty rough?"

Arleigh nodded quietly but without alarm. "You put up with people in the theater. If they're bringing something to it. But Seton's tempers—his arbitrariness—worst I ever saw in any playwright. Weeks ago I realized if it didn't go Seton's way there'd just *be* no production. Actors are afraid of him. Afraid to ask perfectly simple questions."

"What sort of questions?"

"Interpretations mostly. They're working hard to give it all meaning, to *comprehend* it all. For themselves. But much that he's written sounds archaic. Unnatural. I'm talking about bad writing. He does a lot of it, Jill. Crowds every sentence. Bloats it. Often what he writes is unsayable. The meaning drifts away before the paragraph ends. Or the listener's attention drifts away. If the cast wants a phrase change, they can't get it. They want it in the interest of clarity and meaning. Of performability. But soon after we started they became afraid. Afraid of his little-boy boorishness really. At the very start he was all right. We were all feeling our way. But right after that the few times anyone has broken rehearsal to stand on the apron and ask your husband a question"—Arleigh waved at the universe and smiled—"you'd think Seton had just caught someone ransacking his bureau drawers. Glare and whiten. Show his teeth. No sense came out of him. Just snake sounds."

Jill could hear them. Arleigh picked up the little plane and walked over to the narrow window where he perched himself and talked to Jill without looking at her.

"Has he been here to see the boy?"

"No."

"Do you need any money?"

"Yes. Badly."

"Did you know I paid Seton two thousand in advance?"

"He hasn't deposited the check. All our bills at the Cape are held up. Terribly overdue."

Arleigh floated the plane gracefully before him. "Would you take a hundred, in cash, right now?" Then he beamed charmingly, his eyes lighting up in mock conspiracy. "And no questions?"

"No, Arleigh. I'll see Seton. It'll clear up."

"Things never clear up with Seton. They just worsen."

"But *you've* found a way. *You* get along."

"I've had more practice. And I've nothing at stake."

"You've a lot of money at stake."

"Normal risk. Any producer. In some ways—as far as the theater goes—he's not too hard. I found this——" He set down the plane here and bent over, studying it as if he'd helped to build it. "If you want to get him excited about something, let him know he can't have it. I wanted Helen Hayes for your husband's play. I should have known better than to suggest her. He ridiculed the idea. Too inexperienced. He won't in another year, with another play. He'll want her then. When he can't have her. He'll want Charlie Westover too. But Charlie will never direct for him again, no matter what notices we get."

"I'm sorry—he seemed the very thing—the very person." She shrugged and looked away. Arleigh handed her the little plane.

"I won't go to the boy's room. I'd be another confusion. Call me at the Players if you need anything."

She was comforted by him, by the cool hands, by the hillside smell of him, but she was also mystified. How could he get so much done in his own life and still juggle so many details? In almost every action he took he seemed anxious to help someone or to compose something. He seemed perpetually interested yet never shocked. What was it she was to hear about Seton? It was terrible to be left with a hanging question like that. When she loved him so much. When they'd survived everything else.

"What philosophy sustains you, Arleigh?"

In six words he told her. She never forgot them.

"Serve yourself. Serve others. Act. Believe."

They walked down the corridor together. Jill was good company. He knew more of her than she suspected. He'd read the manuscript that H. L. Mencken had rejected and the one he was going to print. And he'd read her first two published pieces in *Smart Set* before knowing who she was. He said nothing of this. He thought of some of the wreckage in his own life—the four marriage disasters. Right now alimony was pouring out of him like air from a dying bladder. The four who had been Mrs. Brayce at various times had taught him much about other men's women if nothing about his own.

He was acutely aware of Jill's sex appeal, a quality in women only lately acknowledged by the public prints but one which Arleigh had been appraising for half a century. There seemed no basis for any marriage problem there—covertly his eye went down the silhouette of her at his side—except her obvious willingness to give herself, and give of herself, all the time; to ask little, expect little, hope much.

"Too good. Too kind," he thought to himself, not knowing these were her thoughts of him.

When Jill brought the airplane to Sean his knees jumped and wonder poured out of him. He made a quick reach for the stick and tried to talk.

Part Four

15

CHARLIE WESTOVER KEPT MOVING BACK AND FORTH
between the water cooler and the door of the lobby office, trying to
read people's faces, trying to pick up a phrase or two of their talk,
trying to keep busy at something, anything, till the house lights would
start to dim.

All the critics were there. At least every one that mattered. It
could be a triumph. Or it could be a slaughter. There was the
New York *Herald*, just coming in now. Yawning. God! Before the
curtain is even up! Here comes the *World* now, arm in arm with
the Evening *Telegram*. Woollcott now, puffing through nose and
mouth, bulging everywhere, toddling about importantly as if he were
the whole New York *Times* and its rotogravure all by himself. God!

Charlie rushed over when the Farriers came in, Seton's mother
and father.

He waved an usher away and personally took the Farriers to their
location. Arleigh Brayce had got them the house seats when he found
that Seton had made no provision at all for them.

Old Dermod had a fearful look. He sat down quickly, even before
his wife did. He forgot to help her with her coat. He leafed the
program without seeing any of the words.

Jill had a suspense of her own. She sat alone in the hospital, wondered where her husband would wait out the uptown verdict on his
talents. In the dreary waiting room where Arleigh had brought Sean
the airplane she prayed for Seton, for his success, for his ability to
hold on and endure until his work could shape itself, until it could go

on by itself without any supports. She prayed that no accident be allowed to mar what he had wrought with such terrible effort. She prayed that drink would not ruin his work or cut his life. She prayed she would be a good wife to him, that she would find the strength to preserve the kind of peace he needed to do his work. Then she prayed for Sean and looked in on him. He was sleeping. Jill went quietly back to the hotel.

It seemed so unnecessary, just now, that *everybody* had to be alone. She went down to the Hellespont for tea. Then went up to her room again to wait for news of her husband or for the return of the Farriers. She thought perhaps Arleigh Brayce might call. Or the bounding Westover. But no one called. She wished she might get just one expression from one single source as to how the play had gone. It occurred to her that there was a theater-ticket service in the lobby of the hotel. She picked up the wall phone and asked for it.

They had heard of the play but had heard nothing as to its reception. They had no tickets but thought they could get some. Jill decided to take a bath, then stretched out on the bed and read the *Saturday Evening Post*. Soon she was sleeping. She woke up much later. It was chilly, and outside, it was quite dark. She opened the bed and got in between its covers. She slept without moving.

Much later she heard Seton. He was in the bathroom. Light leaked in from beneath the door. She could hear the sound of his toothbrushing. Then he gargled. Then he began to sing. This was rare. It sounded soft and loving and far away. She lay still, listening. Was he drunk? She heard water running, then the squeak of the faucet being turned off. She heard the rattle of the towel rack, then something being set on the glass shelf above the washbasin.

The door opened quietly. She could smell soap. Seton was standing in the frame of the door, the light on his back. He looked very tall and splendid. He looked calm and noble and serene. He was naked to the waist.

"Jill?" he called softly.

"Yes," she said at once.

He came over then and knelt down by the bed and reached a cool clean hand in to her throat, then slowly and lovingly patted her breasts. He kissed her temple, began to thread his fingers slowly through her hair.

"I may not be an overwhelming success but I'm whelming, at least. I'm on my way."

"Oh, darling." She began to crawl up toward the head of the bed. "Of course you are." She kissed him quickly and hungrily three or four times on the cheek. "I *knew!*"

Seton pulled up a chair and threw a folded blanket across his shoulders. He looked boyish and absurd. He crowded down over her. In this moment she felt safe and protected and necessary and loved.

"What have you heard? I'm *dying* to know! Have you seen anyone that was there?"

"I've *heard*"—his voice became mysterious and he continued in mock whisper—"that I'm a dramatist of *'terrific force.'* 'Terrific force' are the only words I'm sure of. Robert Gilbert Walsh said 'em, but that's all I heard."

"But who's got any other reviews? When will we see them? Are there any plans? What did your mother and father——"

"We're supposed to go to their suite and sort of wait there for the great judgment to come in."

"Go there *now*? What time is it?"

"It's seven-thirty in the morning. It's the morning after."

"You mean we're supposed to go there now?"

"Yes. Sure. Any time. Our getting there early though, it won't change a single word in a single review."

He reached into the bed for her.

At nine they tapped on the Farriers' door and came in. There was a good smell of coffee and there were flowers on the console table.

Dermod took a long tormented look at his tall son, opened his arms, and walked across the living room. He held him for a long time. Seton was flustered. It was something that had never happened. The old man was shaking with sobs but no word came from him. Finally Seton freed himself. Dermod grinned, backed off a little, smiled at Jill, waved them toward the coffee table.

"What are you trying to make us all *do*, Seton? Go out and commit suicide? My God, boy! What a play you've written!"

"Where's Mother?"

"She's in the lobby ordering more papers."

"Could I see one?" Jill asked shyly.

"*Could* you! Could you see *one!*" Dermod handed her a sheaf.

"Oh, here's Woollcott's review!" she shouted.

"Read it, lass. Out loud to your husband! I've read it four times."

Jill looked up, tentatively offered the paper to her husband. "Maybe you'd sooner go through it all by yourself."

"No, I'll be a good boy." He picked up his coffee. "I'll sit down and I won't say a word. I'll think about other things."

"Mr. Woollcott writes for the *Times*." No one could tell whether this was an impromptu title she had just given to the reading to come but neither man said anything. Great words, each a piercing delight, sprang up from the page:

> "*The diet of pap, poop, and flapdoodle that Broadway has had the gall to charge admissions for during most of this present season has come to a sudden end with the production last night of a heavily counterweighted but magnificent new play. It is magnificent in its reach and in the profundity of its significance; in the torment it lays out for us to look at, in the far greater torment it insinuates into the mind and conscience. It has left this reviewer—a person of strong stomach—quivering and aghast. And exalted.*"

Jill's mind raced and her pulse ran with it.

> "*. . . to behold words and concepts and concatenations of power and dramatic drive that were put there with fury and compassion and truth and incandescent realism——*"

Here Seton cut in like a lash. "Concatenations! By God, it's a good thing he's on the *Times!* They wouldn't know——"

"Hush, son. Proceed, daughter." Jill looked back, and continued:

> "*. . . incandescent realism—so and so and so and so—the play has greatness in it and marks Seton Farrier as one of the most luminous and gifted——*"

Seton looked quickly across at his wife. She was crying softly, had lost control of her voice. She could go on no longer.

"Oh, Seton." She handed the paper to her husband's father, who rose and continued the reading. It was a splendid moment for him. But Jill could only hear it in snatches—

". . . *spaciously endowed, nobly attentive . . . though basic ideas of simplicity are often slowed down by an overabundance of verbiage . . . the processional of Man, self-perjured, his eyes bandaged, his heart locked, but the march to the gallows of his Fate as steady as Life—as cruel——*"

The old actor folded the pages of the New York *Times* as a minister might close the pulpit Bible at the end of the presermon reading. He looked down quietly at Jill, who was sprawled out, unconscious of her position, her head down on the arm of a deep overstuffed chair.

Slowly she turned and looked up for Seton. He had gone.

"To pick up Mother, I do not doubt," old Dermod said.

He passed other reviews to her. She devoured them hungrily, even when they exasperated her, as did the New York *Herald*:

Poetically moribund, philosphically nihilistic, and morally comatose, this rambling, tormented, overwritten, underripe monstrosity is the most moving experience this reviewer has had in a theatre in more than thirty years. We are in the presence of a great original writer. We are in the presence of a great original play. It shakes and galvanizes and electrocutes. It smothers by its very pessimism, by its unrelieved, fatalistic hopelessness. It crucifies. But like the Crucifixion, it lifts us also—the beholder—into the skies.

Jill wrinkled her nose at this critic, then spied the phrase that Seton had quoted—"terrific force." It was in the *Telegram*. She read the next phrase aloud to her father-in-law, and Dermod stood there like some benign dowager watching her ward making a successful debut.

" 'It reveals his mastery of the larger forms.' "

"Indeed it does, daughter! What a son I have! All the years! All the years! And the lonely nights. And not hearing. God bless us all, it *is* true—you give it away and it always comes back. Always in better form, too." Gaelic phrases scrambled about his face, caressing the air, magically brightening his eye.

"Now read Towne, daughter."

> *Seton Farrier, whose accomplishments have been, up to now, sufficiently modest to keep them invisible, has broken through the chilling opacity of being unknown, and by his defiance of convention, and a powerful play, has put his name in front of the whole city.*

The World called it:

> *A crashing, thundering success. With no concessions to current popular expectations; without compromise to the effete play-goer who goes merely to be pleasured, this new barbarian has toppled human feeling and spread it out over the stage with a screaming and self-righteous savagery not recorded since the Old Testament.*

Jill put the papers aside and stood up. Dermod had been there, he'd seen her husband's show, seen every action, and seen it with the eyes of a professional man of the theater.

"What was it like, Father? Describe every feeling that you had. Would you have wanted to play the old father? How good was the acting? To another actor, I mean? Tell me everything!"

"That I will! That I will! Have your seat again while I get you some coffee, Jill. But you're married to a great man and no doubt of it now. I feel a little ashamed, I must say I do."

He poured for her. His hands were not steady. The house phone rang annoyingly and Dermod snatched it up. Then he nodded, looking across at Jill with a touch of regret, even of embarrassment. "Well, we'll be here," he said shortly into the phone, and hung up.

"It's Mother," he said, a little too quickly to be casual. "She and

Seton. He's all out of shirts, it seems. They're going up to Lord and Taylors to get a few shirts. They'll soon be back."

He passed her a plate of biscuits. Jill took one. She knew the old man felt bad too.

It seemed an odd time to need anything like a shirt. It seemed an odd time even to think of a shirt.

Dermod set down the plate and looked over uncomfortably at his daughter-in-law. Suddenly he began to break up and tremble. He came over close to her, shaking his head miserably from side to side. "I don't know, Gillian. I don't know, my dear one. You'd think he could—come up—be with us."

Jill took his hand and pulled it over her shoulder and looked out the window, but she could not tell what kind of a day it was going to be.

16

ONE MONTH AFTER SETON'S TRIUMPH, PATRICK WAS coming up out of another one. Seton had made the mistake of giving his brother two hundred dollars for a new wardrobe.

The Woodbine was outside Lexington, Virginia. It was a sanatarium for "intemperate Christian men." It guaranteed their cure in ten days. When Mrs. Farrier described the treatment, Pat at once accepted the institution's philosophy. It was a private hospital that was run without benefit of doctors and that worked on the theory that a man who was forced to drink incompatible mixtures of intoxicants day after day would get so sick he could never face a drink again.

"There's rest and prayer too," she added a little dubiously.

Gin, beer, rye whisky, and rum were served on the hour, from eight to twelve o'clock noon, in that order. A rest period after lunch was interrupted for a two-o'clock toddy. There were no prayers. At four a pint of stout was urged on offended stomachs. The toddy was the only drink that was mixed. Everything else was straight. The quality of all the liquor was good.

To ensure the results advertised, the Woodbine proprietors gave each patient a daily dosage of apomorphine. This drug was put in the toddy. No one before Patrick, not even Tennessee mountain boys, had ever been able to survive the ten days. No one had ever been cured, either; but then neither had they ever asked for their money back. Each time such an action was suggested, the Woodbine mentioned, with wooden directness, that they would be happy to have the matter judged in court. No man would insist he entered the Woodbine a hopeless drunkard and had remained so.

It was not so with Patrick. "First time I ever got my money's worth!"

He told it, later, to Seton. His dismissal had not been for refusing the blunt regimen or the obscure theorizing of the place. It was for stealing and concealing liquor. Patients (they were called "applicants") were encouraged to walk about the grounds. Queer sounds and queerer conduct were common. One afternoon Patrick found an applicant waving a stick in the hen house, trying to get the chickens out so he could find room to lie down. The nest of setting hens, from that day, became the place where Pat would hide his bottle. He became quite used to drinking the whisky warm, heated by the hen's body and shoved in among her eggs. Once he'd seen a hen cock her head sideways in a clucking outrage at a fresh bottle, scratch at it, and try to bill it to one side. He was relieved to see her unable to deal with it. The hens always puffed out their bodies and their feathers protectively when anyone approached. Pat was physically afraid of the chickens, so he shielded his face with one arm while fishing underneath with the other for the bottle, hoping that these minatory attitudes would keep others away, too.

This way he could get all he wanted and drink his favorite bourbon between the crazy rations provided by the management.

They had a meeting over him. It was decided to send him back to New York. He refused to go. They threatened to call police. He puzzled them by at once approving. He took the receiver off the hook and handed it to them, drunk, but polite as they, and far calmer. He was not fresh about any of this. "I'm trying to co-operate," he said, feeling that this was so. He just felt he was in a good place. Southerners always soothed him, made him feel welcome. He explained this to them.

When his ten days were up he said he would take another ten. But a reading of the brief agreement told him that they had him there.

"You leave me no recourse," he told them. "I *have* to sue."

They gave him one hundred dollars and agreed to tuck two bottles of Park & Tilford Special Reserve in his bag, and get him on the C. & O. for Jersey City.

When he got back to New York he planned to tell his mother that everything had worked out fine and that he was now cured.

He had a bottle left. Outside his hotel bar it was raining lightly. There was a man at the bar explaining to the bartender he was afraid to drive his car downtown to the Union Square Garage, that he'd left his license in another suit.

"Glad to do it for you," Pat said easily. "Got my license right here." He patted an empty breast pocket.

The car was a small Franklin. Its top was down. The man kept thanking Pat and watching the sights whirl by. Pat turned south when he got to Park Avenue and sent the little Franklin chugging cheerfully around to the Grand Central ramp.

"Keep us out of the rain a little bit," he said, sensing his companion's alarm.

Coming down the slight incline, southbound on Park, the car owner was horrified to realize Pat was not driving over to the right to stay in the lane for passenger cars. He was heading direct for the trolley tunnel that opened right here in front of them.

"Stop!" he shouted, clutching at Pat's arm. But Pat planned to go through the trolley tunnel.

He realized he'd wanted to do this all his life. It seemed wide enough. There were two tracks. Northbound and southbound trolleys could pass each other in the tunnel. Did it hundreds of times every day.

"Nothing to it, friend," Pat roared out with amiable bovine reassurance. "Do it hundred times a day! Two trolleys can pass. Why not a trolley and a Franklin?"

They whirled through the half gloom of the trolley tunnel, then came into the open again at Thirty-fourth Street. But the owner was too shaken to go on.

"What's the matter, friend?" Pat asked defensively. "It kept us out of this rain, didn't it?"

"Let me drive! Let me drive!"

Pat wasn't one to quarrel. He pulled over to the right side of the street and stopped, getting out, looking back approvingly at where they'd been.

"Have a drink," he said, offering his bottle.

The owner shook his head, engaged quickly and clattered on down into the Twenties. He hadn't even slammed the door shut.

Pat turned west for a block, then south to the entrance of Madison Square Park. There were a few bums sleeping in a subway entrance. In the gloom of the park, rising clear above the trees, was an enormous replica of the U.S.S. *Oklahoma*, constructed originally by the government to stimulate the sale of Liberty Bonds, and now resurrected for the annual drive of the Red Cross.

He sat down on some scattered lumber by the protected side of the *Oklahoma* and took a couple of snaps of whisky out of his bottle. He was getting wet and chilly. He realized that although he was very close to the Byzantium now, he could not call on his mother. He realized he was in that arguable state where he knew those looking at him would call him drunk, unless they were drinking with him, but where he knew he was stone sober because he'd just driven through a tunnel. By God, he must be stone sober!

He wanted to hum, but the rain got a little thicker. He rose up and peered inside the timbers of the battleship. Interior ladders seemed to rise to invisible decks and spaces above and he began to climb up, hunting for a dry spot. Inside, it had the fresh outdoor smell of a saw mill. He groped and stumbled about over scantlings, props, two-by-fours, and found the housing that was supposed to represent the bridge. A great heap of shavings lay on the floor below the wheel. Pat leaned back against the boards in relief and began to drink.

Thirst and daylight woke him. He had no remembrance of where he had been, no clue as to where he was. He was covered with sawdust. He pulled himself to his feet by gripping a spoke of the *Okla-homa's* wheel. There was a terrible rip in his trouser leg and paint on his shoes. He could hear horses somewhere. He could hear the Metropolitan chimes. But he couldn't orient himself. The roar of a subway seemed familiar but its precise significance would not quite come clear. He stepped from the wheelhouse to the bridge and immedi-ately looked down upon a terrifying complete set of turrets, with guns of some sort, feeling his present circumstance might be blurred by an upheaval still going on. Then buildings that he knew—Green's Hotel, the Flatiron, the mass of courthouse buildings at Twenty-sixth Street, and the unmistakable mass of the Garden—all closed in to comfort him. He choked up with relief.

He came back into the wheelhouse and found his bottle in the edge of the shavings. He still had two inches. Gratefully he drank, then, holding his bottle by its neck, he went out to the flimsy deck to try to find his way down again, and find his way to water. He leaned on a gray painted railing, looking down. He felt sorry for all the people going to work, or coming from work. It was dusk or dawn or something, a poor time to have to be in motion.

He waved his bottle to salute them all, shouting his concern and proclaiming his own freedom and his affectionate presence. He realized one man, quite near and with his back to a telephone firebox, was a policeman and that he was watching him. Indeed, he seemed to be grinning up at him, rocking to and fro just a little, swinging and then catching his night stick in neat but monotonous rhythms.

"Hey, Admiral!" the cop shouted. To Pat it seemed a nasty sarcastic Irish kind of a voice. "When are ye plannin' to come ashore?"

17

AT FIVE O'CLOCK ON LABOR DAY CATASTROPHE struck old Dermod. He was taking a careless diagonal in front of the Lambs and a taxi hit him.

When the news was phoned to the Byzantium Hotel, Seton's mother answered. She was playing rummy with her son and waiting for Dermod to join them. It was Seton's last night before the Detroit opening of his latest play—*The Barren Goddess*. As usual, no one knew where Patrick was, but he would have been hard to reach, had they known, for he was part of a dance marathon that had been thrown out of Newark by the board of health but that was continuing in vans—the couples dancing to Victrola music—on their way to a more friendly Trenton.

"Your father is in Columbus Hospital, Seton. He's unconscious. He's been struck by a taxicab."

Seton looked up from the card table. She saw no comprehension in his eyes, only the bright opacity she had come to know as a shield to protect his inner thought, to keep out feeling, to flee action.

"Will you go right over, Seton? Right now."

Still her son did not move or react. She gripped his right shoulder and lightly but firmly shook it.

"Seton! Your father! He's hurt! You must go! I have to put things together for him."

Seton rose up slowly without looking at his mother. He had the uncertain movements of a man confused by the sight and speed of an unfamiliar city.

"Patrick—I'll try to get Patrick." He hung on to the back of his chair.

"Call Father McShane and go with him!" his mother shouted. This time she shook him harder, turned him about, walked him to the phone, and purposefully shoved the receiver into his hand. "If he isn't there, walk across the street to the Parish house. Get *any one of the priests that's in!* Be sure he brings the Holy Oils."

Seton nodded. Mrs. Farrier left him. From the bedroom she shouted:

"Columbus Hospital! Hurry now."

When she came out a minute later with a small bag of her husband's shaving things and a flask of whisky, Seton had left.

He was not seen again for six days.

Dermod was the most taxing patient the hospital had ever had. He swore great oaths and hurled silverware. He spat. There was no need for the Holy Oils. He had no fractures and when his doctors agreed that his slow but probable recovery could just as well take place in the hospital in New London—a removal he whined and whinnied for—the Columbus authorities were so pleased to be rid of him, they supplied an ambulance without charge.

This was the second and last time Jill was ever to be alone with the great actor.

She was drafted to make the journey. It was not too inconvenient, for she had been visiting her mother on the Jersey shore where she could leave Sean. And she was glad to make up in some measure for her defecting husband. All were embarrassed by his absence. All were silent, pricked with apprehensions of their own, all explaining to each other, in different terms, what they all so tiresomely knew and shared: that Seton fled trouble and always would; that small troubles sent him into the ropes and a real crisis knocked him out. The Farriers never spoke of artistic temperament. The way the men behaved was a family disease. It was all part of the same cancer: Patrick's women, Dermod's pinched retirement, Seton's runaways. They were men in reverse, cursing the world's scenery for going the wrong way, never thinking to correct it by turning around themselves.

On the slow ride up the Sound, Dermod was a cheery man. Jill could smell whisky. That was nothing special. Whisky was the first characteristic of the breath of the Farrier men. She could smell camphor too, and remembered that Molly always made her husband wear a chamois bag around his neck, full of camphor. She said it kept diseases away, all the communicable diseases. That Dermod had never had a disease was proof that this was no Irish superstition.

Jill had never been in an ambulance. It was surprisingly roomy and well fitted. She sat in the attendant's side seat, at the foot of her patient, her back to the driver. The driver was separated from them by a glass panel. He slid this open when they slowed down or stopped at intersections, looking sideways and catching Jill's eye to get her response to his unspoken query about the condition of their passenger. She'd nod quickly and brightly. Dermod was just fine, it seemed. Once the driver took a good look at Jill, saw how pretty she was and came around to the rear of the ambulance when they stopped for an open bridge over the Harlem. Dermod didn't want to stop, nor did he want to share Jill, so he glared at the man and told him he felt uneasy with no one at the wheel and the brake not set. But the brake was set and all knew, for they had heard it.

He dozed lightly, muttered often, sang softly in Gaelic, and forever kept reaching his hand out, feeling for Jill's, and each time she would extend her own.

Presently he began to giggle. He told her it was he himself who had insisted on getting Jill to make this journey with him.

"The nurses—they fuss me too much," he said. "And Molly, she's quite a weeper, you know. And a worrier always."

They passed a forest of masts at Southport and Dermod reared up quickly to see better. The sight of a friendly bay, full of little boats, some tugging at buoys, some bouncing about on the stage of the harbor, each with a pennant fluttering, delighted him. He asked Jill to prop him up so he was half sitting. He had a great need to talk, and, as she soon realized, to confide.

"What kind of car is taking us, daughter?"

"It's a Packard, Father," she said quickly. "I saw the red paint in the center of the hub caps."

"It's a way to tell, surely. By the hood, too. Or even the sound. Did the driver tell you how many cylinders? Never mind. He'll only stop again."

He took Jill's hand and gave it a friendly squeeze.

"What's wrong with my sons, Gillian? I put a floor below their feet. By God! Me and their mother. But can they stand up? No, they cannot! And a mountain of work and loneliness to give 'em both what neither me nor my Molly ever had. And one's a whoremaster and the other's a godless monk with a poor-mouth habit and a tongue like the devil's fork."

He looked out the wide window of the Packard ambulance at a great sweep of waving marsh grass. But his eyes were on sights that were within his mind and memory, and not on the creeks and backwaters of the Sound.

"Is he an artist? Does he have greatness about him? What does your own father think? He's an artist. All I can see is a big darkness. All his people condemned. They curse the place but never move out of it. 'Twas me that come out of the bog, not my boys. I lay down me savings before the bursars of the univairsities and where's the money now? And the good? Patrick takes it in one bite, takes the whole four years of it, then he throws it up like a sick animal and it's like he never read a book in his life. But Seton—the scrawny jackal— he leaves his education on the shelf. To this day he's got no more notion of the reproductive system of the female or the great distance to the Pleiades than his brother has a notion to say his prayers or get his laundry to a Chinaman. He's a bum. They both are!"

"But a lot of things *do* interest Seton, Father. And he reads a lot."

"What's in *life* should interest him. But Seton only reads to find new ways to plague it." There was a tense silence, then Dermod looked into her face with a kind of impassioned tenderness.

"Is he a good lover, lass?"

Jill thought of her answer before giving it.

"We have a good life, Father. We have a great deal."

"He's no good. I can tell. You're a fine girl. But you're not a strong woman, Gillian. You should cuff him."

"Cuff him? You mean strike him?"

"Of course!" He whipped it out instantly as if it were the remedy for Setons everywhere, and universally practiced.

"You mean strike him *with* something?" Jill, whose mother was English, could be literal.

"Indeed I do, ma'am. With anything. There's no peace otherwise."

She had never been in such a conversation.

"But I don't have anything. And I'm quite sure he'd take it away from me."

"Don't let 'im. Don't go offering it to 'im. Just hit 'im. You'll get more respect. And he'll stay out of your kitchen. You've stovewood there. And a poker. You'll see, daughter. I know the world."

He seemed very sure of it. Jill realized he was old and injured but he didn't look or sound either. The lurching of the heavy ambulance concealed the small convulsion in her shoulders, but she had to turn her back on her father-in-law to hide her merriment. He was too intensely serious, too Irish, too grotesquely solicitous, to bear the disillusion her face would surely bring him.

"But I don't hit people, Father. I never think to."

"You should begin. The English—they didn't manage their history by standing at the edge of the fight."

"But we never fought without the King's command," she temporized.

"Nonsense," he said, unimpressed, his voice gravelly. "Split his head," he encouraged. Then he snatched up her hand and kissed it quickly and set it down again. "But you don't *seem* English. I'll say that for you, Gillian."

"Oh, I'm very American, Father. I've been here my whole life nearly."

He twinkled lovingly at her, gave her a little pinch. "Did you ever hear of Dermod MacMurrough, daughter?"

"Of Ireland?"

"Of Ireland *of course!*" he stormed.

"Yes, I have. He lost the kingdom of Leinster."

"Aye, but he won it back. And Dublin, too."

"But he needed an English king to help. He had to call Henry the Second."

"An English king!" He was up and fuming. Jill pressed him down again, and tried to pat him quiet. "You should come to Ireland and know the truth! Hand me the whisky. We'll say no more."

"All right, we'll say no more. And I'll let you take me to Ireland. Anyhow, I know you never struck Mrs. Farrier."

"No, that's the truth, Jill. She's a saint." Jill thought she saw pain cross his face. "And quite self-managing too," he added, as if he'd prefer it some other way but knew better than to disapprove of accepted virtue.

In the middle of Westport old Dermod propped himself on his elbow, reached over and took a noble swig out of the neck of the whisky bottle, then held the bottle for Jill to cork.

"Have a nip, lass."

"No, I'm the nurse. Try to rest. It'll be soon now."

"Rest!" He spit it out like a berry seed. "I've never had such a ride! With a Packard too! And a young man to steer."

He was enormously enjoying the ride. Jill realized that she was too.

"Why don't you tell me about coming to America, Father?"

It was the perfect suggestion.

"I was a child of the potato famine, Gillian, and though we hated the English, as any who knows them cannot help, I was a deep respector of Gladstone and am today. I mention it to keep the judgments fair." He patted her to emphasize this.

"We were cottiers, Gillian, poor as a beetle in a flue. Seventy-five shillings brought me here—think of it—and I was dumped in a lazaretto on Staten Island. I had the ship's fever, or maybe the typhus. Few could walk off the pier. It's a savage thing they did—the owners. No food a man could swallow. Kegged water to drink and tiny animals you could see with your eye swimmin' about. I strained me drinkin' water through me shirttail. No doctor. No medical officer of any sort a-tall."

He talked for the rest of the journey about the abominations that beset the Irish on their way to America in the middle of the previous century, of schemes to rob them; of the apathy of the average voyager; of his illness, his terror, his unbelievable ignorance. Jill knew that if her husband could be listening, he would be embarrassed.

How many of Seton's fears were rooted here, in the knowledge of the desperate origins of his father? Seton would see no valor here, only squalor.

"We sat in our filth, Gillian, with our eyes shut. Forty-four days. In bad weather they roofed us over so we could not even get to the privies. And it's true, some come aboard with no notion of sanitation whatever. Any dark place would do. Thirty-seven died on the voyage —the captain with them—and the officers too sick to get them over the side. So into New York Harbor we sail, our decks loaded with our own dead—smelling like a slaver. A whole *pile* of dead, white and skinny, under a piece of canvas above the forepeak. Two of them young mothers with their babies survivin' but none to tend them. It was worth leavin' this earth entirely to get the ship behind, and the smell of her, and the sight of her miseries."

"Where did you go?"

"Albany first, after the lazaretto. Then for a year I worked on the locks at Middleport. I got me strength back and went on up the canal to Buffalo. I had strong hands, Gillian."

He held them up and turned them over as he might look at

merchandise in a store. "I went to work in a foundry. Fourteen hours. Fifty cents."

"Fifty cents an hour?"

"Fifty cents a *day*. I slept in a shed. Bathed me body in Lake Erie. Then I got me some extry work—in a pool-hall saloon Saturday nights and Sundays. I did a bit of brawlin' there"—then he quickly added, his eyes tight—"not much, you know, but I was young and I was handy."

He watched the scenery pass, his eyes misty, his mouth working.

"It's wrong to think of the Irish as people of the soil. They've no instinct a-tall for it. They hate it. Except for Dublin and the seaports, Ireland is a great farm, but its people even so are city people altogether. We never go near a farm if we can help it. In America, with her cities goin' up, the canal busy, so many new railroads—I worked six months setting sleepers for the roadbed of the Montreal-Portland— we could turn our backsides on the prettiest meadows and never miss 'em. A wage and a woman and a drink. No, an Irishman is a city man. We'll never be different."

He began to mumble in Gaelic, then reached again for the whisky. Jill handed him the bottle.

"Why don't you just keep it by you, Father?"

"Yes. That's a good plan."

He drank eagerly, then picked up the folded edge of the sheet to wipe his lips. "The famine days—God's mercy. I knew what a naked woman was like when I was a spalpeen. Poor creatures, there was none with the strength to dress the corpses and there they lay, a shame to the eye and a curse upon the Crown. In heaps, Gillian. Days of it. In Sligo we covered them over in a gravel quarry. I saw a thousand women stark and stony—their eyes open to look at me lookin' at *thim*—and it's like yesterday and it's seventy-five years, for I was ten and it haunts me right now."

He knuckled his eyes softly. "Goddamn my sons, Jill, why'd you marry aither one of 'em! Has anyone heard of Patrick? I suppose not. Or Seton? Does he know I'm hurt? It's been six days."

"We've not been able to reach Seton, Father," she said, not untruthfully. But he knew.

"Pat's on the bum again." For an instant he looked like a racked saint. Then a stronger look—broad anger and bitter reprehensions —reanimated the old frame, and the eye brightened.

"I put a floor under them," he said again, earnestly. "Why don't they walk on it! The only one decent thing ever he did—my first boy—is never to go propagating hisself. We should be thankful."

"He takes his mother to church all the time," Jill reminded.

"Indeed! He could drown in holy water, Gillian, and be no closer to heaven! He wheedles his mother this way."

"Wheedles?"

"Wheedles, yes! For money! There's only a few of us undeceived by it—me and the Lord and a priest or two, in that order o' knowin'."

"But Patrick prays, Father. That's a good sign. I've seen it."

"Prays? His mouth moves. It's telephone numbers he's recitin'. It's memorizin' the address of some woman he's running. It's the scheme he's conjurin'. He's a runaway scamp. If I have to die to be rid of him, I'm glad of it. And I'll resurrect myself and die a second time if I must! They're that endurin'. Both of them!"

"Don't talk of your sons like this, Father. It's too easy to place blame. It's painful to me to hear it. Seton needs much understanding."

He shrugged and whimpered. "I *wouldn't* place blame if they was here," he begged, quickly melting. "Only where are they?" She knew how forlorn he felt. His was a different abandonment from hers, much older, and far more bitter. Jill had just started the struggle. Dermod had given it up.

Let him talk more of Ireland, she thought.

"How did you live, Father? In the famine time, I mean? Can you remember enough to describe——?"

"Can I *remember!*"

He was on his elbow then, his free hand clutching scenes out of the cheerful atmosphere of the ambulance and reshaping them for Jill to behold and himself to marvel at. "On boxty bread, my daughter, an' turrnip skeddy. Vetches, sometimes. We lived on water-whelps and sowens. Flummery, too, which is boiled chaff juice. And we drew blood from the veins of the stock——" Jill winced. "It's the living truth of God, we did it—a pint from a sheep, a whole quart from a cow by a slight nick in the side o' the neck and carry it home in a jar or a bucket. Cut them ourselves even, if we couldn't wait for the bloodletter. The children searched the trees and the bogs for eggs. For dock and sorrel. We ate nettles, Gillian. Frogs and snails, too. And sea birds knocked from their roosting in the dark.

"Take out the cork, Gillian. I'll finish the bottle before New London. I know the doctors there."

Now he rubbed his mouth in anticipation and gave her a roguish smile, the same sudden guile, the sudden witchery that Patrick could summon when he wanted something improper and right away.

"The famine—it brought out my histrionics before I knew they were in me, Gillian."

"How do you mean, Father?"

"Well, now, in an Irish village every man knows all about every other, whether it be true or not, and 'tis hard to deceive, but in the famine time, with town warders watching the distribution of the food from a common kitchen and but one pint o' stirabout to a person—do you know, daughter, I could slip away and disguise meself and come back in a shawl and a skirt off a corpse an' me feet bare and get another pint? Sometimes two? Oh, I was a slick one! Inventin', too. And there was work, lass. Sometimes. Road mending and drain making. Shoveling, y'know. Fourpence a day. Twopence when the schemes provided a noggin o' stirabout. For the same work the women got half a noggin and three halfpence. And they'd fall down exhausted while wheelin' barrows! Women! Think of it! And me own mother, she got the bad sickness—the fever, you know—and she knew the signs of it—you can tell by the color of the urine if you know the meaning—and she had the knowledge of the cure too—it is two-milk whey, Gillian, with a thin cake of yellow buck, but we had not a farthing and she tried to work, and did so, handling a shovel with a gang of men on a boundary wall. There she died, Gillian, and she was never buried that I know of, for me father hid the body to keep the ration."

He wept quietly.

"The awfulest part of it, Gillian—God save us—the dogs were as famished as the people. They roved the empty houses where corpses lay—whole houses of dead people, daughter—and they rooted in the scailps and the bramble patches and brier lean-tos, eating the dead."

Jill sucked in her breath. He was not making it up. He'd seen it.

All his life it had been burning in him. Could he really be eighty-five? Even smashed up and half drunk he looked knotty and vital and quick.

He seemed to notice the view beyond the windows now. They were approaching the bridge over the Thames River. Jill's eyes went there too. Was it possible? There, indeed, wet and gleaming and two miles up the river, was the tidal boom where Seton had tied his launch on those miraculous Sundays when he'd swum in, towing his wine, with the poetry book tied to his head!

She told her father-in-law, and before the ambulance left the bridge, he caught himself the glint of the marker. Her story held him speechless, in a long wonder, in dubious forgiveness perhaps. But it was momentary.

"If he had it, it's gone, Jill."

"No, Father. Why do you say that?"

" 'Tis a weak man who believes nothing—just to escape the hurt of living. Seton's afraid to know where I came from and what I am. He's afraid of the story of his mother. He's afraid of the story of mine. He's afraid that something will get *out!* That we rose above it, that we survived a-tall—and he would not have, the cowerin' cave-dwellin' bivalve!—it should give him strength, Gillian. Braveness anyhow and a kind of pride too, maybe. But he's ashamed. Ashamed always of the wrong things, Gillian, and proud of the worst. Why do you believe he's to be a writer? He can't even think! 'Twas the luck of Providence he caught you in a full moment. He'll never have another."

Now he smiled winningly.

"Take out the cork, Gillian."

He finished the bottle this time and sighed comfortably. In a moment he was sleeping hard and he did not wake in the traffic of New London or even in the transfer to his own bed in the hospital.

At six o'clock a doctor came. His name was Randall Cedric. Jill had heard of the name. They were a complaining lot, the Farriers, and the names of many doctors were known to her.

"I didn't realize it was the old gentleman. I was afraid it was just Seton again." He smiled and walked quietly to Dermod's bedside, taking the sleeping man's wrist.

It seemed a strange thing for a doctor to say. "I'm Seton's wife," she said, to prevent any embarrassment before it started.

"Yes," he said, looking at her with a kind of remote approval and patient curiosity. "I've seen pictures of you. I was the family doctor."

He didn't seem old enough to be the Farriers' "family doctor," hardly as old as Patrick. He had the tousled boyish look of an athletic coach.

"I'm a chest man now. I won't be on this case."

"Oh." He caught her tone of disappointment and wonder.

"Molly Farrier called me. Said a private ambulance was on the way. So I thought I'd pop in. I'm not even on the staff here any more. In fact I'm on my way to Saranac. The hospital there."

"You mean you're going to join its staff?"

"Yes. I'm going to run the whole joint."

He seemed to Jill very American in all ways, in his easy acceptance of success, his casual proclamation of it, his quick way with people, his not feeling a need to be introduced, his sureness, his gay tie. He seemed secure and happy and able to act. He seemed like Arleigh Brayce, only younger.

"Congratulations. It's very kind of you to come in to see him."

"Thank you, Mrs. Farrier. I love the old boy."

The hands were exploring the liver area now. Dr. Cedric was all attention, then concern. He became conspicuously alone with his patient.

Jill saw the expression and slipped out. She looked up and down the great wooden corridor. It seemed garishly featureless, like a hotel closed for the season, its rugs rolled and stored. There were some stale palms at the end, bravely dying in uneventful tubs. Jill sat down on a bench by a wicker table. An old copy of a magazine called the *Outlook* peered back at her with a sterile severity, offering its cover story: "The Decline of Lloyd George." The hospital didn't seem to have any patients, any people at all. Far away a telephone rang. Well, that was something. She'd wait here till Dr. Cedric came out again, then find out the name or names of other doctors. She'd get all she could, then call Molly. Maybe they knew where Seton was by now. There might be news of Sean too. Whether he missed her. How he liked the shore. Anyway, she'd give her mother-in-law a comforting report, even a merry one, about the ride they'd had in the ambulance, and nothing, of course, about the whisky.

Then the thought came to her that there might not be a full examination until the next day and that Molly might want her to stay over. She only had six dollars, barely enough to get her back on the train. Well, perhaps the hospital could cash a small check for her. It wasn't degrading, having no money. It was just unendingly inconvenient, forever forcing improvisation on situations that were bad enough alone and that should be free of it. But there would be money soon, lots of it. Seton had the mark of greatness.

She thought of Sean, running around the big yard near the Jersey shore, trying to climb a tree or pedal one of the numerous velocipedes the children had there. There seemed a great deal of cement. She hoped her sister would get the boy to the water where he would feel at home. Well, she'd be with him in a day. She only wished that she were with him now, swiftly to grab and hug him, then swiftly set him free, as would be his wish. The bright image of Sean made all of life's discomforts seem very small, the reward for living very large. Even so, she wished she had him now.

Far away she could hear footsteps. They seemed to come on with excessive weariness.

Seton appeared, shuffling, slope-shouldered, looking about for help. When he saw Jill he stopped dead, leaned forward a little, a startled look beginning in his face, then giving way to a gray gravity. He tried to smile but could only stand still before her with his face breaking up.

He had been through some awful days. Jill knew by the sight and circumstance that his queries would quickly turn to querulousness, perhaps to quarreling at nothing but strain and impotence; that they could not talk now, and that his first action, once he had looked in on his father, might be to dismiss her.

"Dr. Randall Cedric is with him now," she said quietly. "He had a good trip up here."

"Never mind about the trip up. How is he now?"

"I believe he's still sleeping. He's right down the hall. Twenty-three. On your right."

He tried to smile, to say something, perhaps to mean something. Jill was very tired.

"Do you want me to stay?" she asked. "I mean till the examinations are completed?"

"What on earth for? What could you possibly do? You have a child to take care of. You should be with him. Right now." Then, with the finality of a caboose, he added: "I've come up by myself. With a suitcase."

She wished so much that he would kiss her but knew he would not. She rose coolly, held his face in her hands for a brief instant, stood on her tiptoes, and kissed him very softly and lovingly on the cheek. Then she walked away without looking back. She heard a faint gasp come from him and knew he was weeping. But there was no comfort she could bring him now. The doctor would have to do that.

In two days Seton's letters began to come.

Jill could always tell, and instantly, whether Seton was having a drinking problem. His unusually neat but tiny letters, the even spacing, the straight, firm line; all this was part of his normal chirography. The lines wavered after much drinking (but only after much) and the spaces between words was uncertain. His extremes of accusation or self-degradation, which were pronounced even in periods of calm, became idiotic and sad—even comical—when he was in the clutches of bad whisky. (He never got any good. Jill wondered if *that* might make a difference.)

She was relieved that the first letters showed no problem.

Of course, now that Dermod, whom Seton had never understood, never tried to understand, never appreciated, never loved, never thanked, never written (and Seton wrote to everyone, all the time); now that the old gentleman was indeed leaving this earth forever, he had become quite dear and important to his younger son. He kept telling Jill what a rich companionship they had always had; how, though invisible, their conscious thought of each other and Seton's own basic filial devotion, how these were spiritual renewing and sustaining to both father and son. There was a word she had never before seen, nor ever heard her husband use. It obtruded, almost obscenely, from a fat paragraph of imaginary remembered goodness. The word was "palship." Pals? Dermod and Seton?

Who *was* Seton? Would she ever know? Could she bear to uncover the whole of it? Should she try? Would the old man's death bring something to a head between herself and her unguessable husband? Would secrets of the past go into the grave with the dead bones and the stoppered mouth of Dermod? Was Seton ashamed of Ireland? Of what his father had been? Of the pitiful, starveling way his grandmother had died? Was he ashamed of the baleful poverty that produced his parents? Or was his self-concern so consuming that nothing of depth or poignance or meaning that was actually close to him or part of him could ever get through to him?

> *Dearest,*
> *Only Father's unbelievable vitality is keeping him alive. I'll stay here, of course, until the end. It cannot be far off. What a fine man is passing! What a horrible, stretched-out passing! Beyond the relief of drugs.*
> *Pat came up. We've been to a nearby horse room a couple of times (when I couldn't take the hospital any longer). Race results come in on a ribbon of type like ticker tape. I won enough on a horse named Sun Bather to pay for my funeral hat."*

In the times when Seton was away, on drunks, in rehearsal, on trips to out-of-town openings, or working in one of his hideaways (Seton was away most of the time, even when he was with her), she tried, with the insect persistence of the immemorial wife, to tweezer out such bits and fragments from the mound of particles that made him up as might join them together and piece out a person that could be seen and explained; that could be made known to himself and to others; that could be cogently lived with; and if not cogently, at least endurably.

She remembered the mighty moments.

She remembered the blanket around her shoulders; Seton's rare tenderness, his real but difficult solicitude, his happy wonder, and the tumult of the unborn Sean within her. She remembered Seton running in the dawn to rouse a doctor. But it was the blanket that he had placed around her shoulders that was the most endearing. This he had really done. This had really happened.

There was the new watch that he flung into the snow, then wept, and rushed out in the dark without his rubbers, absurdly digging.

There was the portrait.

There was the flash of it, the sun shooting back from its shiny face, then the unbearable vandalism and the insane fury of Seton, trying to wound Jill, torture her (and quite succeeding)—bashing the canvas down into the end of the fence post. Up and down went the frame, breaking and bursting like a cheap suitcase. It was the portrait of her father, painted by Thomas Flesch. It lay there in the yard like something left by Comanches. Seton could not have tortured Jill more had he tied her father and forced her to watch while he took out the eyes, cut away the nose, and skewered him.

Why? Why? God's mercy, what are you doing?

"Goddammit! You're an hour late! The photographer won't wait another minute! You need to be taught a lesson!"

"But we had a tire to mend! Seton! Seton! What are you doing! *My God! Not the picture!*"

Dearest,

Pat came up again today. He's in another show. He's been going to Stillman's Gym to get back in shape. He has a very difficult eccentric dance (marvelous to watch—real Pat Rooney soft-shoe, too, mixed up with the more strenuous stuff). Last night he danced clear down the dark corridor, humming or whistling the rhythms to himself. What nimble elegance he has in his legs and feet. Nurses with trays or bottles stopped to watch. (He's already picked out one for to-night!) How he does it I don't know. I think it has something to do with his positive (not pretended) assurance that he will not be rebuffed. That he knows he can take any girl to bed and that this takes away any opportunity to set in motion the the little systems of protest or demurral that is their proof of virtue. Pat just smothers all of this before it starts.

One of his sources of income (always mysterious—did you know Father had cut him down to 25¢ a day! Hardly more than cigarette money) came to light yesterday; he can get fifty dollars a pint as a blood donor any time he wants! And seventy-five if it's a direct transfusion! One of the nurses (probably the one he's sleeping with) told me about it this morning. What a man! But why a transfusion from his arterial system is not instantaneously fatal is one of the marvels of New England fortitude.

Father's eyes brighten each time I enter his room.

I finished the second act of "Treasure." It looks pretty good, considering the conditions under which it is being put together. I'm still so seething at Brayce that I'll not let him see it, although I plan to let him know it is being readied. Let him squirm for once. He's let me do enough of it!

Now it was summer. Jill and Seton were standing in front of another painting—rich, strong, bold. The artist was there, trying not to look Italian. He saw the lively admiration in Jill's eyes. He saw the husband whisper. He could not hear.

"It's great!" Seton murmured. Jill was touched. "Do you think *we* could afford one of his portraits?" Seton asked. Jill glowed. She knew what it had to mean: the Italian never painted anything but women, never painted anything except women under thirty-five. She was about to tuck her arm through Seton's. By what preternatural instinct did she hold back?

"I was thinking"—Seton went on staring, his voice went on purring— "I've only had the one painting—the Buehler——Perhaps Boriello— perhaps he could make an exception." Here Seton had looked away—a little rakish, a little fatuous, in his self-apology. "I mean—when he knows who I am. Not that it——Well, I guess——Oh, come along."

Jill Dearest,

I find I've brought the checkbook by mistake. Sorry if you have been inconvenienced. You could have telephoned me here at the hospital. Since you have not, I suppose things are all right. It is now (it must be) only a matter of a few hours. I'll call, of course, at once.

The bright sun that illumined the sounds and expressions of Sean (What joy he took in living! Patrick, for all his bawdy ways, had some of it), was this to go on and on, unseen by Seton? Unknown to him? That he had a happy son? What of Seton's own smile? (And he had one.) When it lighted his face, it came not from inner warmth but from something apart and beyond, like the sun's light when reflected to the eye from the rim of a dead planet; a bleak albedo peeking down pallidly upon the surface of a polar sea, chilling what it brightened, then vanishing with boreal silence.

The same quality was in the prose of his plays, she thought. Great gaping clichés, bare as icebergs and just as ponderous and settled in their drift—these dragged along the turgid pages in heavy draft; in glacial and mysterious impassivity, foreign, disdainful, impressive, chilling all they touched, too cold for the tern or the bittern, glinting with the minerals of rivers frozen for a million years. Mists rose, a Triassic breathing in a prehistoric void before the elements had sight or feeling. But Jill could see something superb in the very awfulness of the places where Seton lived. She saw that whatever he did, however mammoth, however grotesque or shapeless it might be, it moved massively, inexorably forward to its own dreadful destinations, unturned by tides, impenetrable to the sun itself.

Sweetest Wife,

Wonderful news! Dr. Randall Cedric (The big strong fellow—he could have been an Olympic wrestler but went into medicine), who probably knows as much about the mechanical me as any man alive (and a brilliant fellow), has promised to keep me in tow even after he leaves here permanently for the t.b. sanitarium at Saranac! Isn't that great of him!

It will be a nice objective for regular checkups, two or three a year. I can stay at the Lake Placid Club. (I've always heard so much about it.) Arleigh Brayce is a member. So is Dr. Mortimer Flowers, the psychiatrist who has so many famous people of the theatre in his practice. (I feel I should have a session with him sometime. Maybe we both should. We might get together on what is the matter. If, indeed, there is anything. There must be.)

*I know you will be relieved that Cedric, even though he'll
now be separated geographically by many miles, will still be
as close as ever. I'm still his "patient."*

Jill remembered a ghastly moment. She thought it must be a
joke. ("Why don't you let Sean sleep in the cellar, Jill? You could hear
him if he cried." "In the cellar?" "Why not? It's warm. You could
leave the crib right next to the furnace. Well, don't *look* at me like
that! All I mean, with him down there, if he *did* cry, it wouldn't
disturb me. Jill! Jill! You come back here!"

*Lovely Wife,
Yes, of course it will be good to have some real money. But
it isn't here yet. And it will be going out a lot faster—when
it's coming in big—than you (or I) can dream. So keep your
mind constantly on our past; keep your mind (and our stand-
ard) adjusted to what we already know so well. Your tooting
off to get new dresses postively astonishes me. You should see
what I have on at this minute!*

*Sweet Jill:
Father died at three this morning.*

Is it true he does not love me because he cannot? Because he cannot
love anything? The desolating thought that Jill had had on the beach
so long ago now came back to her.

If he did not love because he could not, could she teach him?

18

TWO WEEKS AFTER HIS FATHER DIED SETON'S AGENT
mailed him a royalty check for $3,944.46. Two of his other downtown
successes were being moved to Broadway, and a third, a trilogy of

one-act sea stories, was looking for an uptown house. His economic situation took a dramatic turnaround. He began depositing royalty earnings of between four and seven thousand dollars every week. Hollywood noticed him. So did Europe. As early as the end of October, Rafferty phoned to say that London wanted *The Barren Goddess*, Stockholm wanted *Treasure*, and Hollywood was anxious to negotiate the purchase of *Rim of Chance*. In fact, Rafferty had just received a firm offer from Superb Pictures for fifty thousand dollars. Did Seton wish him to close the deal for that figure, hold out for more, insist on a percentage of the gross earnings of the picture, or say no to everything? (Rafferty knew how Seton loathed Hollywood.) "If you want some quick money and a new experience, I can get you assigned as writer of the screenplay. I can probably get you three thousand a week for from eight to ten weeks but you would find it quite different from the way you like to work."

Seton settled for 2 per cent of the picture's earnings provided he had right of approval, provided it was in distribution within eighteen months, 3½ per cent if it went beyond eighteen, and a "forfeiture fee"—new in such negotiations—of an additional twenty-five thousand over the purchase price if the play was still on the shelf after three years. The purchase price was $62,500, the simple compromise between the original $50,000 offered and the $75,000 asked.

When the money finally came in, Seton took the pink check and deposited it.

He hired a chauffeur-driven limousine and went out to Fairfield, Connecticut, where he bought a house.

He had heard it described one afternoon by an actress who had recently weekended there.

The property had a private lake with an island and a gazebo, three and a half acres of lawn, a colonial house with eight Doric columns, a greenhouse, two fountains, two tennis courts, and a pool.

With noncommittal mien and a majesty he did not feel, Seton walked slowly through the endless rooms. In the library there was a ladder on a track so volumes on upper shelves could be reached. Off the library there was a combination billiard room and solarium. Seton lifted a cue from the cue rack, set it down flat on the green

felt of the playing surface of the table, and slowly rolled the cue to
see if it was straight. He'd seen Patrick do this at Thum's.

"Oh, this equipment is in perfect shape, Mr. Farrier," the real-estate
agent assured him. "Mr. Watrous was a gentleman. A *real* gentleman."
Seton didn't care for this emphasis.

"What are the taxes out here?"

"Moderate! V*ery* moderate! Especially considering the exclusive-
ness of the place. Nothing but real gentry here, Mr. Farrier. The most
well-to-do-people in the East. Even more so than Brookline. If possible. People who've always had it, you know. People like yourself.
None of this Johnny-come-lately stuff. No war profiteers. No Jews.
No foreigners. Fairfield just won't have it. It's Harvard, Yale, and
Princeton all the way."

The bobbing, agreeing, comforting man—Jasper Horner—seemed
most anxious to preserve the town's purity. He took a long chance:

"You *are* a Harvard man?"

Seton looked down with benign protectiveness.

"Yes, I was at Cambridge," he said.

They moved into the dining room and stood under one of its
two chandeliers.

Imported wallpaper, created in Lyons and depicting in unflattering
particularity the utter rout of England's gallant but luckless Light
Brigade at Balaclava, covered one entire wall. Obviously the work of
a spirited Anglophobe, it found half of England's horsemen to be
already fallen, the other half either in the air or in the embarrassment
of being run through. One persevering lieutenant was still in the
saddle, even though the Russians had cut off his entire head. It was
rolling rapidly along with the rest of the gallop, staring with interest.

Seton liked any picture in which the enemy appeared to be pre-
vailing over the British.

"How much is Mr. Watrous asking for the property?" he asked.

"You've only seen the house and immediate grounds. Wouldn't
you care to see the lake and the boathouse?"

They walked two hundred yards on a tree-bordered path of a
substance Seton could not identify. It was soft and springy and it gave
him a sense of a great ease and elegance.

"What is this path surfaced with, Mr. Horner?"

"Cork. Chopped cork. Mr. Watrous imports it from Portugal. It's self-cleansing."

They came now to the lake and boathouse. There was a fixed serenity about both. In the overhang of the boathouse there were slips for three powerboats.

"This is very lovely. Very secluded. How far up does the lake reach?"

"Mile and three quarters."

"What is he asking for it, Mr. Horner?"

"Well, to answer your question, Mr. Watrous won't break up the estate."

"Yes, I realize," Seton heard himself saying, though the information was new. "How large is the estate?"

"Oh, there's no more buildings. You've seen all the buildings."

A black swan glided by, looked slowly over and slowly back.

Whether it was the black swan or the cork path or the tennis courts or the gawdy mural of the British in defeat, Seton would never be able in the days and years ahead to say what he had seen or felt that told him this was the place that must be his.

He knew he was going to buy it, no matter what it cost.

"I suppose there *is* a figure," Seton offered.

"Indeed there is. And there's a complete, an absolutely complete inventory."

"I hope it doesn't include the boats," Seton sounded testy.

"The boats?"

"Yes. They don't seem to be here."

"Oh yes. To be sure. Mr. Watrous took the boats. No, they're not part of the inventory, naturally. The powerboats and the single sculls. He took them all to Florida. But everything *else!* Everything."

"The single sculls?"

"Yes. He was a great oarsman."

"Does the estate have a name?"

"Oh, yes. Glen Lochen. Known all over the state."

"And what did you say Mr. Watrous is asking?"

"A hundred and forty-five thousand. Of course you'll want to study the inventory."

Seton looked about as if everything were rather sad; as if these acres had been his all his life.

Horner was impressed by the fine head, the low laconic speech, the appraising eye. You could tell Harvard. Every time.

When the hired chauffeur saw Seton's approach he stepped out quickly and held the door. Seton looked at the great house again.

"Mail the inventory to the Vanderbilt Theatre, Mr. Horner. Thank you for your time."

He turned his back then, stepped into the limousine, and sat down in the cushions with a convincing imposture of melancholy, patience, and an ancient and aristocratic weariness.

Actually his immediate thoughts were quite romantic.

Seton had just seen his own daydreams. All his life, from the age of sixteen, his inland reveries had had a fine spread of lawn, beautifully kept. In the reach of suspended fancies, he could usually hear the sound of grass being mowed. Now on the ride back to New York the daydream lingered. What he had just seen in fact, and what he had so long and so yearningly seen in fancy, now began to move about in his mind, the real interchanging with the chimerical in delicious patterns of tranquillity and hushed splendor. His daydream had always centered about a great mansion, remote from the road. On its shaded porticoes, and from behind high boxwood hedges came the plunk and ping of gentlemen's tennis. There was an occasional crunching and churning of bluestone in the turnaround of the driveway.

On hand at all times was a nameless chief steward—silent, courteous, tireless—who took care of things: bought the tickets, made reservations, checked itineraries, table covers, paid the help, turned the wine bottles, filtered the pools, put up the flag each morning.

Across these felted lawns, among these columns, Seton saw himself, at one portion of the day, as a resourceful diplomat beset with insoluble problems of statecraft; at another, with vigorous but floating involvements of polo or tennis. Sprinkled through his day were the same rich choices that Milton Sills was meeting in motion pictures: the reading of the will, the setting forth upon the safari, the painful home-coming from the base hospital just outside Paris, the disarming of the intruder, the advice between rounds.

Women were frequently to be seen in the stands and boxes but they were never too near. Neither Jill nor his son Sean was known to these acres nor were they ever seen on the gallery suite, a carpeted recess, where small but cultivated groups gathered for afternoon music. Even these people were, by his arrangement, just a little beyond his touch, physically separated from him by a glass partition, and when the music was over they merely disappeared.

They were his guests, yet he did not know them.

What would have been strange to some other but what was most appealing to Seton was that the whole estate was domed over, transparently but impregnably. No one could get in but him if he so chose, for he alone could revolve the dome.

The three basic elements of his fantasy, that he was safe, dignified, and exclusive now dissipated. The limousine had come to the end of the Bronx River Parkway. The squalid featurelessness of the journey from there to Riverside Drive brought his mind to city things.

Seton hesitated a little before picking up the speaking tube—he didn't know how much voice to use.

"I want to go to Abercrombie and Fitch before it closes."

Seton thought he might get Abercrombie and Fitch to install a very small but functional gymnasium—exercise bars, chest weights, punching bag, perhaps a rowing machine. At Glen Lochen he could build up his body marvelously.

Abercrombie and Fitch was closed. Seton was jarred by this. He paid the driver, then walked through the Roosevelt and the underground passageways to the Western Union desk in the concourse.

Here he wired Jill—she'd gone back to the Cape—that he had bought the Watrous house in Fairfield, Connecticut; that it was ready for immediate occupancy; and that she should get everything packed and sent. He was sorry he could not help but he was too busy in the theater. Send Terry for the sand wagon.

19

IT WAS TYPICAL OF THE OLD ACTOR—WHO HAD SPENT his life worrying about his money and his wife—that he should die intestate, leaving the widow with the greatest worry of her life. But the physical activity of slashing through the financial wilderness of her late husband's affairs was a merciful thing for Molly.

Dermod Farrier had accounts in nineteen banks. He owned forty-four pieces of real estate. He owned South American bonds of dubious yield but impressive appearance, stock in Gary Smelting, Duluth Ore Terminal, Necco Wafers, Morley Phone, Zip, Sunshine Biscuit, Hudson Traders. He seemed to be the president of a company that planned to build a fleet of powered oil barges and put them in abandoned canals as soon as legislatures granted the diversion of necessary water. He was a director in a number of unborn corporations and the principal stockholder in two that were dead as flint.

One day in the late spring, while Jill was trying to make sense out of Glen Lochen, the phone rang. It was Molly. She did not sound like a lost widow.

"Jill! Get away from all your troubles for a few days! Bring Sean. I've taken another room. He can have his own bed."

"But I've a million things, Molly! I'm frantic! We're not *half* settled. You never *saw* such a place!"

"But you've servants to help now, Jill." Her voice had a touch of pleading in it.

"*Servants!*" she thought. Had Seton told his mother they had *servants?*

"Yes, it isn't that." She was puzzled by the call. Molly was concealing something. "Is there anything the matter?"

"Yes, there is!" There was spirit in the reply, spirit and cheer.

"Do you know my wretched son has four plays going at the same time and I've seen exactly one?"

"Well, you've seen exactly one more than I have."

"I know, I know. I just don't under*stand*." Molly was hurrying through this part. Jill realized the old lady was now trying in some way to make up to Jill for her losing out in the great moments preceding and following the triumph of *Rim of Chance*.

But that was over and done with. It was only six months; it seemed six years.

"I've just called your husband's agent and told him a thing or two!"

"Called him about what, Molly?"

"I've got splendid seats for you and me! For *everything* of Seton's that's running! And I've got the Catholic sisters arguing over who's taking care of Sean. Now *do* come, dear. You *need* this. And I do too."

And so it was that Jill came to New York and saw her husband's plays.

It wrenched her and exhilarated her, made her richly proud, nobly composed, quietly objective. She who had been so close to the long labor of their assembly; who had been at his shoulder when he wished, or who had remained out of sight when that seemed the prudent thing; *now she was here*—inside these catacombs and these cathedrals, these charnel mansions and bloody deserts, these waterless bladed savannas—Jill herself, taking the slow tour of her husband's awful mind, inspecting its agonies one by one, inspecting the swept verandas of its pity, the spattered vaults of its revenges, the burning trees of its brief laughter, the deep still cistern of its pessimism beneath the round stone of despair that covered it.

All this Jill saw, in fascination, abhorrence, respect, wonder, sorrow, and hurt, and with such a wild reaching out from herself to touch the artist who was her husband that it was like an arrow in the flesh not to be with him now.

And where *was* Seton? Not a mile away at any time! Sometimes only a block or two. He was in rehearsal again, this time with *Crown of Thorns*, all night in the Wentworth, croaking and moping around the half-lit theater in the day; in both places leaving the harsh order he was not to be interrupted—"no matter what."

It was an order Jill never violated.

She who knew the plays as well as he; who had the courage to separate herself from what he had wrought—in truth *how* close was she to him, to his mind and life; to his need? To his future?

Was he healing, in this way, from the grief of his father's passing? Or was he, for that matter, grieving at all? Was it not perhaps fortunate that Seton was working this hard right now, just as it was fortunate that Molly, his mother, had the exacting problem during these very same days of making sense out of Dermod's chartless voyages across a world he didn't know?

Perhaps this was the best possible thing for Seton. Surely it was producing a miracle in Molly. She was finding what many widows had found before her—that marriage to a difficult man had made it impossible for her to discover what kind of woman she was in her own right. Just in the six weeks since his death she was finding herself an altogether different person from what her husband *thought* she was and certainly far different from what he wanted. What *he* wanted she had tried to be, and she had succeeded. But it did not resemble what she was.

She was a sharp businesswoman. She had a natural cunning with figures. If she had handled her husband's affairs, the wealth he sought for so long would now be theirs. But the discovery of such a stripe of shrewdness in his wife would have hurried Dermod to collapse, for Dermod, who knew nothing of business, was the perfect person to be impressed by a drummer he'd never before seen. It was the vast, relaxed liar in the Pullman smoker who was always Dermod's discovery and Dermod's authority.

Seton was that gullible too. But to Molly belonged the capability of instant calculation. She'd given it to Patrick, who, if he'd had any business morals, would have made a great handicapper or a successful casino manager, but who, lacking them, got by anyhow just by knowing the angles and the odds.

Molly did not know these words. But she began going to her late husband's banks, asking questions. Presently she saw how money was made, saw the mistakes her husband had been making from the start. Molly began to sell and to buy, to seek the counsel of men whose only business was putting money to work.

Now, when Molly spoke of money, a cold practicality came into her eyes and phrases. It was obvious to Jill that she regretted—perhaps resented—her passive role in the business side of her husband's gambles and investments.

In the kitchen of the Byzantium suite Jill sat on a red folding stool. Molly was cutting up a chicken. Pat was coming for supper, and Seton, too, if his rehearsal would let him.

"I was talking to Mr. Rafferty. And to Vivian Sable. Seton's worse than his father was. About money. Vivian Sable can only handle the publishing of Seton's work. And Rafferty can't run Seton's office. He can only protect or improve his contracts."

"But Seton has no office, Molly."

"Exactly."

So that was it!

Jill was intrigued at what she assumed Mrs. Farrier would now propose: that Pat be allowed to do for Seton what Molly had never been allowed to do for Dermod; that people who understood the uses of money be given a responsibility over it and be paid for it.

Molly was very direct about it.

It made sense. But Jill knew she must be cautious. Though Seton loved his brother, he loved a dollar more. Now with money coming in—in the past week there had been almost seven thousand dollars, twice as much in that one week as she and Seton had made together in the first two years of their marriage—she did not think Seton would look with approval upon any plan that would threaten his sovereignty here.

"Even his brother?" Molly asked.

Jill didn't answer at once. *Especially* his brother, was her thought. Instead she asked:

"Is Pat well enough?"

Mrs. Farrier powdered the chicken pieces with flour, set them in a pan, and slid the pan into the broiler.

The thought came to Jill: This is a woman who can do everything and who has never been allowed to do anything.

"Pat isn't well enough now," Mrs. Farrier allowed. Then she looked right at Jill closely and steadily.

"Do you think Patrick's drinking is in the way?"

"It will surely be easy for Seton to say so, anyhow."

"But Seton drinks. *He* drinks, just sitting in his umbrage!"

"But Seton hates it. Pat loves it."

"If he hates it, why doesn't he quit it?"

It was not a new question in this family.

"I think he will quit, Molly, as soon as he finds he *can* quit."

The buzzer sounded.

"Will you get that, dear? It's the front door."

Jill went through the pantry door into the living room.

The hotel suite since Molly occupied it alone was completely different. The costume cases had gone. There were new window drapes, bright and fresh. The room had lost its mummied look and more than half its furniture. It seemed open and friendly and twice as large.

Jill opened the door. It was Seton.

He looked down sternly from his dark eminence, then glowed in real surprise at seeing her. He picked her up and held her, kissed her forehead, her hair and temples, cheekbones, eyelids.

"I smell chicken," he said, setting her down.

"Oh, Seton, your mother and I have been on the most wonderful binge!"

"Binge? Mother?" He went into the kitchen, Jill following.

Success really *had* released him. Seton was fulfilling every promise he'd ever shown.

Seton kissed his mother with great tenderness. Then he looked at them both. He had the darting look, the eager turning of the head that had so caught Jill's young-girl's mind those forbidden Sundays on the banks of the Thames River.

The phone rang. Molly dried her hands on a tea towel and hurried to answer. Seton wanted Jill to explain the "binge."

She looked at him saucily:

"We've been to all four of your Broadway plays."

Seton seemed enormously pleased.

"You *have?* But, my God—all *four!* How could you *stand* it, Jill? They were all stale stuff to you—every one. Why, you *typed* them!"

"Oh, my dear, beautiful, gifted, hard-working husband, you are a dummy!" And her arms circled his neck. For a brief instant there was no one to see how they clung to each other.

Mrs. Farrier came back untying her apron in some impatience and tossed it to Jill.

"Take care of dinner till I get back. I'll bring Sean. He's with the sisters across the street. The phone was Mr. Ferguson. I've got to run down to the Midland Marine Bank."

"But it's way after three, Mother. How can you get into a bank?"

"He's waiting for me. I'll hurry back. Seton, set the table for Jill. Show him where things are, Jill."

She was gone.

Seton helped his wife into the apron, then would not let go of her.

"Let's go into Mother's bedroom, Jill," he whispered into her ear. His hands slipped stealthily and firmly cupped each breast.

"We *can't*, Seton!" She was whispering too. "Later. Tonight." Then with some petulance: "Why am I staying here while you're at the Wentworth?" She began pulling back his fingers.

"No, here!" he insisted.

"Pat's coming. He might come in!"

"Hell with him!"

"But the chicken will burn."

"Hell with the chicken. Turn it off. We'll go to Lüchow's." He had a devil's grin and a python's grip.

She wished he had asked about the progress she was making in the great house in Fairfield.

Then a quick tremble went through them both, for to their ears now and tumbling through the tortuous corridors of the Byzantium, the magical flute sounds of Pat's whistling came floating in.

Jill and Seton broke apart.

Seton was annoyed.

"Why the hell couldn't he come at suppertime! I had a present for you."

Without grace he pulled it from his pocket and thrust it at her. It seemed like a volume of poetry, it was that size, but it was wrapped in tissue paper and tied with ribbon.

In a moment she heard the brothers talking, the glass stopper twisted from the decanter.

Why didn't Pat come in to say hello? Should she go out? Perhaps a little later, after they'd visited together and alone, she'd hand the silver to Seton, the table linen and the dishes to Patrick, and say hello that way. Anyhow she had dinner to make.

Wondering what Seton had given her, waiting to open his present when the others could be there too, she began to peel the potatoes. She could feel her husband's arms around her. It had been a long time.

Before long she sensed a change in the quality of the men's talk. Urgencies of some sort were coming out of Patrick. And they were being as quickly repelled by Seton.

There was a tiny, diamond-shaped window in the pantry door. Jill peeked in. Pat had his finger up, something Seton hated, but he was getting Seton's fullest attention. Jill wanted no quarrel. She wanted her husband left alone. She didn't have much of him herself when a new play was building. She didn't have much of him any time at all, certainly never as much as she wanted. She felt it important to know what they were talking about, partly to protect the plan that Molly was thinking about for the two brothers and partly to preserve Seton's present feeling for Jill.

Very quietly she slid the grocery pencil between the door and the jamb. Now she could hear.

She might have guessed it. It was about the damn Algonquin Hotel again. Patrick had an obsession about Seton's belonging to its famous Round Table. Jill knew her husband was periodically invited, that the invitations were increasing in frequency and solicitude as his fame grew, that it could do a lot for Seton. But she knew Seton better than Pat did.

"You don't have to go every day, Seton. Not even every week!" he was saying. "If you just *joined* it, once a month would be enough. Just to *belong* is the thing."

Jill realized her brother-in-law was being what he considered his most tactful and persuasive.

"These are the people that run your end of New York, Seton! They're *exciting* people. Not a dummy in the gang! And *they're* excited about *you*. F.P.A. and Woollcott. Broun. Frank Sullivan. Some high-rated bimboes too—Elsie Janis and Dorothy Parker. Edna Ferber, Alice Miller. Alice Miller's *society* for Chris-sakes!"

Pat was being effective in here, Jill felt. He'd even impressed her.

"You can *use* that! And enough fellows your own age to make it easy—make it fun. Pemberton and Benchley and Johnny Weaver. Deems Taylor. Donald Ogden Stewart."

Jill's eye swept the tiny window. Her husband's lip was beginning to curl. She knew the look. Leave everything just where it is. Say no more.

But Patrick felt he'd lost, when he'd almost won. He couldn't resist a sudden, embittered sarcasm:

"You don't think you need 'em. You think you're too good, don't ya?"

"I *know* I'm better than they are! What's more, I know what I want. And what I *am!*"

Though she did not see it, she knew her husband had risen up, that he was circling his brother without looking at him.

"Several months ago Arleigh Brayce tried to force me to meet the press. He tried to *force* me!"

Here his fist smashed down on the table top.

"He'll never make that mistake again! I don't give a damn for the press, Pat! And I'm not interested in famous people. I'm interested in the stage! That's every bit and forever all I *am* interested in!"

In her mind Jill could now see her husband standing at the head of the bare table, leaning forward, supporting his weight on the finger tips of his strong hands. It was a way he had when he laced into someone, a position he took before the kill.

Now in deadly calm she heard: "I've had fame and I've had de-fame and one's the same as the other!"

But Pat was quick to parry this and press the only point he was trying to make.

"I'm talking about *money*, Seton! Money-Money-Money! Money that's lying right there on the sidewalk! Waiting for you to pick it up!"

There was a dead pause then.

"*You* pick it up, you no-good yellow-gill!"

Seton was screaming like a woman now. Jill peered in again. She was afraid the brothers would attack each other. Her husband was advancing upon Patrick, shoving him, dispersing him.

"I'll never join the Players. I'll never join the Friars or the Lambs. Or the goddamn Algonquin!"

"Your own father's picture is *hanging* in the Lambs!"

"Let it hang! And him with it! You can take the Algonquin and burn it down and I won't even piss on the fire! I'm a writer, goddamn you, not a public billboard! If people want to know what's in my plays, let them go see them. If *you* want to know, here it is: *I'm* in them, God stiffen you! That's all there is of me. There isn't any more!"

Jill heard a slight scuffling sound, and after a moment a door slammed.

Pat was rushing down the corridor. She knew the step. But she did not know the two brothers were never again to see each other.

With relief, with a sudden fillip of expectancy, she thought of the present her husband had brought her. In her thanks for this, she could calm him and disperse the tensions. Excitedly she unwrapped it.

It was the published version of *The Barren Goddess*.

Eagerly she thumbed the pages, picking out a line here and there. As she read in quick snatches, her mind raced through the sights of his endless labors. She could see the torn sweater he wore on cool days. She could describe the kitchen towel which he hung as a signal in the window of his work shack on the Cape when he was ready for his milk and his sandwiches. She remembered the day they'd gone to Truro to buy a pencil sharpener.

She fluttered the pages from back to front, then saw with real excitement that he had written something to her on the first blank page:

"For Jill: You have kissed my cheek with the gentle touch of a bird's wing. You have lighted the candle in the night and come in to me, prayed for me. On this my lonely journey—oh, best and loveliest of women—stay near, stay near."

Jill caught her breath, holding the book close to her body.

She ran out into the living room to kiss her husband. She wanted to cling to him for a long time without speech. It was all right he had said nothing about the country house. It was all right he had not asked about Sean. Seton loved her and needed her and nothing more mattered. Nothing.

But Seton was not there. He was not in Molly's bedroom, or in the bathroom. There at the table where the quarrel had broken out were his fingerprints, photographically clear and visible, the whorls and tented arches of his finger tips sitting on the dark mahogany like labeled evidence of his temper and his outraged self-respect.

This instant, of all the time she wanted him to be with her, was the time she wanted him most.

He had never given her anything before.

Jill went back into the little kitchen, set the book quietly on the oilcloth covering of the pantry shelf, lowered the flame under the chicken, and sat down on the neat red stool by the window. With Seton gone when she was overwhelmed with her love for him, she had to push back the great rush of feelings his rare tenderness and his dark passions could build in her.

She felt dizzy and lost, locked out of life. With her hands she seized hold of the narrow boards of the stool, stiffening her arms and pressing them tight against her ribs. She closed her eyes. Her head fell slightly forward and tears that she did not feel or notice tumbled down upon the light blue gingham of her apron, making it darker where they fell.

20

TANAGER BOLT, WHO HAD NOTHING TO OFFER THE world but an effective platform style and her astonishing beauty, nonetheless knew where she wanted to go and was emotionally geared to get there.

Certain of the traditional restraints and reticences that other women might have had did not fall in Tanager's way. The matter of who owned what, for example, had no meaning for her at all. In the matter of money she was economical in knowing how to use other people's. Housing, often, was the same way. Right now she was living in Marion Vogel's brownstone, an elegant third-floor high-ceilinged place on West Eleventh Street, just off Fifth.

In New York she had had a comparatively easy time, for she'd picked easy targets. In mid-Manhattan in the mid-twenties there were a good many of these.

She was a slick thief really, and well ahead of other women of her age and inclination who might want many of the same basic satisfactions and primitive comforts (including, if possible, a husband) that Tanager wanted. But there was this difference: to most women the hard fact that a desirable man might already be encumbered with a marriage of his own set certain limits.

Tanager viewed these situations somewhat differently. She could disregard another man's wife or another man's marriage with the contempt and impunity of a helmeted fireman going up a ladder with an ax, bouncing hot shingles off his hat.

This worked to her advantage and served often, indeed most of the time, to keep her in funds. But it was no longer solving the problem that was growing about the core of her life. Sooner or later she would have to come to grips with the fact of her age. Since she could not indefinitely keep setting back time she would presently find it desirable to find something for herself that was permanent; a setting that would preserve her present glitter; if possible, a setting of such stability—if such were about—that the flow of its benefits would continue after her beauty had gone.

Boldly she had thought of Seton Farrier. With steady eyes, with hardly a lift of pulse, she had decided to go after him.

Tanager was forty, she looked thirty or thirty-two, and said—usually with a coy and somewhat impatient dismissal—that she was not twenty-eight (which was, of course, true). And she'd had a long time to look around New York. Very early—it was a characteristic part of the economy of her thinking—she had come to a cold conclusion: New York *had* no eligible men.

New York had many men who were wealthy, well sexed, well schooled, well positioned, marriageable, and under thirty-five. But of men who were wealthy, well sexed, well schooled, well positioned, marriageable, under thirty-five, and still unmarried, New York did not have a single one.

Where *were* all the best men? They were all in the grip of a union previously called the Four Hundred and now spread to some forty thousand. Even so, they were still expertly endogamous, curiously fearful of their own extinction, and self-perpetuating, although more through the influence of Newport or Palm Beach or the National City than through any splendid compulsion to have children by the wives assigned them.

It wasn't that Tanager disapproved of this. She merely regretted not being in it. She did the next best thing: she spent no time looking there. She looked somewhere else.

And she looked always for money first, marriage second.

This explained why, in two full decades of being egregiously available and persistently nubile, she had never brought anything to bed but other women's husbands. But she had beaten a good income together. She could wear clothes, and she could give parties. For these two things she lived.

Arleigh Brayce, who knew her without wanting to, called her a "strong" hostess.

Tanager had this double anxiety: being forty and still passing with fair success for twenty-eight, her bloom, departing, would meet menopause on the way in. Being a born dissembler, she had the added anxiety to hide both, not only from the world but from her professing self.

Her lectures brought her about twelve thousand a year. Besides this income, Tanager lived conjugally with married men, but fiscally she lived for the most part on old ones, taking money from wobbly widowers, foundation presidents, art-museum directors, retired bankers—men usually desiccated, rich, and accommodatingly impotent (though a few protested this).

Tanager took the money not at all for the money but as her due for the aesthetic concinnity she supplied to these occasions as a minnesinger might do in Provence, or a minstrel at Dumferlin. She read poetry aloud, sometimes recited it to mandolin accompaniment. Charles Westover had told her to cut out the mandolin as it dated her with Home-run Baker and the chafing dish, and she had put the instrument away. This was around the time she and Charlie were breaking up, when Jill had seen the woman at Dermod's party.

Tanager was not an unhappy woman, but because of the bounce of her sex life, her bed had been subjected to such a variety of pressures and her pillow to such a sussuration of entreaties—not always grammatical—that she had recently been suffering from what the town's psychiatrists were calling psychic nervosities. Tanager's mother would have said the girl was fidgety (her father had shorter words), but in any case Tanager kept changing the décor of her apartments, changing their addresses, and actively worrying about finding a man who was either already successful or manifestly on the way; one who, above all, she could hook, fight, gaff, boat, and hang up over her own fireplace.

In two seasons in New York, Tanager had an Aztec period on Minetta Lane, a Directoire on Fourth, a Tudor on the Mews. Between times, while paint was drying, she'd spill over in the Pierre Towers. She'd sell everything oriental or French or English or whatever it was at the moment and move, taking only New York's most famous bed.

This was everywhere known as the workbench.

It was sixteen feet across and could be disassembled for moving. Not so the mattress. This had to be carted each time in one piece and for some years had represented a real engineering problem for a number of downtown movers. Manhattan Storage finally solved it by rolling and taping it lengthwise, passing it through a front window, and letting it by ropes into the street, like a fieldpiece.

Though she took money not only from the men she slept with but from those old men whom she merely exhilarated and sang to or whose victrolas she wound, she could prove she was no common person by virtue of the peculiar duties of an unusual maidservant, Deirdre—the only servant ever to stay for long in her employ. To this Deirdre, whose other chores were not distinct, Tanager dictated poetry.

In the early flush of first acquaintance, when Charlie had asked Tanager what Deirdre did, her answer came at once:

"Deirdre is the only secretary I've ever had who could take down my poetry as it came to me."

"Poetry!" Charlie had said, amazed but gratified, "*I* didn't know you published poetry!"

"Oh, never to *publish*, silly man! To recite. Before a fire. Before a few friends. Poetry, like the dance, is an evanescent thing. The spontaneity of its utterance, the spontaneity of its acceptance—both must occur at once." Here she'd waved illustratively. "The life cycle: to give birth, to shimmer, then to burn." Here she'd come a shade nearer, her voice dropping dramatically. "Like making love. First the embrace. Then the rapture. Then the quiet death. . . . Yes, I dictate them to Deirdre as they come to me—then recite them to my friends as *they* come to me—then——"

Here Charlie, not yet her captive, surmised "then" might be when Deirdre took out the poetry and burned it and set another life cycle to going on the street where the municipal trash wagon could pick it up and haul it to an East River scow.

Tanager knew she could never be called anything derogatory like "whore." There was never a whore who could dictate poetry. When she thought of it, there were damn few who could write it at all.

Tanager's ready rationalizations against her being a whore were achieved by somewhat the same reasoning that Patrick Farrier employed when he wanted to assure himself he had been stone sober when he had been stone drunk, and who could arrive at these composing judgments merely by driving a car through the Park Avenue trolley tunnel without killing himself; then asking himself if he thought a drunk man could do such a thing; then soberly informing himself that of course no drunk man could do such a thing, he'd bust his goddamn neck!

Of the two lives, however, Tanager's was the more comfortable.

Its quality of comfortableness on this particular night was suddenly scattered and it was not to be reassembled for many days. There was a knock at her door. It was ten o'clock at night.

Tanager was a firm person. She opened the door firmly. For an instant surprise and physical loathing disfigured her face. It was Patrick Farrier. He was a little drunk, visibly so, but not to anyone's danger, she felt, or to his own impairment.

He bulled past her and barged right in.

She was wearing an aquamarine mandarin coat, richly embroidered, and tawny silk pajama trousers that exactly matched her hair.

Whether Pat's arrival at her door was protective or merely meddlesome, there was none to say. Tanager suspected little more than the aimless explorations of the meandering drunk. Certainly he had not come to admire, though the fiery smoldering that hung about her movements would have caught any eye.

The room itself was not too neat. There were curtain rods in a corner, an unhung drape. Tanager had spent the afternoon and evening trimming and mounting a number of newspaper clippings she had gone to some trouble and expense to get. This debris, with its snips and discard, was on the piano. There were, of course, all the new ones of *Harbor, Oasis*, and the road company reviews of *Rim of Chance*, but there were many hundreds of little scraps from years ago, items he'd written for newspapers, a few poems (quite bad, she realized, though she had memorized them).

She had nearly completed a huge scrapbook of the life and art of Seton Farrier. Its purpose was to indicate to Seton that if his critical position in the world of dramatic art was in some dispute, there was no doubt as to her own position. It was to be given to him (loaned, at first) at the proper time. She'd been using the grand piano as a working area and a bridge lamp cast its glow on shears and paste pots.

Tanager snapped off this light, tossed a scarf from the piano bench to the main surface of the work, and hoped that Pat's errand—she'd now guessed its purpose—would explain and dispatch itself before he saw what she was at work on.

She kept the cheapest scotch—a brand called Thistle—in the crystal decanters on the sideboard and dispensed it to people she didn't care to impress.

Pat was drunker than she had at first thought. His movements were cloudy. So was his eye. She had a sense of dull fear. She wondered if the superintendent of the building had seen him.

"How did you get in, Pat?" she asked, not unpleasantly. She poured out an old-fashioned glass full of scotch, and handed it to him.

He nodded, drank off half of it before saying anything, then sat down on a straight chair opposite her.

"I want you to stay the hell away from my brother," he said. There was a jagged edge to his voice. "My goddamn brother doesn't know what's good for him. He spurns the Algonquin and he bums around with nobodies. Leave him alone, Tanager. Leave him alone or I'll put a lid on your pot."

"Why don't you tell him to stay away from *me?*"

"He doesn't know women. Not your kind."

"Then why don't you tell his wife to protect him?"

His reply to this was quiet, almost gentle.

"She doesn't know it's necessary. She's a simple person."

"I don't know her."

"Seton is a sap, Tanager."

"I've no idea what he is as a person. I'm interested in your brother's career. I'm *not* interested in your brother. I'm a professional woman myself."

"I'll say."

Again Tanager refused to react.

She set the decanter before him, took out the stopper, and poured a tiny drink for herself.

"You've been going to rehearsals. Meeting after. None of my business." He filled his old-fashioned glass again.

"No, it isn't."

"Woman gets the mileage on her your clock is showing, she's *got* to look at other men. That's all right. Way it is. Only not Seton."

"Maybe you think he's here. Maybe you'd like to look around." She opened her arms hospitably, the loose hoods of her sleeves hanging open invitingly.

"No. But I'd like to water my snake." She showed him where the bathroom was.

She remembered the whole agonizing humiliation she'd suffered at the hands of this monster; his flinging her into the hotel corridor stark naked; the humiliation of begging at his door to be let back in.

He had something coming to him. He'd had it coming for a long, long time.

She knew he'd drink as long as she would pour. That would help. At least it would immobilize him. But how to get him out? Wait till he passed out and call the police? Call Seton? Better to call an ambulance, she felt. That way she could give the whole ugly episode a Samaritan look.

("Your brother used me quite badly, Seton.")

She could put a good quaver into that sentence, then look away while Seton groped for thanks. Or she could drop Seton a note, or a wire. She was leaving first thing the next morning for a winter weekend at Lake Placid with Marion Vogel. She could be safely away from it all by the time Seton would hear of it.

It nearly turned out that way.

Patrick appeared again. He was bare to the waist. He had a dirty look. Though he could hardly walk, he was goatish and attentive. Interest and disgust mixed themselves in her eyes. There would be no problem now but a few more ounces.

"Finish your drink," she said, not looking directly at him.

With a quick, simian jerk at her coat, he tore the sleeve out and yanked the heavy silk clear off her. Then he snatched off her brassière. All the red and black furies of her life poured their savagery into her blood stream. She spun hard, breaking his grip on her. He tumbled over, grabbing at the piano scarf. A shower of papers went to the floor with him.

Tanager picked up a curtain rod. In the half-dark its metal made a blurred arc. She brought it down on Patrick's naked back with all her might. When it hit his flesh it made a report like a paper bag burst at a ball park. Then she struck again. Pat quivered like an animal in the cold. His eyes glazed over, then closed. Three times more the rod whistled and cracked.

Tanager stood still a moment, breathing hard like a winded race horse. Another shudder of revulsion shook her. She kicked Patrick in the side of the temple with all her might. She felt the old account was beginning to square.

Outside, it had begun to snow. No other apartment lights were on. She set the curtain rod back in the corner. Then she pulled down the blinds and carefully picked up all the clippings from the floor. She put them all loosely into the scrapbook, took this into the bedroom and placed it in the bottom of a bureau drawer. Pat's shirt, undershirt, and suit coat were on the bed. She picked them up and came back into the living room and began putting Pat's clothes back on his limp unconscious body.

She had no sense of fear, and no guilt.

It took her a long time to dress Pat. She did not hurry. She

buttoned his shirt and his fly and put a good knot in his knitted
tie. It was like preparing a corpse for showing. When she finished
the tie she dragged him to the piano and propped him against the
piano leg. Here she rocked him forward so she could put on his
overcoat.

She had a strange sense of mercy and solicitude.

She turned off the bridge lamp now and opened the French doors.
The garden was quiet, just starting to whiten with new snow. It had
the sweet smell of clean snow, untouched. She could hear a victrola
three or four houses away—Abe Lyman and "Canadian Capers."

She did not know how badly she had hurt Pat. She did not care.

She let her eyes grow accustomed to the dark outside. Slowly and
fully she opened one of the French doors. A little snow sifted in on the
floor. She took firm hold of Pat's overcoat, grabbing the material in
the double thickness near the shoulders, and dragged him out on the
landing of the fire escape. She came back into the large living room,
found Patrick's hat, and dropped it over the fire-escape railing into
the garden below. She could see his breath in the dark. It delighted
her mind to think of his confusion—and his first movements—when
consciousness returned. Where would he go? How long would his
pain remain? A week? Two? Then she locked the French doors.

Tanager was a good planner and a good manager. She was already
packed for tomorrow's early departure. Now she folded and put away
the ruined mandarin coat, tidied the bed, dressed carefully, put her
toilet case and her large vanity case in her bag, rinsed her mouth
with Lavoris, reshaped her eyebrows, went down the carpeted stairs,
and out to Eleventh Street.

At the corner she turned south and walked to the canopy of the
Fifth Avenue Hotel. It was snowing a little harder.

She smiled at the doorman.

"Would you get me a cab, please?"

In a moment she was driving north. She felt safe.

She shouldn't have. Already Pat was stirring. In his agony as the
cold air revived him and consciousness came back, he slid his arm
across the snow on the fire-escape landing and clutched at an iron
support of its railing. Blood was coming out of his nose. He felt the
same fires that had blazed in his belly when he drank the alcohol

in the Columbus hospital but now the fire had moved up into his lungs.

He saw his hat down in the garden, lying in the snow.

He knew he could never make the iron stairs. He knew what Tanager had done to him. In frightful pain, he realized what Tanager had done to him and he admired her. She had got him.

He tried the door, knowing it would be locked. With his fist he could not strike hard enough to break a pane in the French door. With his right knee he could. He reached through, and turned. In a moment he was in the apartment again, bleeding on the floor.

He closed the door by lurching against it with his shoulder. He thought of Tanager's whisky and went to it. He flopped down on the sofa.

Many hours later he woke up. He thought he was dying for sure. It was dark. He was thirsty. He had to go to the bathroom. He crutched himself through the dark room by clinging to chair backs.

In the bathroom he drank, cup after cup, letting the water run. He relieved himself, then snapped on the mirror light, shielding his eyes. He was a ruin again, just like Springfield.

Where could he go? He had run out of places. He thought of the Luxor Baths on Forty-sixth Street. Open all night. They'd take him.

Patrick went down the carpeted stairs like a tiny child, bumping gently down each step on his buttocks. In the dark of the vestibule he breathed, then tried to organize himself for the ordeal of appearing on the street.

What would he say at the Luxor?

What would *they* say?

He couldn't say he was rolled. He couldn't say a woman beat him. Maybe he'd say some sadistic perverts caught him.

A cab picked him up. Pat monkeyed his way in. He could not lean back.

It occurred to him in the cab what to say at the Luxor. He would merely say that on his very first trip he brought a load of alcohol to the wrong warehouse.

They helped him undress. They laid him down on his belly and washed the bleeding stripes. Then they put collodion in the wounds to check the bleeding and Patrick passed out. At seven in the morning the house physician from the Nassau Hotel came over and put white vaseline all over Pat's cuts, then laid long strips of cotton up and down his back and strapped these on with adhesive tape.

For four days he stayed in the Luxor, eating soup that Ted, the assistant manager, brought, taking light massage from the rubber. Pat was a curiosity. He knew it. He let them think what they wanted.

The morning of the fourth day he realized he needed a haircut. Teddy told him that Ralph, head barber at the hotel adjacent, was in the steam room. By and by Ralph came out.

"My, my," he said, friendly and serious. They sent a boy to the hotel for Ralph's kit.

The barber was chatty. He'd cut Pat's hair before, but never like this.

"Don't move," he said. "Lemme do the movin'! Lemme do all the movin'." Then he went on: "Your old friend Gwennie What's-her-name was in las' week."

Pat was pleased. "You mean Gwennie Durgan?"

"Yeah. Went to Hartford. Some kinda Japanese show. *Big* show. She was gettin' a mannicuah."

"You don't say. Nice woman. Real nice woman. You know, Ralph, I oughta settle down and marry that woman. We were in the same show together. All through the Middle West."

"Yeah, she was tellin' me. She says you knocked 'em dead again. With the Jenny Cooler. And the whistlin'. Gee, you're some whistler."

He snipped quietly for a moment.

"You in an accident some kind?"

"Yeah. I showed up at a wrong address, Ralph."

"Too bad, kiddo. You pretty near got it, I guess, huh?"

"Yeah."

"You see a doctor yet? A real doctor with his own practice?"

"When I leave here."

"You better, Pat. You don't look no good."

"Well it's a good thing Gwennie Durgan don't see me like this."

"Like this she *should* see you, Pat. I get the feeling she wants to take care of you."

"Too much has happened, Ralph."

"It's happened to her too, but she's no bum. Right away you can tell she's no bum. She never peddled it."

Ralph's fingers made him feel drowsy. A throb of organ music came into the bare little room, then the sound of a full choir. Pat realized it was Sunday. He was right next door to St. Mary the Virgin. It had a famous choir. He could never get away from churches, it seemed. The music took his memory to the bright porch of Daisy Glad's boardinghouse in Atlantic City. He wished he'd been nicer to Gwennie on the road. Or had he been nice? He couldn't be sure. In the years he'd known Gwennie, he'd been in her bed fifty times but he could only remember being in her bed once. The last time. And he remembered her crying. But he hadn't shoved her out in the hall.

"Can I cash a check at the hotel, Ralph?"

"I don't know the Sunday manager so good, Pat. You want some money? I got three hundred. Right in the locker. Maybe you want a hundred?"

"No, fifty."

Ralph's towel fell off but he paddled away in paper slippers. Pat heard a locker click and bang. Then Ralph came back, holding up his trousers by their suspenders, and fishing into the pocket. He pulled out a roll of bills and counted off five tens and handed them to Pat without saying anything.

"Thanks a lot, Ralph."

"You know I want you should do me a favor now, Pat."

"Sure. If I can."

"I want you should whistle at my daughter's wedding. The same like when the fire commissioner's daughter got married."

"Sure. You bet." Pat loved to whistle at such things. "When is it?"

"Just a week from yesterday. Right next door here. It's eight o'clock."

Pat took a cab to Grand Central and went down the ramp to the Oyster Bar. Here he had lobster pan roast, very nourishing, he knew. Then he got on a train for Hartford.

He went into the Euclid Hotel, asked for an outside room, and told the desk he'd be in the bar. As usual, he had no luggage. In a few minutes a bellboy brought him his room key. Pat gave him fifty cents and told him to go out and get him a *Courant*. When the boy came back with the paper, Pat flipped its pages open to the theater news. Gwennie's show was right next door to the hotel in a theater called the Lyric. Her show was called *Japanese Virgin*.

That was a good show title. Anything with the word "virgin" was pretty near sure to make money in the theater, even here in Hartford, Pat felt. With a Japanese hook in it, Pat knew Gwennie was in a probable success. He would go see her show, then go backstage and pick her up and ask her to marry him.

This thought briefly lighted his mind. But it was Sunday. He'd have to wait another day. He didn't feel well.

He stepped out on the street and walked to the theater. It was all locked up.

He didn't want to be alone. He was sick and frightened. He wanted Gwennie. He wished right now he'd married her a long time ago. He wanted to do something civilized with Gwennie, something that would please and surprise her. What should it be? Just once to sleep with her when he was sober, stone sober. Probably she'd appreciate that. Or get her some flowers. Or some nice underwear. But he didn't know Hartford. And he was secretly becoming more and more afraid that there was something really wrong inside. He wanted to lie down in a quiet room for a few days and have someone take care of him. Gwennie would take care of him for a few days if he could find her.

It was a despairing time of day. He began to tour bars.

Bar drinkers would always shove over a little to give him space at the mahogany. He had the look of a man who belonged to bars.

In Hartford the bars were quite dark. To a tyro they would appear sinister but to Pat, who saw no difference between gloom and glitter where whisky was being served, the Hartford bars were fine. He had forty-three dollars of the fifty that Ralph had peeled off for him.

In the Two-Star the radio was going. It was Floyd Gibbons and the news. He was talking extremely fast, too fast. Everyone was listening hard. After a few minutes Pat felt they had all listened long enough. He felt Floyd Gibbons was beginning to monopolize the pleasant feeling in the bar. He was talking about Pilsudski taking over in Poland.

Pat tapped the edge of a five-dollar bill on the bar and slid his glass over toward the bartender for a refill but the bartender was listening to everything Floyd Gibbons was saying as if it was the most important thing of the week. Pat had sharp eyes and quick recognitions and when he looked over the men in the bar, he realized he was in a roomful of Polish Americans. That would explain their interest in what was going on in their native country. He decided that was fair enough. But even so, there ought to come an end to it, and in his own feelings, wanting to be part of the group as he always did in any gathering, he tried to listen at least till the Bond Bread trio would break in. Suddenly Pat remembered the day he got a crying jag in New York right on Fifth Avenue while the parade for Kosciusko Day was streaming up the street. He'd wanted to join the parade but he couldn't because he wasn't a Pole, he was Irish.

Now he clapped his neighbor on the shoulder to tell him the amusing story of how he wanted to march with the Poles. His companion glared at him and held up a quieting finger. Pat resented anyone trying to teach him his manners in a saloon. He very well knew the etiquette. He resented everybody here. He couldn't make the bartender turn around. He began to bang his glass on the bar. The bartender turned and picked up Pat's glass and went as if to put a drink in it but stood there in front of the radio beside the cash register listening to Floyd Gibbons and not getting anywhere.

Pat stepped up on the brass rail and leaned clear across the bar and shoved the radio off the shelf to the floor.

Rather grandly he turned then, and in the stunned confusion walked to the door. On his way he flung a handful of silver against the mirror behind the bar.

Near the door, in the dark, someone grabbed him and sent him flying into the street, tearing his coat collar.

A few blocks away he found another bar. Here he was able to buy a bottle of liquor. It was put in a brown-paper bag for him. It was an innocent-looking paper bag that had recently held a sardine sandwich and the fish oil had run into the fiber of the paper, making it transparent in some places. Pat had two drinks at the bar. He tried to diagnose what had happened to him at the Two-Star. He couldn't be sure whether to be mad and go back and settle it all. His Irish didn't come up very often but it was rising now. To the rage of humiliation, pain was adding itself, and a surrounding fear like a wall of fog moving in and down. Here in this new place—it seemed to be called Collie's—the strange, alarming sensation came to him that all his thoughts were being read by the man on the radio and were being revealed out loud right here.

He realized his most secret thoughts were now being penetrated by a hostile power and that they were being spilled out before these strangers for the sole purpose of giving them the evidence they needed.

He could see it in their eyes. They'd listen to the radio, then look down the long bar at him. Just waiting their time, waiting for the clincher. He knew he wasn't drunk because he was able to count his money. He even knew what pocket it was in. And he had his key to the Euclid. Now in a freeze of horror he waited for one more false accusation from the radio. It came in that very second: "—and is at this very second on his way to Washington to see President Coolidge."

"It's a lie!" Pat screamed, trembling. "You can see it's a lie! How can I be on my way when I'm *right here!*"

He ran out. He ran down the street to his hotel. He locked himself in his room. Then he drew the blinds and peered down through a tiny crack into the street to see if the crowd had begun to collect yet. He could see no one. That was ominous. They were coming for him the back way. He struggled across the room to the door and put the chain through its slot. His hand shook. He slammed shut the transom. In the bathroom he opened the bottle and poured out a full tumbler of the raw whisky and drank it down, then filled the glass again.

When he woke up it was day, though the blinds were still drawn. Moving hallucinations of pursuit, of persecution and torture, hovered near his conscious recognition. He remembered crowds chasing him. He knew he was in a foreign country. An insupportable anxiety clutched at his eyes and bit his chest. He hurt all over now. He drank from the bottle's neck. He had slept in his clothes. A persistent, lurking desire to look normal—to try to look normal—sent him into the bathroom to inspect himself. His eyes were discolored. There was blood on his shirt. He realized he'd slept with the windows shut but he was afraid to approach them lest he be seen.

He groped for water. In this desperation all he seemed able to remember through his whole life was thirst. Thirst and hotels and no money. The whole cavity below his diaphragm seemed congested. It seemed to be expanding, filling up, slowly exploding but without releasing any pressure, to be packed with organs swollen to bursting. He felt suddenly as if he'd inherited the abdomen of an animal that was trying to calve but could not. Pain and gravid distortions of equilibrium sloshed and rocked back and forth like water in a tub. Now the bag was made up of a ball of constrictors, interlaced and sliding through each other's bodies, poking their heads against the inside muscle wall of his belly, trying to get out. He was afraid to open his trousers and look down. He knew he would see snakes. He knew one of the snakes had a nail in its mouth.

As he stood uncertainly in the bathroom wondering where he was and what to do, a dragging pain that began between his lungs just under his sternum ran down into his belly behind his navel. It seemed to bind here and increase, building up its own strength to go on. By and by, as he stood there clinging to the washbasin and gasping for breath, the pain gathered impetus. Down, down it went, poking lower to an exact point he could touch with his finger. It was where his pubic hair began, two inches below his navel. Here the pain spread right and left, reaching out to the soft portions above his hips and below his ribs. That would be the snake with the nail, he realized.

His pain and his terror became so extreme that he began to cry. He made no sound. He merely breathed harder. Tears fell into the basin as he hung there. He felt as if he were committing hara-kiri from the inside. He felt as if his intestinal cavity were now blown so large he could move around in it.

He stumbled away from the basin and sat down on the little chair by the writing desk, rocking forward. He thought he must call a doctor but he knew he could not speak. He groped about for the bottle and drank again. Then he flopped down on the bed and drew up his knees.

He had no more sensations that his mind could record. He remained in this position for six hours. When he came to, the quality of the outside noises had changed. It was night now, though he could not say how he knew. He tried to comb his hair but could not grip the comb. When it fell to the tile floor behind the basin in the bathroom he could not find it. He finished the whisky and reeled out into the corridor.

The whisky spread out inside him.

He sat in the theater trying to identify which particular girl was Gwennie. If it was a strip show, he could tell all right by the scar, but it wasn't that kind of a show. It was very hard to pick out Gwennie. It was a costume show. All the girls wore obis and they all had their hair pulled back tight to lift up their eye corners and give them a Jap look.

Pat was too close to the orchestra but at least nobody was bothering him. From time to time flashes of the faces of some of the men who had been mean to him the night before began to flicker across his memory and bring back quivers of the uneasy, jumpy suspicions that they had caught up with him. As the conspiracy in the Japanese Emperor's palace became clearer to him, he felt that he was beginning to identify with increasing distinctness certain of the very men who had been out to get him. Even though they were mincing around the stage in Jap costumes and samurai swords, they couldn't quite fool Patrick.

Pat's eyelids would half close, then a crack from a temple block or a snare roll and cymbal crash would jolt him quickly back and he'd sweep the stage again looking for Gwennie.

Suddenly she was right there in front of him. They were burning her bare back with an iron. She screamed. Her hands were tied over her head to a bamboo cross. She was tied up and they were going to torture her before throwing her alive into the volcano. There it was, the volcano itself—smoking and roaring, and red fire all around. You could smell it.

Now they began dragging Gwennie up the side of the volcano. Pat began to tremble and shudder. His leg muscles stiffened, lifting his buttocks clear off his seat. In a searing flash he realized no one present had the courage to interfere, that the men were going to do to Gwennie what they had planned for Pat, and that no one around him was going to pile in and fight.

"STOP!" he screamed. "Stop! Stop! Stop!"

Pat vaulted the low railing of the orchestra pit, knocking over stands, players, and sheet music. He heard nothing. He felt nothing. He could only see the men who were killing Gwennie.

Grabbing the inner edge of the footlights trough, he sprang to the stage just as Gwennie was flung into the fire pit of the volcano.

Now he could hear a great screaming. He scrambled up its sides like an ape, then he too screamed and plunged headfirst into the crater.

21

JILL TRIED TO THINK OF THINGS OTHER THAN THE errand that was taking her out of New York. She had never been to an insane asylum. That's where Patrick had landed.

She could not fit Pat's story into the coherence she wished. He'd gone to Hartford apparently—gone there soon after his last quarrel with Seton, the quarrel that Jill had heard from the kitchen. He'd got himself in trouble in a string of bars, then interfered with a stage performance of some kind. That's all the manager of the Euclid Hotel was able to report.

Jill guessed that he was trying to say that he suspected the Hartford police had put Pat in a mental hospital. But this phrase—mental hospital—never quite came out. The word "disturbed" came out. So did "delusions." And the name of the place he'd been sent to.

Seton was prostrated by the news about his brother. Jill put in a call for the asylum. Pat was indeed there.

She took a cab to Grand Central.

In the solitude of the train, snatches of obscene song, couplets of lecherous rhyme and winking fancy paraded across Jill's mind—all the songs she'd heard Patrick singing.

Pat struck poses when he sang, always performing. With the fervor of a choirboy at the end of a long season, Pat could burst out singing a smutty verse from a tab or turkey show, a song he'd picked up in a free-and-easy, a purple quatrain he remembered from the Dewey Theatre on Fourteenth Street. And Pat could do it as if he held a hymn book.

She remembered the time he'd taken her to the Dewey on her promise she'd never tell her husband. It was a new world to Jill, congested with an evil gaiety, a sweating lust, and a throbbing prurience. Hookers and hustlers crowded right up to her, tried to push her away from her own escort!

> *There was a young girl who retired for the night—*
> *She was both young and handsome—*
> *She took off her shoes and the rest of her clothes*
> *And the rain blew through her transom.*

To recall some of the wild times that belonged to Pat in days past now helped to keep Jill's mind from guessing at the wreckage she was on her way to see.

She never had told her husband about the Dewey. Or about the Spit-Box either. That was worse.

> *Oh, Tommy and Molly*
> *Were playing in the sand,*
> *Enjoying their youthful folly——*

She remembered no more of the verse, but the sight and the smell of the Spit-Box she'd never forget.

The Spit-Box was patronized by degenerates. Jill knew nothing of this when Pat took her. There were four boxes for women. Because Seton never took her anywhere, she tingled with a sense of illicit gaiety. There was a comedian dressed in red underwear, crepe whiskers, and a pink wig. There was another named Snuffy the Cabman. There was an obscene dance with the lights dimmed, then the lights coming up full and sudden, as if by an electrician's fumble, for the curtain. The chorus line was all men, some impersonating women. At Pat's suggestion Jill looked down into the front row. It was occupied entirely by middle-aged men and old men, jaws hanging, tongues working.

"They meet later." Pat tapped her knee to explain. "They pick out the ones they want. Like chorus girls. The old men bring silk underwear and perfume. Even flowers."

Most of them had derbies on their laps. From time to time they tipped up the derbies toward the stage. All had opened their trousers and were exposing themselves. Jill felt unnerved and nauseated. She felt embarrassingly betrayed by her brother-in-law. She felt dirty and degraded, publicly fouled.

Then the violence of Seton, and the sound of him in that last quarrel came roaring back. Was it only last Sunday?

The train came out of the tunnel at Ninety-seventh.

What an absurd thing for grown men to fight over! A sadness pierced her. Somewhere there *was* something splendid in Patrick, or there surely had been or could have been; something that needed a different kind of stage for its showing; that needed the force and urging of a different kind of stage manager, different at least from that arranged by his parents, or by circumstance, or by the shock that occurred when Pat's brilliance collided with his bounce.

For the first time she saw that for all the years she had known him, Pat was not trying to live but trying to die.

Now all she could remember of the quarrel was the mouth of her husband, a mouth permanently curled by his long habit of truculent thought and open snarling.

She was sitting on the left side of the train. As it drew abreast of the Naomi Hotel for Women, it slowed down, stopped, and stood there on the elevated tracks, taking on passengers. Jill looked across to the defeated loft building on the north side of 125th Street. There was the same old weather-beaten sign, still readable though it had been there ever since her own girlhood, and how many years before that the Lord only knew.

GUS HILL'S MINSTRELS.

She'd always meant to ask Patrick about Gus Hill. She could remember a long time ago as a child seeing a billboard advertising a Gus Hill but all he seemed to be was a man in an 1890s mustache and a gymnast's costume, severely holding a set of crossed Indian clubs. Patrick would know about Gus Hill.

On her way to him now, to his "emergency" (if the hotel manager's report were in any way true), thoughts of Patrick, thoughts of the things he'd done, the cruel and the heartless and the merry and the mad and the debonair and the crooked, sifted about in the empty seat beside her like a fidgety but unspeaking travel companion.

She felt far away from her husband. It was not the first time. But it was the first time she realized it was not the first time.

The train left the Sound, turned north, and followed the dry boulder-spilled bed of the Housatonic till evening.

Leaves were falling. Though the air was mild, autumn was well on. Empty trees like children's drawings—dead twigs for fingers—scratched quietly at the horizons, then became still once more against the blackboard of dusk. Tentative, unfinished, abandoned in the dark, they watched the train pass, and the bright unwinking eyes of Jill, looking out, wondering if she would be able to do the right thing, wondering what she'd do if Patrick were dead when she got there.

A brakeman came through Jill's car, a strong smell of kerosene with him. The train slowed politely, stopped gently. It seemed quite proper of New England, she felt, as if she were herself being recognized.

She had no bag to lug. She stepped off lightly. It was nearly dark. No one got off with her.

Lights were on in a few houses in the little town—tiny in the dusk—but the station was untended.

There was no taxi.

Across the street from the station she could see the shadow of a man's elbow rocking back, then shooting forward. It was a pool hall with the street shades pulled. Jill walked across the open tracks and tapped on the door. Nothing happened. She opened the door and peered in, half smiling.

Two tables, both busy, stopped their play at once. All the men were in their shirt sleeves and their vests. All had their hats on.

"I wanted to get to the sanitarium," she said. "The Leeward Hospital."

"She wants to get to the nut house, Morris," one of the players said, turning from Jill and looking over his shoulder to a man seated on a high stool, reading the paper. "He'll drive you over, ma'am," he said. "It's seventy-five cents."

They were in the dark street. Morris had a 1920 Overland. They drove in silence for a quarter of an hour toward the two mountains she had seen from the train window. Morris asked without turning, "Got a relative out here, ma'am?"

"Yes," she said quietly. "My husband's brother. He was hurt. In a car wreck."

"They won't get him mended of much."

They drove through an unlighted entrance between two wooden pylons, through a deep park, and stopped before a course of steep stone steps. Jill gave Morris a dollar, which he straightened and flattened and folded in with some other bills.

"Shall I come back, ma'am?"

"Yes, please," she said cheerfully. Then she had no idea when. "Maybe I better call. Do you have a card?"

"They know. Inside. Just crank the phone and ask central. I'm the only one. Most of the time in the pool palace."

Jill always counted steps she climbed. There were eleven. The building itself was gray stone, vast as an armory. A brass-plated door gave on an enormous and useless hallway.

In an office to her left a woman had pushed back from a typewriter. She was just beginning to set a hat down on the back of her head.

"There's no visiting today." The hat came down with deliberate expertness, maneuvered to its final berthing with little tugs and nudges.

"No," said Jill, disclaiming that sort of errand. "The police called."

"What was the name?"

"My name is Mrs. Seton Farrier."

"No. The patient's."

"Oh, Patrick Farrier."

"Oh yes," the lady said, not writing. "He can't see anyone."

"But I was told—they told me he might not live."

The lady at the desk got up and walked away without saying anything. Jill realized it was after hours and that her own appearance, unannounced, was just another distraction. There was no one else in the huge office, though there were nine desks.

On the departed secretary's desk was a light blue card, typed:

"Harriet McClure. Admitted June 20, 1894. Husband committed 1877. Believed deceased. Three children. Children refuse visiting privilege. Return mother's letters unopened."

Jill shuddered.

She glanced at one more card. "Sedalia Plymouth. Admitted January 1901. Brother visited July 1902. No visitor since. No mail. Believed Protestant."

Dr. Niarhos came in. He was a quick-moving small man, important in manner.

"He had to be pumped out, Mrs. Farrier. He's in hospital bay. Maybe Dr. Sommers . . ." He sat down and picked up a phone. "You are not supposed to be here."

"But they *called* me. I've come from New York. I'm all alone." The item did not seem to interest Dr. Niarhos. He nodded as if he already knew. He was a European of some sort; Hungarian, she thought. So many new accents had arrived on America's east coast after the war.

An attendant in a white canvas jacket and white sneakers stood in the door. He held a ring of keys. Dr. Niarhos got up.

"Take Mrs. Farrier to CW-19. Dr. Sommers will meet you there."

She went into the enormous hall with the attendant, his keys tinkling. Jill could still hear no sound of human habitation. The building could be empty or asleep. The first door opened without a key and took them into another corridor, narrower but longer. On each side of it doors opened into small offices. Each door had a porcelain plate with a man's or woman's name. Rolled fire hose hung on protruding hooks and there were several red sand pails.

At the extreme end of the corridor the attendant unlocked a door. There were stairs in front of them. Jill could hear sounds now, a strange unison murmuring, a congregational response in a Sunday service.

"How is he, do you know? My brother-in-law?"

"Lady, there's three thousand here." He said no more.

At the top of the stairs the attendant opened another door that gave on a ward where two hundred men were moving about. A patient lay on the floor at their feet. The attendant had to move the man's body out of the way, shoving it gently with the door as a plow moves snow. Thirty or forty men lay on the floor, inert, uncomplaining. It was not possible to tell whether they were asleep.

In the air was an overwhelming stench like an accumulation of unflushed toilets. Most of the men who were on their feet kept walking. Around and around and around—fish in a great pool—some muttering, some laughing, some lost in the puzzle that had brought them. Some were ancient but there were boys not over fourteen. Along the walls were rows of heavy chairs. Most of them were occupied by men with vacant eyes or men sleeping.

A sense of panic struck Jill. The room was as featureless as a gymnasium, big as a drill hall, but it was so packed, and the stink of it was so tangible, that she could think only of flight and fresh air. The stench had an adhesive penetrative quality. It settled in her hair. It attacked her skin. It seeped into her clothes, got under her nails, got down her back, between her legs.

She had a horrifying certainty that if she opened her mouth she could taste it.

Jill and her companion walked right down the middle of this long elliptical clock-wise promenade and the sound of insanity roared in her mind as it cackled and susurrated at her side.

Men rocked and swayed. One beat his own ears till they bled. Jill was too stunned by the visual horror of what was about her to realize that very few of these lost and suffering people had any idea she had entered the ward. They could look right at her and not see her; look right at her and not even sense her. She wished the attendant would speak or take her arm. Men walked like saints, their mouths praying, their hands pressed; phobic messiahs with the secret of heaven in their eye sockets, saliva in their mouth corners, their hair wild, their shoes split.

The floor shook slightly as if it had contracted the chill of the moving population it supported. Wires and wall fixtures torn out by violence years before hung down from holes in the plaster. Light came from bright bulbs covered over with protective metal baskets. There was crying and laughter. A man of seventy was pretending to eat an ear of corn—the empty spool of a roll of toilet paper. Another man, young and athletic, packed with muscle, bursting with euphoria, was the entire Red Sox infield. A man made an impassioned speech for Sacco and Vanzetti. At least a dozen were stark naked, daubed with feces. A man of sixty, weeping softly to himself and feebly finding fault with something out the window and beyond the trees, shook his finger at it, cautioned it, warned it, then urinated on the window sill, spraying the stream back and forth with the focused concentration of a small boy urinating his initials upon a fresh snowfall.

A florid muscular attendant, deep-chested and hard of eye, stood at the opposite end of the frightful room. He watched Jill approach without interest. Automatically he drew his keys to permit their exit when they had reached the door he tended.

As they passed through a dark corridor on their way to Patrick, the wail of a woman came out of the dark from some blind alcove.

"Somebody *please* take me to the bathroom! Please! *Please!*"

They went up a half circle of iron stairs. Even when she could hear nothing, agonies seemed to leak out from door cracks like blood from a corpse.

There were blocks as quiet as famine.

Across the hall at the top of the iron stairs was a door with Dr. Sommers' name.

The attendant opened the door without knocking, made a half gesture to Jill that meant "Here we are," then left. For an instant she was again alone. She took a fresh handkerchief from her purse, dipped it under the faucet of the water cooler, and carefully washed her lips.

Perhaps Dr. Sommers made up for an inner embarrassment about being attached to a mental asylum by making sure everyone knew he was Scotch and a graduate of Edinburgh Medical College. These facts repeated themselves several times from the walls.

He came into the office with quick strides. He was strong and pale and severe. To Jill, he seemed a man who would have preferred to be in uniform. Or perhaps to be taller. He was about five feet ten but seemed straining to appear a full six feet.

Coming in quickly and bringing with him an odor of collodion and lilac water, he gave Jill a mute magisterial review, a dry twist of smile, then sat down at his desk.

Here he sat very tall, chest up, chin in, and looked down at papers, supporting his clamped jaws with white fists.

When he spoke, something very real came into the face. A sorrow of his own?

"No hospital has to smell," he said quietly, without looking up. "These people don't *prefer* to be untidy, you know."

"No, of course not," Jill agreed. "Of course they don't."

"Many visitors—who come here only once, like yourself—don't know this. They merely go away thinking no one cares. I am in the emotional-rehabilitation business, Mrs. Farrier. Truly, these patients are people just like us, only more so. Faster, more extreme reactions to the same stimuli."

Jill thought to herself: "But Patrick isn't insane. He's just hurt. Why doesn't he get around to Patrick?"

"Are you the next of kin?"

"Mr. Farrier is my brother-in-law." Her heart jumped a beat. Was Pat already dead? Was Dr. Sommers expecting someone else?

Then it occurred to Jill that it might be he was reluctant to take her to where she had to go, that in the doctor's view it was her husband who should be there, not she.

She tried to answer both his unspoken questions.

"My husband—Mr. Farrier's brother—is ill, Doctor. I had to come alone. We had no warning. I've—I've already been through one of the wards."

"Yes, I know. I'm sure it was shocking. I wish these places were better laid out. I wish we could find some money. Or an architect who could inhabit the mind of these poor creatures." He became simple, very quiet, very direct. "State hospitals are built like warehouses, so much space for pianos, so much for trucks, so much for short-storage eggs. But there are only two kinds of people here really—those who have been scolded too often and who are scolding back"—he walked around the end of his desk, crossed the office and opened the door, holding it for Jill—"and the ones that were never noticed, never loved, never wanted. Lost at the very beginning and never missed."

Like Patrick? she thought. Is that what he means? Then she thought of the wards.

Jill wondered if she could stand the stench again. She felt her right elbow cupped tightly, reassuringly, in the strong hand of the doctor. Was he really kind? Then why did he pose?

"How many wards are there?" she asked.

"Of the size you saw we have about fifteen."

"I saw a man chained to a bench."

"We have to do that. When they attack others. We can't isolate all the assaultives. Or dress the nudatives."

He was walking fast, too fast for her.

"But don't you have . . . special places?"

"Surely. Padded cells. But they're full. For three thousand sick people we have twenty-eight nurses. For three thousand sick people we have twenty-two hundred beds. This means that the bed ratio is better than the ratio for nurses. But it also means we have eight hundred patients with no bed. So the eight hundred sleep on the floor. Two hundred of them right here. What we do with the insane, Mrs. Farrier"—here he spoke with a surgical edge, and strange sardonic mischief lit his eye—"is not cruel, it is just unendingly senseless."

Suddenly Jill saw through the pose, saw his reason for the need of one: Dr. Sommers was the most tortured of them all. The strain on his compassion was beyond endurance, his fury beyond speech, his impotence beyond feeling.

This knowledge calmed her. It calmed her in the same way the quiet bespectacled Lieutenant Munoz had, that day on the beach at the Cape when she was having trouble with the new pump, the day Sean got the fever.

"I want to treat them as people. Not as insane."

He drew a bunch of keys and leaned down, clicking them over with quick familiarity, then rammed one into the keyhole.

"It'll stink in here too. Not so bad as the one you hit first. Bad enough, though."

He opened the door. At once the odor rose and showered invisibly over them. Then Dr. Sommers closed and locked the door. A charge nurse, gray and quiet, turned her face up to his from work at her desk. The desk acted as a barricade against the patients but the woman seemed an assured person. She was gentle, even grandmotherly.

"You better have Willy moved to D 4, Doctor. Or change his sedation. He's made some trouble and it's going to climb. Joe says the new attendant can't handle him."

"All right, pill him." Then to Jill: "Your brother-in-law has had two alcoholic convulsions, Mrs. Farrier. Two days ago. And there's a strange pattern of bruises clear across his whole back. Never saw anything like it. You might have thought he'd been lashed. I don't see how it could have happened in a car collision."

"Has he been X-rayed?"

"Yes. No fractures. But we don't know what's keeping him alive. He seemed dead when he got here. Spiritually he seems to have been dead for a long time."

Patients came up, some mute, all tentative, all anxious for the doctor's attention. He put them all off with quick phrases: "I'll be back, Charlie,"; "You bet, General"; "Don't worry about it, Mr. Moses"; "Yellow pill for you Willie, right away."

To Jill he said: "He's been a terrible rummy his whole life, hasn't he? Your husband's brother, I mean."

"Well, for a few years anyhow. But the bruise—it couldn't have happened here, could it, Doctor? Truthfully?"

"Well," he said, honoring her directness with a candor of his own, "we can't let one patient kill another. When they get rough, we get rough. They have to be subdued."

He let it sit there a moment in her mind. Then he relieved her quickly:

"But it didn't happen here. It happened about five days ago. Where was he then?"

"I don't know. He lived alone. And never in one place very long."

She realized miserably they were both speaking of him in the past tense.

"Could it have been a fall?"

"No," he answered with finality. "Not a fall. Not a whip either. The bruise is too deep for a whip. And too straight. The area of capillary rupture is too wide."

"What do you think?"

"I think somebody gave him a terrible blow with a steel rod, Mrs. Farrier. More than one. And I think he was undressed at the time."

At the foot of the ward, Dr. Sommers opened a slatted door. Inside was a semicircular alcove with six beds about two feet apart, all of them occupied.

A nurse attended an old man in the bed farthest from them. This was the only movement. The patient was sitting up while his bed jacket was being changed. His right arm trembled with a waving, continuous *paralysis agitans,* so pronounced it made his bed jiggle.

Her eye ran swiftly down the line of dozing men, stopping at the bed in front of her. Was this Patrick?

A spent figure, breathing slowly, lay back on a pair of pillows, half recumbent, his arms wide apart and relaxed. The grotesque apparatus of *gavage* tubing supplied the sleeping face with a pair of brick-red antennae reaching above to a jar on a hook.

Jill looked questioningly at Dr. Sommers, who nodded back.

"Are they pumping his stomach?" she whispered.

"We are feeding him," he answered just as softly.

The Scotch doctor stepped quietly over, close to the bed, turned the glucose bottle in his hand, saw it was empty, then gently began to pull the tubes from Patrick's nostrils. They came out like mammoth night crawlers, supple, slimy, endless, and elastic.

The nurse came over and handed gauze pads to the doctor. He wiped the lips and nostrils clean, and the nurse washed the face. Patrick's eyelids fluttered, then he seemed suddenly awake, his faculties intact. Intelligence revisited the face, recognition lit it up. Dr. Sommers took the wrist. Patrick turned his head and smiled. It was hardly a smile, more a swift evanescence of apology or surrender, and a puckering one-sided twist of regret. "I guess I'm not very much," it seemed to say. "Please excuse me. I'm just going."

Then he saw Jill. His whole body jerked. He lifted his free arm, holding it for her to take.

"Jill! My darling!" She took the hand, squeezed and patted it. "Is Seton here?"

The eyes roved the room in a quick sweep.

"He'll be up later, Pat. He's in the midst of another play. He caved in a little himself."

"He never knew when to lay off, did he? None of us did. Is it going all right?"

"Sure is," she said easily. "Another great one. You've got to be well enough to see it. To take me to the opening."

"Yeah, sure." He turned to Sommers, who was wrapping the right arm preparatory to taking his blood pressure.

"I've got a famous brother, you know."

Sommers bulbed the pump and took a reading, then pumped again and took another. There was a weak hiss of escaping air. The stethoscope left the inside of his elbow and Dr. Sommers began going over the back.

"Inhale through your mouth, please."

Through the open back of the hospital gown Jill suddenly saw the bruise. It looked like a black skating strap with purple edging. It looked like a blow that could kill a man. She gasped and turned away.

"Pulitzer Prize," Pat said. "He's won two, Doc. First time he didn't even know it was worth money! Imagine!"

He laughed a little, but pain stabbed at his face. Dr. Sommers put his hand on Pat's shoulder.

"Keep as still as possible, Mr. Farrier. You've been one hell of a job to untangle." He rose up. "I'll be in at eleven to give you a hypo."

Pat was docile. He was licked too. Anyone could see it.

Dr. Sommers began clicking his gear together. Outside there were confused sounds and a sharp cry. The doctor was there at once, cold and ready and conspicuously alone. He went out on the ward, the nurse following.

Instantly Pat grabbed Jill's hand.

"What city am I in, Jill? Is it a city hospital? Is it a *state* hospital?" His questions came in a whispered rush. "Is this a laughing academy?" Jill didn't know the expression. "What the hell have they got on me, Jill?" Then the real terror: "Is this a nut house?"

She realized he'd been told nothing. She knew then that his banter in the doctor's presence merely covered a wild and horrible suspense.

"It's a sanitarium," she said, standing close. Even though that was what it was officially called, it sounded like a lie when she said it.

"I've been in a jam, Jill." She waited to hear his report of it. "I can't remember it, though."

"Were you in Hartford?" she asked, seeking for clues herself.

"Yes! Hartford! I went up to see Gwennie's show. But it was Sunday and I couldn't find her and I started drinking to pass the time."

"Who's Gwennie?"

"Show girl I know. I always liked her. I got to thinking about her. I guess I was even thinking about marrying her maybe. But I got drunk. Jesus! I got *beastly* drunk! But what happened?"

"Oh God, Pat! How can anyone tell? You do the damnedest things when you go on a jag. You just *go!* Can't you remember *anything?*"

He shook his head. Fear, and a destroying weariness, came into his eyes again. He rose up suddenly, pleading with her.

"This *is* a bug house, isn't it, Jill?"

"There's some disturbed people here. And a lot of hangovers." She tried to make it light. "But you're not committed, Pat. It's nothing like that. Not nearly."

"Well," he mused, his eyes filled with despair, "maybe it would be a good thing if I *was* committed. I've never been any damn good. Not to anybody. I was always on next-to-closing. I can't even help Seton. Maybe I helped Mother a little. Once. A long time ago. But she's never needed anything from me . . . never since then. And no woman ever wanted to marry me." His eyes filmed over.

"Does she know where I am? Does Mother know?"

"No one knows, Pat. Just me. You're in a good place." He reached for her hands and hung onto them desperately.

"I feel all broken inside, Jill. Like a punchy fighter. I feel as if I fell down a shaft. Christ, they took some blood out of me yesterday. But what for? What the hell for?" He grinned horribly. Something was fading out of him. "There's nothing going through me any more but old spirochetes and raw redeye." He tried to grin.

The racket outside got worse. She moved over closer to him and sat down on the side of his high bed. Pat clung to her. He was almost childish.

"I guess my salad days are all over, Jill. I guess I've run out of French dressing."

He smiled feebly, as tears fell down his riven face.

Something, or someone, crashed against the lower part of the door of the alcove, shaking it in its frame. Then the kicking of some wild patient split in two or three of the slats.

Pat lifted his head to study the meaning of the sound. A strange eagerness lighted his eye. He suddenly slid his white knees from beneath the sheets and slipped out of bed.

Jill was surprised he could even stand.

"They'll all kill each other!" he said, quick with alarm.

He was opening the door!

The nurse saw him from the ward. She misinterpreted his appearance there. She dodged and darted through the running men and rushed at Pat, trying to force him back into the half safety of the alcove. But Pat merely stepped aside. She hardly brushed him.

In the futility of his weakness, in his sorry bedclothes, he walked out into the flood of flailing arms and flying knees. Unbelievably he began to whistle, high and merry, warbling melodiously as an entranced man coming out upon a crowded sidewalk after a gay and tuneful musical comedy.

Barefoot, ridiculous, vulnerable as a child learning to walk, he assumed a disdain for the reek and the risk and the confusion all about and slowly walked the full length of the enormous room, whistling high and shrill and haunting.

Jill shook all over, clung to the door, and wept.

Patrick was indifferent to the roar. Attendants appeared at each end of the ward, grabbing at the most agitated, overpowering the assaultive. Jill saw Willie, the redhead, taken out in straps, lunging and biting and spitting, trying to hit back even with his arms bound.

Yet Patrick, by daring the whole room with the absurdity of his own defenselessness; by flaunting his incongruity, remained untouched. What strength had come to him here? What had brought this steely composure? Frightened men began to watch, then actually to listen. The overwhelming anxieties let loose just before were going down a little. In spite of his nightgown ludicrousness, there was a strange dignity in Patrick's walk.

It was a quiet walk, labored too, as if the floor were steep, but his high trilling and the pure quality of aeolian sounds that came from his lips—sounds that seemed to descend rather than to rise—ethereal, vagrant, transporting, mysterious—brought a stillness upon the room.

Sommers came in, watched, listened, cocked his ear. He came over to Jill, his forehead ridging up.

"It's something he did in theaters," she said. It wasn't quite the way it was but it would do.

Patrick turned and started back. Coloratura flutings and flageolet glissandos fell, then rose again, with his approach. Something magical was happening. Jill had heard of it once from Dermod. She'd heard of it many times from actors who had been there when he had performed at the Friars or the Twelfth Night or the K. of C. And she'd heard just a little herself only a few days before when Pat was coming down the hotel corridor before the fight began with Seton.

The disturbance had subsided now. Pat moved slowly, still whistling, from one cluster of men to another, sharing his ghostly serenade with the tormented people he had found here at the end of the road, and all the beauty of daybreak shivered and quivered exquisitely in the sad squalor of listening faces, of shriveled memory, of places that were no more, of voices gone and pictures put away.

He started to sit down in an empty chair by the wall, reached back to feel for its arms, bent forward slightly, and fell down on the floor. The patients stood about, staring down, wondering what had happened to the music.

Sommers rushed over, saw that Pat was not able to rise, picked him up, and carried him back to the alcove. Then he hurried off. The nurse too disappeared. On the bed Pat clasped his two hands and locked them between his knees, groaning. His eyes rolled. Then they closed. His whole body began to shake.

"Jill, Jill," he cried in a hoarse whisper. "Come quick! I'm going under."

"No! No!" she pleaded with him, stroking his arm and his forehead, pulling up the blanket. But his body went on shaking. "Pat! You'll be all right. The doctor has gone for medicine."

"There's no medicine," he groaned. "No medicine. Nothing now. Only a short——" He broke off the sentence. He placed a hand on her wrist. He was ice cold now. "Jill . . . one thing . . . Tanager."

Tanager?

Jill couldn't relate the woman to the moment.

"She's after Seton." He turned over on his side, speaking in broken phrases, breathing fast and light. "I knew Tanager—a long time ago. You're away too much. She's been coming to rehearsals. Seton's afraid of her. Doesn't know how—to throw her out. I went to her place. I was going to—take care of her. But I got drunk there. Keep her out, Jill. She'll kill him. She kills everybody—she's near."

"Did Tanager—hurt you?"

"Yes—Marion Vogel's apartment—I remember—falling. Falling. Then she hit me—I couldn't get up——"

His hand slid back on the mattress. His breathing sounded like a man going under ether. It slowed and became heavy, fluttering his palate. Then she saw he was breathing no more. He looked quiet, tired out, like a man resting after a long illness.

Without tears or feeling she turned away from his bed and walked out into the day room where the jungle disorder had just occurred.

It seemed a long time ago. Now the room was empty. The patients had gone off to bed. The nurse had left her desk.

Jill walked to the door through which she had come with Dr. Sommers. It was locked. She came back to the desk and sat down wearily to wait. Sommers came in, started to run across the ward, saw Jill, and came over. She merely shook her head once, hardly perceptible. But he knew. He set the bag on the desk.

"Wait here. I'll be right back."

She heard him speaking to one of the patients in the alcove, then he came back, picked up the phone, and squeezed Jill's shoulder.

"This is Dr. Sommers," he said to the night operator. "Call the morgue. Send up Jamie with the wagon. Twenty-four. First bed."

They walked slowly out, down the long halls where the overload of patients had to sleep. Dr. Sommers had a flashlight and walked ahead of her. The corridors might be accommodating disaster victims. They had that look—something set up hurriedly by the Red Cross.

He opened the door at the end and looked back. All was quiet.

"Fights start here too, sometimes. So close together. They accidentally strike each other in their sleep."

She thought he was trying to keep her mind off the tragedy of Patrick.

In his office she asked him the question that had been on her mind from the start.

"But why *this* hospital, Dr Sommers?"

"It was a police order. Your brother-in-law thought all the radio announcers, news and sports reporters were reading his mind. Exposing his thoughts to the public—Floyd Gibbons, Graham McNamee. Then he got the idea he could tell what they were going to say before they said it. He was going into bars and pushing radio sets off their shelves."

Jill didn't know who Graham McNamee was. She'd heard of Floyd Gibbons, had once seen a newspaper picture of him with an eye patch, but they had no radio at the Cape.

"Your brother-in-law seemed a fellow who could attract a crowd, too. Bellowes' furniture store became involved. Mr. Farrier was sleeping in a Queen Anne sofa, right in the front window. Four in the morning."

"How could he get in the store?"

"Its front window had been smashed by a backing truck. He was tired, he was drunk, there was a place to lie down. Stepping through the plate glass would be nothing to a drunk. They'll go up the outside of buildings if they feel like it."

Dr. Sommers had forms to fill out, calls to make, a death certificate to sign; papers to which Jill had to put her name.

Then they walked through the silent building to the main office.

"You want to take his body down tonight?" Dr. Sommers asked.

Jill could think of nothing else to do, even though Pat's burial would probably take place in New London. She nodded her head.

"I'll speak to the night operator. See if we can get a train to stop."

Jill found a ladies' room nearby. Here she washed her hands and face, the back of her neck, her ears. She touched up her hair with a tiny folding comb she kept in her bag, put a little coloring on her cheeks.

She felt better.

She sat down in a large leather chair outside the office that Dr. Niarhos used.

Pat was going to die this way sooner or later. He was scheduled to. For a long time she'd known he had no liver, that the cirrhosis was so advanced the hard enlargement seemed to extend through his abdomen and to project beyond like a wild tumor.

Toward the end he'd even stopped going with women. The sight of himself was too abhorrent. He couldn't take off his clothes. He kept the thing to himself, kept it away from whores, bar pickups, from women he'd slept with a hundred times. He had a strange shame of it. Seton told Jill about the condition and exacted her promise she'd never mention it to his mother. Mrs. Farrier told Jill, then swore her to secrecy, not wanting to upset Seton.

Death could be so kind. There could have been so many other endings for Patrick. Death might have come to Patrick as something brash and public and three-sheeted. It might have come in a whore's bed.

But he had merely fallen down quietly, exhausted altogether, in a wilderness of despair, a bird singing above the roar of a senseless battle. How long had he been there? Five days? What did it matter now?

Jill could feel regret but she could feel no sorrow.

In her mind she kept avoiding a return to what Patrick had said about Tanager. She knew she'd watch for it from here on. But with the horrifying speculations his last sentences had forced upon her mind; with the threat to her marriage that was implicit in the center of his warning; with this most urgent of entreaties, his own eyes starting in their sockets, came her own fear that she herself must now bring forces into action she did not even know how to mobilize.

One terrible truth was clear to Jill: if Tanager wanted Seton, there were limitless ways she could get him. For one thing, Jill would never fight to keep him. Pat himself had touched the quick of her whole vulnerability in one short sentence: "You're away too much."

But whose fault was that? It was no one's. Seton hated New York, hated to have Jill anywhere near one of his theaters, but his output was so rapid, he had to be there nearly half the time. It was the way circumstance and necessity had laid out their life.

She had had no time to absorb the shock of death. It was too early, too swift, too dramatic. She was in shock herself and did not know it. The messages Patrick crammed into his last minute of communication visited back and forth in her mind, keeping out the need for immediate planning, letting her rest. Dr. Sommers was doing everything that had to be done right now.

He appeared and held out his hand. She thought he had come to commiserate. Then she saw he was holding a capsule in his palm. She took it and sipped some water which he'd brought. After that he poured a tumbler of whisky and set it down beside her.

"I'll go with you to the station."

"There's no need."

"As superintendent of the hospital I have to go anyway, Mrs. Farrier. Whenever a body has to be put on a train."

He picked up the cards she had been looking at.

"You know why these are lying out. *They* all died today too." He was looking at the card for Harriet McClure and read aloud: "Children refuse visiting privilege. Return mother's letters unopened."

They heard a car outside, heard the front door slam.

Dr. Sommers handed her an envelope. "Your doctor will want this." She tucked it into her pocketbook. "When you get off at Grand Central, walk up to the baggage car. There'll be someone there to meet you. Just stand by the baggage car. By Mr. Farrier—his box. They'll lift it down and place it on a hand truck." He looked at his watch.

"Is it time yet?"

"Yes, it's time. Take a little more whisky."

It was not a car from a funeral parlor. It was a small truck that smelled like garden tools, fallen leaves, and greenhouse gear. There was a young driver in overalls. He was sleepy but he smiled at her. Jill sat in the middle.

"Give this to the conductor on the train," Dr. Sommers said. "I called the numbers you gave me. Mr. Brayce will meet your train."

She wanted to thank him, to listen to him. She didn't want to be a problem to him, he had so many others.

"What is the greatest need in your hospital, Doctor?"

"People who care," he said at once.

The train came in to the deserted station. Dr. Sommers handed Jill a fresh pillow.

"I thought you could get a little sleep maybe," he said. "It's four hours. You'll be in just about sunrise. Try to think that it's all over. There's just one thing . . ."

"What is it?"

"It's ugly. But I have to ask it."

"All right," she said, turning from the step, her hand on the rail.

"It's about those bruises. I want a doctor to see them. A New York doctor. Before the embalmer. I want his report in the record."

"But I know about it. I know who did it. Patrick told me. It was the last thing he said."

"Is there anything I should do, Mrs. Farrier?"

"No, I think not"—he reached up and shook hands with her—"but there may be something that *I* should."

She went up the steps, turned at the top and leaned down a little. "What about the pillow?"

He made a scattering gesture with his hand.

"Courtesy of my hotel."

Jill went in and sat down, the pillow beside her. She was very tired. She had not felt it till now. It occurred to her she had not eaten anything since luncheon in New York. It was now almost three o'clock in the morning.

She wondered without spite or interest where Seton might be by now, what solaces he'd found, what places to hide, what hand to comfort his forehead, what kind of whisky he'd encountered, where he'd cashed the first check.

The face of Arleigh Brayce came into her mind, as if looking in upon her from the darkness outside. His words, simple words in a magic sentence, came back to her now: "You cannot live with anger."

Jill patted the pillow smooth, tucked it between the back of the seat and the window. Then she relaxed into it and waited quietly for the night to pass.

Part Five

22

THE FARRIERS BEING SUDDENLY AT LAKE PLACID WAS
Jill's idea. It would give Seton a chance to drive the new Pierce-Arrow.
This had been a good selling point in their long discussion of the
trip two or three days before, when they sat for a long time after
dinner in the great dining room of Glen Lochen.

Jill had not found the right moment, or perhaps the necessary
courage, to tell her husband she was pregnant. Nothing had been the
same the whole spring and summer after the death of Patrick. Though
Molly called from time to time, Seton didn't want her to come out.
He didn't want anyone. He resented the press photographers who
came one Sunday afternoon to take pictures of Seton playing
tennis, Seton swimming, Seton overseeing the potting of bulbs. He
posed a few times, once in white flannels and blazer, once holding
up sixty pounds of bar bells. Then suddenly and for no reason he
dismissed them all. They were glad to go.

He banged doors and gave orders. He ate little. For two months
he wrote not a line. He kept the tennis courts rolled and marked but
he put away his rackets and used the area for sunning and reading
and being by himself. He cut down the Italian contractor's duties
to keeping the lawn clipped. He shut down the greenhouse, drained
and covered the pool. He spent most of his time reading in the
boathouse or swimming by himself in the lake.

Jill felt as if she and her husband were a pair of caretakers on a
property of great beauty and imposing historical significance but that

their privacy was so vulnerable it might at any moment be broken in on by visitors who paid twenty-five cents to be taken through.

It wasn't the look of the place. It was what Seton did to it. Of its twenty-six rooms, they lived in four.

In the course of that awful summer, in the midst of its visible but untaken beauties, Jill received positive word that Seton's son by his first marriage—his name was Derek—was anxious to make a direct contact with his father. She had communicated with Seton's first wife in the matter. Neither woman knew what to do. Derek's mother was in a distressing situation. She was even willing—if Seton were— that the boy return to his father. She did not want to give him up but she had no way to support him.

Jill knew what an explosion such a proposal would make.

Then she thought of Dr. Randall Cedric, of his transfer to Saranac Lake. And this was all Seton needed. They were under way in less than three hours. Seton had even kissed Sean when he swept him up and placed him in the front seat with his mother.

It was a happy ride. Seton was en route to a critical checkup. The findings might be his death warrant. He was continuously courteous all the way, once even holding open the door for his family when they stopped for a late lunch in Hudson Falls.

The Lake Placid Club suited Jill. Everything, of course, suited Sean. The main building was huge and friendly.

"That's Mirror Lake, Mrs. Farrier," the young man at the desk told her. "Fools everyone at first. Lake Placid is a couple of miles off."

As she looked about the open lobby, she could see nothing but happy people. On a large blackboard nearby, the day's activities were listed. Ping-pong tournament, shuffleboard, tennis, dancing, folk dancing (for children under ten), swimming lessons (beginners), camera club, bird watch, church service, skeet, riding, interpretive dancing.

"I saw your husband smoking a cigarette," the polite desk clerk observed pleasantly.

"Oh yes," Jill agreed. "Isn't it all right?"

"Oh yes, ma'am. Only so many guests forget that there is no smoking in the dining room."

"Well, I'll be sure to remind him."

But it was not necessary.

Seton had taken the car on to Saranac to have his first session with Randall Cedric. Some hours later he called to tell Jill the tests might take two days.

The period had its uses.

It gave Jill time to get acquainted with the club, with its sprawling layout, its odd rules, its legendary breakfasts, its planned but not-too-strenuous-life out of doors. She took Sean with her everywhere. He devoured it as if it had been a busier extension of Cape Cod.

Jill found it all pleasant. She admitted guiltily to herself that it was a relief being away from Seton but the second night she became uneasy and called Dr. Cedric at Saranac.

He didn't care for the call. She remembered his blunt antipathy to Seton in New London.

"Oh yes, he's certainly here, Mrs. Farrier."

The doctor didn't sound as if he were enjoying her husband's visit.

"How long do the tests take, Dr. Cedric?"

"Oh, few hours. He's passed everything. A beautiful specimen."

"Well, why isn't he coming back over here? I mean——"

"You mean what's keeping him? Well, not me, I can tell you. I've got people here who *are* sick. I think he went for some whisky. But he's all right. There's good Canadian whisky here." Then, perhaps suspecting he might have sounded gruff to her, he asked kindly:

"Are you all right, Mrs. Farrier?"

"Me? Oh yes. I'm all right. Thank you. Good-by."

She hung up and went out on the endless verandas. People smiled and spoke. Everyone was relaxed.

Then she saw the Pierce-Arrow. She hurried on to their cottage to see if he had come in. She did not get there in time. He had come in but he had gone out again. A bag and a jacket were there. He'd apparently opened one of the bags to take out a sweater. He loved sweaters.

She looked in on Sean. He was sleeping hard.

Jill sat out on the porch. There in the dark she prayed for her husband, for the preservation of his powers as an artist, for strength to meet life, strength to meet his brother's death, strength to meet the problems of disappointment, to meet the problem of drinking.

Jill went to bed.

In the supernatural quiet that stands still over these ridges for the breathless moment between the last cry of the whippoorwill and the first flute sounds of the Wilson thrush, there is a suspension of sound and of movement so arresting and so fearsome as to suggest the primeval mood of these mountains before ever they rose from the sea's floor.

Anyone who has been up, or awake, on a black Adirondack night has felt this. Now Jill felt it. It can be touched with the hand; yet instantly receding from this touch, for in that currentless half hour before dawn man seems wholly to have departed. Or seems never to have been at all. Flowers are closed. No insect stirs, and steeple clocks from Placid to Keene stand in the chill silence like charms painted on a sarcophagus.

It is not possible to hear any sound whatever, for there is none. It was this that had wakened her.

She got up. Seton was still out. Jill put on a wrap and went through the cool grass in her bare feet to the edge of the golf course: Sometimes she'd seen him walking about the immense lawn at Fairfield at three or four in the morning. She came back and looked in the Pierce-Arrow. There were three bottles of whisky in the back seat. She took these inside the cottage and went back to bed.

In the dead center of the moments while the malign potential of night stood congealed over the flower garden a tall thin man, with a sweater tied around his neck, walked slowly and wonderingly through the cold grass, moaning musically to himself. Seton had no objective. He felt peaceful now but he would have terrified anyone who came upon him at this time and in this condition.

Seton was drunk and did not know it; he was barefoot and did not care.

First light disclosed a half circle of rustic benches where wives sat in the afternoons to watch their husbands practice dry-fly casting; where Jill that afternoon had held a rod for Sean. Now Seton sat down here in the dark, sticking his bony feet out like a spilled dancer in a comic ballet. His head wobbled up and down as if tugged from behind. An incoherent fragment of song came out of the hanging mouth. He drank from a bottle that he carried by the neck, pulled his knees up, got his feet under his body, and began walking again. A fish leaped lightly from the lake's surface and the man turned his head at the sound, his body steadied by the back of the bench. Mournfully he waved back at the ripple marks as drowned people—their hands drifting limply—wave in the companionways and dining saloons of sunken liners. Then he started down the road once more, his torso bent forward as against a wind, though the atmosphere had not moved.

When he left the shore road of Mirror Lake and entered the wood road to Placid deep darkness enveloped him. He began to weep now, and a feeble glow from the dry earth beneath his feet showed him the road's margins. He could hear the click of the earpieces of the stethoscope as Dr. Randall Cedric folded the instrument and tucked it in his pocket. And he could see a string of X-ray pictures clipped to a wire before a window. But he could not now remember just when this was or what it had had to do with him.

A new sadness shook his spare frame as the sound of organ music and the stagnant smell of funeral flowers came to him through the trees. He had lost his father and his brother, in quick sequence, each dying with an obstinate deliberateness hard to think of now, harder to sit beside; lost them all with their last words coming from blind mouths insensible, monopolizing all his time with their endless dying.

Feeling it might be toward one of these funerals that he was now moving; sensing he was only one man in a long line of silent mourners, he turned his head slowly from side to side without breaking his forward steps to see who might be in the procession behind.

He saw that his feet were bare. To him it seemed ceremonially fitting. He regretted only that he was not a priest. He turned about with quiet solicitude to bless the pious people behind him, whoever they might be, and saw only the wagon bearing the casket.

Softened by the darkness, it passed in creaking dignity, with the driver frozen at the reins. Suddenly the driver stared right at the walker as though the walker had become the corpse. Then he rose up from the wagon seat and slapped the reins, and the wagon disappeared in the woods.

Just ahead, shrouds of mist lifted into the open tops of the birches.

Lake Placid sat in its cup before him, its water as green as oil but still as rock.

Two men stood near a rowboat, one looking out over the water, the other looking into the sky, as if in prayer. Something lay on the ground beside them. It looked like a drowned child. Seton saw that the man who peered into the sky was trembling, that tears were coursing down his face. Was this from the cold? Or was he weeping? Weeping for the dead child? What child was it? What had happened here?

The barefoot Seton moved more slowly, thinking to spy out the exact situation before intruding on anything so private. It was possible the form lying so still on the ground was not a person at all but a bundle of camp luggage perhaps, or a blanket roll. Yet he was certain he could make out the wax contours of a dead face.

He squatted down on a damp log, holding the bottle in one hand, and studied the silent men. One of them wore a pair of oil-stained white flannels. Behind him an ax leaned against a Norway pine. It suddenly flashed through his mind that there might have been a killing here; that these men were about to take the body into the lake and sink it.

Seton took a huge pull from the bottle's neck and shook the liquor down.

He was crouched out of sight in a thicket of blueberry bushes. For the first time the hard chill of dawn went through him. He drained the bottle, regretting he had no more.

A parallel track of rusted rails, nearly invisible in the undergrowth, ran down to the water's edge. To launch a powerboat, no doubt, and to haul it from the water at the season's end. He'd seen it often enough along the open beaches of Provincetown. But here in this pale light the tracks had a suggestion of life departed. There was no boathouse. Perhaps the tracks at one time had led to the eye of a mine shaft, now blinded by disuse and sealed up.

Thoughts of the world's lost energies, of mankind born and buried with nothing but disappointment, thoughts of his own disasters and the sense of doom that clung to his preoccupations brought him staggering and uncertain to a walking position again. He started toward the men.

He remembered that he was bound for a funeral.

The incongruity of the whisky bottle signaled itself to his right hand and he lightly dropped the bottle behind him. It broke in a pleasant tinkle upon the track. The men at the shore looked over. Then they moved closer together. The one near the Norway pine picked up the ax.

Seton emerged like a crazed and mumbling messiah from the protection of the underbrush and stood meek but hectic before them. Now he looked down at the face of the drowned child. Death had come so recently that the face still seemed alive. The girl's eyes looked back, and a little beyond. The mouth was delicately turned, as if it had been stopped by the water while still speaking.

A great sigh of pity escaped Seton. A sense of inexpressible compassion shook his mind. The men seemed so immobilized in their sorrow, the form of the girl seemed so cold that Seton wept at the misery before him. Slowly he removed the sweater from about his neck and covered the thin wet shoulders of the child. Words from the burial service came into his mind and framed themselves appropriately for utterance. But he found he could make no sound. Only his lips worked. He raised his hand in benediction, blessed the two unspeaking mourners and looked up into the vault of the dawn's darkness for some answering sign.

In a searing stab across the full quadrant of the heavens from Ampersand to Haystack a great blinding meteor tore open the sky. Seton covered his eyes and rocked back to catch his balance. The two others stood amazed.

God had received the child.

He turned away, seeking the road again. Daylight was perceptibly closer. He passed the boat yard, passed a huge wooden hotel, its porches vast as empty dance floors, its rocking chairs lined up and tipped forward like Chinese prisoners bound and waiting quietly for execution. In the empty yard at the end post of a croquet set, two high stacks of shutters had been piled. Summer was dead. One of the flower beds at the side of the hotel was already covered with heavy muslin.

Summer was dead and buried.

Ever so far away came the sound of an outboard motor refusing to start. Reflexively his ear waited for the sound again but it did not come.

The barefoot man was alone in the universe, just as he had been from the day he entered it.

The night clerk of the Lake Placid Club was intensely interested. He was a senior at Middlebury College. His name was Chidsey.

"Even though nobody's awake, we couldn't take a chance."

"Well, how'd he get upstairs then? He could hardly walk."

"Yeah, how'd he get up the stairs? He kep' fallin' down."

The Middlebury senior jerked his head. "Trunk elevator. Took him up after you dumped him off. Porter's room right now. Family's in one of the cottages. Wife anyhow."

He drummed on the blotter, then looked up at the mountain men who had brought Seton in.

"But he kept sayin' there was a kid drowned. Then he'd bawl some more. How can a skinny guy like that carry so much booze! Prohibition too. Musta had a barrel in 'im."

"Bottle anyhow. Me an' Eddy heard it bust. Then he come out, barefoot and the blind staggers an' liquor you could smell to Rouses Point!"

"Hunted, he looked," broke in the other. "You could buggered me through me overhauls! I picked up the ax. Jesus! I'm just leanin' against this tree, rewinding the armature. Not five yet!"

"Cryin' an' prayin' and even sorta hummin'."

"Scared me at first."

"Scares me now."

"What about the drowning?" Chidsey asked. "No boat turned over, did it?"

"Hell, no. Just a great big cryin' jag. Kept rolling around, puttin' signs on us both like he was the Pope."

The men turned the sweater over and looked at the label.

"It's a good sweater, all right. Musta cost nine-ten dollars. Abercrombie and Fitch. I'll get it wrapped and sent over to the cottage."

The clerk came back behind the long desk and began to fold the sweater. "You know who he is?" he asked idly.

"No, he didn't innerduce himself."

"He's Seton Farrier. He's the most famous playwright in the United States."

"He was sure the drunkest." He laughed at his own words and dismissed the incident.

The other man sucked his teeth.

"I can smell cinnamon buns. We better get outa here, Piney, 'fore all the rich folk find them a native right here in their lobby."

"Yup."

In a moment Keith Cloverleaf, the undergraduate from Bates who drove the club's station wagon, bounded cheerily into the lobby. He'd seen the fishermen in the road, and the Farrier name meant a great deal to him.

"What'd you do with him?"

"Eddy dropped him in the porter's room next the back fire escape."

"You going to tell Dr. Flowers? You better tell Dr. Flowers."

The phone jarred the privacy of Dr. Mortimer Flowers, who, at the moment of the ring, was shaving. He was a cross and successful man who didn't like to work on his holiday. He'd been coming to Placid for more than thirty years. He knew all the young college bucks who did the work around the place, even recognized Chidsey's voice before his whole message was delivered. Many considered him New York's most reputable psychiatrist. He was surely its most independent.

The porter's room, where Farrier lay sleeping, was a cozy little nook seldom used. Two miniature dormer windows hung out over the tennis courts far below. The cot was between the dormers.

Dr. Flowers didn't look at Farrier except to see he was there, and dry. The clerk handed him the sweater that he'd brought up from the desk. The doctor tossed it to a canvas deck chair.

"May I bring anything, Dr. Flowers?"

"I think not," he answered. "It all seems to be here. How many know about"—he gestured toward the cot—"about this?"

"Harry, the night man. And Eddy. Eddy brought him up. Eddy and Piney."

"Who are they?"

"Local. They have a boat concession on Placid."

"But no connection with the club?"

"No."

"Did you see Mr. Farrier yourself?"

"No. I come on at seven."

"You might send up a pitcher of water. And there's an unopened bottle of Canadian Club on my chiffonier."

"More? To drink?" The clerk was horrified.

Dr. Flowers opened the door for him, then nodded him out. "Better to let him have it. That is, if you want the front office to stay where it is now."

White creases appeared in the young man's forehead and he hurried away.

Flowers turned, after fastening the door, to look at the sick man. He was instantly struck by the look of strength, the almost dramatically masculine beauty of bone formation. His hair was thick, anvil-black, just beginning to gray. The eye sockets were deep and widely spaced, the nose long and thin and inquisitive, the brow high and a little pinched. To the doctor's eye the main indications of strength were gathered in the region of the mouth and across the jaw line. The cheeks were so sunken that their concavity exaggerated the outcropping of the jaw far more than it might in a man of normal weight. More mask than face, it seemed a barricade behind which a person of great complexity and cunning kept his silence and watched and recorded continuously, but responded rarely.

He was in deep alcoholic sleep, and it was easy to believe, because the pallor was so pronounced, that he had at one time suffered with tuberculosis.

The wrist was sticky when Flowers reached forward to take the pulse—it was racing at 136—and although the body lay as still as a fallen tree, the blood was pounding through it so hard the cot jiggled.

The hotel was awake now. Because of the interval between the springboard's quiver and the splash, he knew someone had gone off the high board at the diving tower. All the tennis courts had become active at the same time. A power lawn mower started up somewhere behind the west cottages.

In a few moments one of the bellboys came with a large pitcher of water. Almost on his heels came a second boy with the Canadian whisky. He dismissed both boys at the door, taking the burdens from them there, then going back into the room alone and setting both water, which would be his first need, then the whisky, which would be his greater, on a bare table at the head of the cot.

The doctor himself left word at the desk that one of the bellboys or housemen be assigned duty at Seton Farrier's door and that he, the doctor, be called the moment Farrier was heard to be on his feet.

Then Flowers went out in the fresh sunshine and strolled down the easy slope to the edge of the seventh-hole fairway where Colden Cottage stood.

He could smell coffee in the cottage.

Dr. Flowers tapped at the door. The young woman who came—and she came at once—wore such an assured and carefree look that he knew she could not be Seton's wife.

"I'm Dr. Flowers. I was looking for Mrs. Seton Farrier."

"Yes, come in. I'm Jill Farrier," she said, holding the screen door.

"Mrs. Farrier, I know that your husband is Dr. Cedric's patient. But I thought you should know where he is and that I've seen him."

Jill passed coffee to him. Her hand was steady, so were her eyes.

"Thank you, Dr. Flowers. I appreciate your coming. My husband is always close to or in the midst of or just coming out of some kind of nervous calamity."

Mortimer Flowers didn't expect to hear so much in a first statement. He could not tell whether Jill was poised or cold or beyond caring. She didn't look cold, she looked warm. She was a beautiful person, beautifully formed and lissome.

"How did you know he was drinking?" she asked.

"The front desk called me."

"I'm grateful to you, Doctor."

She picked up a small bicycle pump from the wicker table and put a couple of drops of oil on the rubber flange of its plunger, then began twisting the rubber back and forth to renew its pliability.

"What in the world are you fixing?" he asked, genuinely curious.

"It's a little hand pump. For my husband's punching bag. Over there in the corner."

Flowers glanced over. Behind a half-pulled curtain a small square platform stood on the floor. About six feet above it, suspended by an oak post, was the rebound ring for a punching bag and in the center of the ring the hook from which the bag hung down. On the floor was the bag itself, unlaced, sad and shapeless without its air.

"We have to deflate the bag when traveling," she told him. "He has another rigged up in the boathouse where we live in Connecticut."

"Does he really use this?" Flowers heard himself inquire.

"Oh yes," Jill answered, fitting the pump back together. "He has several sets of exercises." He felt her eyes on his face and looked intently at her, hoping she would add more. "Does it seem queer to you?"

"Oh no." But of course it did seem queer.

He could not analyze his own feelings about Jill. Behind the exterior candor there was a hurt look, hurt and wary. Something else, too. Was there a great fear? and a greater self-control? Or a fear that wouldn't say so to itself?

Then he knew she was asking for help and could not do so in words.

The huge absurdity of the little pump, the woman's eagerness and competence to fix it rolled up into meaning. He could see heroic patience and accommodation.

He knew he would do what he could, not just this morning, any time she sought him.

"Has he ever promised to stop drinking?"

"Oh yes," Jill answered, putting the pump aside, "many times."

"And tried?"

"Tried, I'm sure. Many times. Hard. It's so bewildering to him. It's easy to describe, but so hard to penetrate."

"What is the pattern of it? Is there one?"

She was nodding thoughtfully, looking off, remembering. "Yes. A pattern. I believe he *thinks* he wants a drink the same as any other man but I believe he hates it. And I believe he knows subconsciously—though he has never related the two—that he *can't* drink as other men drink. That it's easier for him to go without."

She had used a phrase that interested him and he asked:

"That he's never related the two *what*?"

"That once he starts, disaster follows. Always."

"Once started, he can't stop."

"Yes. Not even if he wants to . . . not even if he *has* to."

"What circumstance would that be—that he has to?"

"If he has a show in rehearsal."

"What happens then?"

"A compulsion seizes him. Locks him. He drifts away."

"Like now?"

"Yes."

"Is it always something special that starts it?"

"No. But it was this time."

"What was it?"

"To find he is entirely well."

She began pumping little jets of air into the bladder of the punching bag.

"He lost his father about a year ago. Then a bit later his brother. He can't get over his brother's death. All these things have come at the same time. At a time when there's one more burden to carry."

"What is that?"

"Next February I'll have our second child."

She slipped the bladder, now taking form, into the leather cover of the punching bag, pumped it full of air, laced it and hung it in the center of its ring. The operation suddenly seemed absurd as Dr. Flowers realized these little preparations were being made by an adult woman for a famous man, rather than by an attendant for retarded unfortunates asylumed so they could bring no harm to others.

"What do you do, Mrs. Farrier, when your husband drinks this way?"

She tried to think. "I don't do anything really. I just pray. I can't think of anything else to do."

"You were thinking of something else last summer."

"What do you mean?"

"You asked Arleigh Brayce to recommend a good psychiatrist."

"Yes. You know Arleigh?"

"Very well. We have a week of golf here. End of every summer. I've seen most of his productions. Most of your husband's too. Arleigh will *be* here in a week."

"We'll be gone by then. I wish he were here now."

Many hours later, alone in his big room, Dr. Flowers remembered the expression in Jill's eyes when she had said that.

Outside, it was very still. The sunflower smell of goldenrod came to his nostrils. It was late at night. But the doctor reached for the phone anyhow and put in a call for Arleigh Brayce. After a few minutes the sound of the producer's voice, ringing with distance but clear and full of life, filled the room.

"No, I wasn't in bed. I just got in from the Habima Players."

"Could you come up a week early? Could you come up now?"

"You mean, while the weather holds?"

"I mean while Seton Farrier is here."

There was a long pause, then the dead word: "Why?"

There was another pause—this one from the doctor.

"I don't know, for sure. I don't believe I know him at all. I just know *about* him."

"But I don't understand why you're making the call. If he's in trouble, I can't help. I *could* come up now. It isn't that. But Seton's had some new plays since I did those three with him. All with different producers. I made a lot of money for that man but we never see each other."

"Well, come up anyhow."

"I don't think I can take Farrier, Mort. I wrote him a month ago. About the 'Joseph and His Brethren' thing—the sketch his father made so famous. I thought it could be expanded into a play. I know it could. Make money, too. You ought to *see* the letter I got in return!"

"Perhaps I *should* see the letter."

"Indeed you should. I'll keep it."

"No, don't keep it. Bring it up. Bring it now."

"Is his wife with him? Is Jill there?"

"Yes. And their boy. Quite a beautiful child."

There was a long silence while Arleigh thought over the use of such a trip. "It sounds from here like a terribly *personal* involvement. A family thing. I don't want to get near it."

"It's beginning to overwhelm the wife. I've met her several times now, while her husband was getting out of a long drunk up here. She's spoken of you. She seems a fine person, the wife. In fact quite extraordinary."

"That's very true. Did she ask you to call me?"

"No. She's never asked for a thing. I just feel that something—something central is missing from this whole complex, without you here."

"I'll come up. I'll be there tomorrow afternoon."

"Thanks, Arleigh. Bring that letter too."

Early in the morning Mortimer Flowers walked over to Colden. Jill was pleased and relieved. Tension lifted from her face. Her movements became quicker.

The three met for tea on the practice putting green under the trees. In the sun, through the trees, from where they sat in the shade they could see the flash of wet paddles, the glint of wet limbs, the bright sky, the sound of shouting.

As she poured and passed their cups, Jill thought: What selfish robbery of their time this is! What has happened between Seton and me that has not before? Why have I asked for help?

"I'm not trying to transfer blame to Arleigh," she said seriously. "But it may be that none of this would have happened if I had not insisted on finding out about Derek."

"The son your husband won't claim? Why do you insist on looking into this?" Dr. Flowers wanted to know.

"I just can't stand not knowing. Then, when we so suddenly have so much money that it would be easy——" She shrugged.

"But why has he kept the reality of his son out of his life?"

"I think," Arleigh offered easily, "that Seton fled the obligation successfully once. Years back. It didn't present itself again. The mother remarried. The boy ceased to be real. He ceased to *be*. Seton can walk away from anything he doesn't like. Or walk out on anything that makes a demand he doesn't want to give. We all know that. I would even say—knowing his situation pretty much from its very beginning—that he's now walked away from so many, there has grown up a whole system of demands to which Seton can no longer respond, even if he wants to."

Loyalty urged Jill to explain this at once, feeling that a wrong construction here might do damage to her husband where he most needed help.

"I think, Doctor—to qualify just a little what Arleigh has said—my husband has never *felt* people with any intensity. About people in general, he doesn't need one more than another. Nor *like* one more than another. In fact, he doesn't really *like* anybody at all. Doesn't even like them around."

Jill leaned back and regarded the two men quietly. She felt safer, just for their being here. For the first time in her life she felt a total falling away of all inhibition. She could not then have told herself what her own central fear really was, for she didn't know. She told them about the great house in Fairfield. She had no special objective yet, in any of these talks, and no overriding curiosity. There was not yet any single aspect of her peculiar situation that she wanted relieved or clarified.

She had a great desire to talk and listen, to understand more deeply, to warn herself, to prepare herself to meet the exactions that the personality of her husband, with its thick overlay of the infantile, its real agonies, its needs, its willful rejections, required in their daily living.

"Not everything about my husband is a paradox," she said. She looked off to the steep shoulder of Whiteface to fix her focus and form her thought. "Nor a contradiction. But there is one anomaly, one persistent riddle—— If he is fighting frustration, why does he flee fulfillment?"

"Because fulfillment cannot fulfill," Flowers said at once. "It could only further congest him. People are very wrong about frustration; about the disease of it. Frustration without expression becomes insanity. But as a disease of artists—there has never been any art fit to behold, or fit to listen to, that was not the natural child of frustration. It is wrong to think of frustration as something hostile, as something negative. Frustration is a force. It is a force in itself, the most intense force in all living."

"But if it's a disease——" She wanted to get hold of his idea.

"Think of disease in a different way, Mrs. Farrier. Think of it, not as sickness, but as dis-ease." He enunciated with exaggerated clarity. "As the opposite of ease."

The quick pragmatism of Arleigh's mind darted back to Jill's intention and desire to bring Seton's older son into the picture. Bluntly he asked:

"Do you want to bring the other boy into your life so as to force your husband to face something?"

"I don't know," she said with equal bluntness. "I want him to have a home anyhow." Both men looked at her, hoping she could say more. A readiness to go on was in her eyes but her thoughts seemed too buried for articulation.

Flowers asked her:

"Why do you *think* you did?"

Jill leaned back and looked up into the cool branches. How could she tell these men what Seton was like? They knew an artist only. Besides, they were men, a limiting circumstance here (a limiting circumstance always, for any woman in trouble).

"Perhaps I could no longer stand the indefiniteness of it. The indefiniteness surrounding the boy himself. The indefiniteness of my husband's response to the *fact* of his own son."

She was silent then, offering the men more tea with a lifting gesture of her hand. Dr. Flowers held his cup.

"I definitely recommend you do nothing about the older son for at least a year."

"All right. I won't," she said. "I'm sure you have a reason."

"I'm sure you know what it is," Flowers answered just as quickly. "He's carrying too much already. For a person who can't carry anything at all."

"But what kind of person *is* it, Doctor—in a psychiatric sense—who can abandon a wife the day he finds she's pregnant? Abandon her forever, never see the son she bore, and never want to?"

Dr. Flowers had a useful habit of jerking his head slightly toward any speaker who interested him and in the gesture to suggest he wanted to hear more, that his attention to the speaker was total. Now he said nothing and Jill resumed:

"The mother went through this period all alone. In fact she's never seen Seton since. There was an annulment. Three years later she married again."

"Did you ever ask Seton about his first marriage?" Flowers asked.

"Once. 'I never talk about it,' he said. 'The whole thing was a mistake. We were innocent as children.' Quite aside from the natural curiosity any woman would have in her predecessor, it interested me.

And not because I was curious to know what she was like"—here Jill grimaced apologetically—"although I suppose that was present too" (and Dr. Flowers was again struck by her candor). "It interested me because he's said the same thing to me about *our* marriage. That it's a mistake. That we aren't meant for each other."

"What has your answer been to this, Mrs. Farrier?"

"I've only answered it once. I told him he wasn't a fit person to be married to anyone at all! That he didn't have the courage to grow up! Wasn't that awful!"

"How did Seton take it?"

"We had two months of real peace."

"Very interesting, Mrs. Farrier. Too bad it didn't begin earlier. The world's penitentiaries are jammed with sinners wanting to be punished. Seeking it. Insisting on it. Husbands are much the same, some of them. Men like *your* husband are exactly the same."

He remained silent a moment, then decided to ask her the main question and to ask it quickly.

"Mrs. Farrier, is it not true that what you *really* dread is that your husband is going to treat his new child, once born, as he has treated the two already living?"

"Yes!" She said this instantly. "I not only dread it, I won't stand for it! If it happens again, I'll leave him. I'll have to. I can stand the collisions of living but I can't stand wreckage. If I have to, I'll make a home and a living for all three of them. And I could." Here the chin asserted itself and Arleigh again saw the sudden look of pride and defiance—the English look—he had come to know so well. "Only I'm afraid it would kill *him*."

"No, it won't," Arleigh contradicted with blunt confidence. "*He* is his only concern. It will never be otherwise." Jill knew it was hard for Arleigh—now that Dermod was dead and Seton's new plays were going forward with other producers—to speak with any restraint. But she knew that his concern, now, was for her and not for himself or Seton or either man's future in the theater. "What do you really suppose, Jill?" he asked quietly: "That he has lived over, in his mind, the days—and the nights—with the woman who preceded you? Or don't you rather suppose"—he leaned forward and tapped the table lightly—"*he's never once given her a thought?*"

Jill didn't answer.

"Don't you know," Arleigh went on, "that there's nothing on his conscience about anything? *Anything?*"

"Yes, there is," she answered.

"What?"

"I believe he thinks he's responsible for the death of his brother."

"Have you told Dr. Flowers about the end of Patrick?"

"No."

"I think you should."

"Yes, I think you should know of it, Doctor," she agreed. "It's been gnawing away at him inside. For several months. He's done no useful work. He's wept a lot. Gotten up at night to walk in the dark. It's why we're here—Dr. Randall Cedric's being at Saranac made the journey seem quite proper for Seton. Even if he's physically well, I'm sure that nervously he's all smashed up."

Step by step, and with unhurried deliberateness, she told Dr. Flowers all she knew about the last days of Pat, the last quarrel with Seton, and all she herself had seen and done.

Jill's face, to Arleigh, was a more remarkable study than it could be to the psychiatrist. His memories of the whole Farrier "period" —the wild Irishness of it, the rich yield of it, the egregious contradictoriness of it in its cringing retreats one minute and bold break-throughs the next; the singing and the fighting and the drinking, the swearing and the praying, the shriving and the conniving, the hoarding and the spending, the containing and the scattering, the search for peace and friendship, the search for God and salvation, the grabbing of things false as quickly as things real, the never knowing the difference, the Irish blindness that never told them the difference and that rushed them all to sudden fists, sudden whisky, sudden rage; when their bad manners defended their worse judgments—these were his memories that circled about and swirled before his eyes as Arleigh contemplated Jill calmly telling the doctor about the two Farrier brothers. And these were his sympathies. They mortised themselves around Jill for her unbelievable steadiness of endurance.

Right now in New York, since Seton had jumped so suddenly from actual want to villatic grandeur, wild stories—comical and fantastic—of Seton the country squire, could be heard backstage in any theater: that a Jap butler-chauffeur-valet had left in dismay when Seton kept showing up at dinner in tennis shoes and a torn sweater; that the full complement of servants (Watrous had kept eleven) had been let go, and that Jill and a part-time town girl were doing the work.

There was no way for Arleigh to be sure of any of this; how much was true, how much exaggerated. Arleigh had driven by the Watrous estate only once since Seton owned it, at the start of the summer just past. The lawns looked well kept then. But it was obvious Seton had taken on too much.

As he thought now of the practical side of trying to live in the great mansion that Seton had bought, the total absurdity of it, in its direct impact on Jill, occurred to Arleigh for the first time. He saw in a flash that Seton the artist would perish in the very week that Jill left him.

That was Jill's real dilemma, without a doubt. Somehow she knew that it was she herself who kept it all going. But why, Arleigh asked himself coldly, did Jill have to go on taking it? And for how long? What, indeed, was being fulfilled for Jill, now that they were rich?

Seton the artist—if Jill left him—would quickly die; yet Seton the man—for what there was—would go on forever!

Damn the Farriers! Damn them all. Especially be damned for what they did to their women!

In a way, they weren't people at all—Patrick, Dermod, and Seton —they were energetic primordials who had lost their fur but kept their fears and their ferocities, kept all the prinking egotism, all the preening, the turkey strut and cockatoo swagger wherever they had gone—his own friend Dermod along with the sons. The only difference was *where* they did it. Dermod did it on a stage, with a great aestheticism at first that quickly wore down to bombast. Patrick had had a choice of gawdy brothels, hotel bars or soda fountains, it hardly mattered. And Seton, indeed the dreariest of men (as Arleigh looked at him now through Jill's eyes), required nothing but the mirrors on his wife's dressing table where, half swooning at his own handsomeness, he could be lost for hanging minutes, deeply happy just looking at his own reflection.

A jam of shanty-Irish superstitions had shouldered right in with

the snowy draft of their culture, too; from Dermod's lively terror
when someone set an empty rocker to rocking, to Seton's refusal to
sign a contract without a session with Evangeline Adams; to buy a
bond before buying a horoscope, or talk to his bank without first
ducking into a Gypsy Teakettle for a waffle and a reading.

Who said it was tragic that Seton had had no university experience!
Had the Fordham Jesuits done anything for Patrick? Education could
do nothing for these men but solidify the prejudices they already
held. If they were firm-willed—and they were—they were all, every one
of them, weak-willed too. It seemed no mystery to Arleigh that they
could be both at once.

You only had to be Irish!

They all had squamous minds. Dark talents, yes, but spastic hearts.
And Seton the worst of all. They had a spiritual precipitate that
was flinty, like a stone passed from a toxic kidney. Seton's heart
pumped no blood. There was none to pump, nothing in his whole
arterial system but gall and urine and sea water.

Arleigh's memory jumped to that charnel morning in the chill of
Grand Central when Jill had brought down the body of Patrick.
Later, at the mortuary and without Jill's knowledge, he had called in
this same man now beside him—Mortimer Flowers—to look at the
wounds on the back of the corpse, and to have these photographed.
But the sight that came to him now was the sight of the spirit of Jill,
of her dealing with the problem, of her doing it alone when it was
evident she could hardly stand from fatigue and mental strain.

How *could* Seton—this selfish, self-willed, redundant man—know
anything at all of the real entanglements of others when he spent
his life fleeing his own? How could he—on a journey he had neither
the courage nor stomach to make—*send his own wife!*

They were all paradoxes. How could Patrick, who had never been
anything but a priapic barn rat, always get into bed with his women
when he always insulted them first? For that matter how could his
own friend Dermod arrange to be remembered as the greatest American actor since Booth when there was hardly a person living who
could remember him in anything but vaudeville? Doing it all backward, how could these men get anything *done*? In any family in
the New York theater had there ever been such accomplishment and

such breakup at the same time? Yet somehow everything the Farriers undertook went through to its own finish—whatever that finish—propelled to set terminals as inexorably as quarry rubble going down a spill, as flowers appearing at the top of stems, as stars coming out or tides returning.

Sometimes Arleigh was a little ashamed of the tumult of feelings his harbored thoughts held for this family, for he knew better than any man living that a splendor hung over their heads. Dermod, though dead, was immortal. Patrick, dead too—and thank God for it—was a living legend on Broadway this very minute. There was even a song about him, a Feist song—the story of his calming the outburst in the asylum had sifted down to Tin Pan Alley. Molly, who was perhaps the most amiably useless woman Arleigh had ever known, had exactly doubled the value of the estate her husband had left her, and had done it in less than ten months. None of these three had ever really *lived*, in the sense in which society understood the word, and Seton, who had never lived at all in any sense had won fame as secure as any writer since Mark Twain.

In his early thirties he was the most talked-of writer in the world.

Arleigh caught his breath and lifted his eyes to the wide sweep of veranda. People were passing to and fro on the cool veranda. Suddenly a sight he saw there—one special face—broke in on his private reverie and sent it flying.

It was Tanager Bolt! It was the Iron Butterfly!

All the disciplines of a lifetime were summoned to him now, in the double demand to disregard her and to reveal nothing by eye, voice, or manner to the others.

But he knew she'd come for Seton.

And in the flash point of this wild recognition came something else, equally abhorrent but just as real: Arleigh Brayce realized he could kill Tanager Bolt and that it would never be on his conscience.

Motionless he looked right into her without looking at her.

Tanager would almost certainly come down the steps and walk over the lawn to them if she sensed he saw her. She might anyhow.

A stage phrase came to Arleigh: slitty-eyed slut.

Arleigh reached deliberately across the table and took both of Jill's hands in his own. He hoped it would appear an unusual sight to

Tanager. It would appear an unusual sight to anyone looking, in a place as sanitary as Lake Placid where the air was so pure one thought of nothing but breathing it. There was never any love-making at Placid, during the day. But he was loving Jill with eyes and voice.

"I wish I were forty, my dear girl. I'd bust your marriage wide open."

Flowers leaned back and crossed his arms, the better to enjoy a tableau so unexpectedly sweet. He didn't see much in life that was sweet.

Tanager slipped away. But Arleigh knew her method. He knew she'd show up somewhere else. Soon too. She was hunting.

Arleigh began to tingle just a little. It startled him to find he could think with such violence. Tanager was almost certainly staying with Marion Vogel. She wouldn't be welcome at the club. He had never thought, even for a rash instant, of killing anyone. He was astonished to discover that the idea, though admittedly monstrous, was turning itself over with a cold and cogent economy and that the whole activity of mind was most pleasurable.

"How much of his own trouble does your husband create for himself?" the psychiatrist was asking.

"More than most men, I would think," Jill answered.

Arleigh brought his mind back to the table.

"I suppose I've known," Jill continued, "all my married life, that my husband is a tortured man. It was some time, though, before I saw for sure how much of this was self-torture—that much of this very self-torture, if it really was needful to him, was just as certainly pleasurable to him."

Dr. Flowers sat very still, hoping she would go on, hoping that if she did she might supply him with clues for her own recomposition, for he realized she was nearer to breaking than she knew. When her voice resumed, it relieved him. It began to uncover not experiences but an interpretation of experiences which he felt quite sure had not before been put into words for anyone. It was too impromptu.

That Jill had studied her husband was clear to the psychiatrist. She had studied him with far more care than most wives bring to the problem in a full lifetime. It had been this doctor's observation that with most women continuous inspection of the same men resulted only in a continuous repetition of the same findings. This merely gave them the satisfaction of knowing they were married to cement blocks without having to acknowledge the same for themselves. Most married women, whenever threatened, and all divorced women—so he had found—merely made new accommodations in their thinking to avoid the pain of making changes in their own intellectual morals on the one hand, or to avoid, on the other, the embarrassment of reshaping their visible personalities. Most of his women patients, if they didn't come out better than their husbands, were slow to pay their bills.

With this quiet woman—Jill—who seemed so immensely present as a person yet so recessive socially; who seemed so willing to sit still in the pronouncement of contrary opinions, it was different. Each return to Seton, in her thought or comment, pricked in a little more sharply the major outlines, made the map plainer.

Her astonishing account of Patrick, of his flight, his fighting, his collapse, his abyssal loneliness and his apocalyptic death, illuminated an entire forest for the psychiatrist. It astounded him that Jill could correctly see Patrick as the one who was really lonely, and Seton only playing at it.

This was a woman who didn't care what the pattern said nearly so much as that the pattern be set down. She said it all in a bleak, neat summary: "All I'm trying to understand is *what he is*."

Then, unasked, came an astonishing revelation about their sex life. Jill's voice was cool, her hands quiet.

"It seems to me that sex—the act of sex, the part of sex in married life or married love—that it takes concentration. That it takes time. And in a sense, planning. It takes great energy. A woman who loves, or a woman who carries about in her mind the image of one man and whose fantasies of love and of making love always involve themselves with this one image, this one man, this lover—she is planning and preparing all the time. With a man it is more special. More segmental perhaps. It takes more effort. Far more than the wild turbulence. But Seton cannot assemble this effort."

Flowers had the sudden feeling, listening to her late-afternoon confidences, that Jill's reading of Seton was the real reading of the *man* Seton, not the mere reading of a person she'd married.

At the same time, he feared that Jill had studied her husband with

more care than she had taken in the study of herself. More and more
it appeared that Seton might slip away from her if she didn't look
to her own protections.

Would that be good or bad?

He would think of this side of it now. His sense of containment
was alerted by her too obvious willingness to spend herself—altogether
and anywhere, it seemed—for her husband. (Later that same evening,
on the club porch when he was alone with Arleigh, he called it Jill's
"unself-preservativeness.")

"I saw that most of his suffering—the worst of it anyway—could be
modified by a few intelligent alterations just in the way he did things
or looked at them. Paying bills, for example. Right now, with more
money than we ever dreamed, he'll put off payments till creditors
become ugly. Then meet them with blasts of his own. Not to the
creditors. To me. We have no money problem really. Yet we have an
immense one actually. And an immense house. His proof, to *himself*,
of success. There's a special perversity here. He knows he could make it
all simple just by paying what he owes, but he holds back. There's a
perversity in this holding back—in his withholding the assertion of
the very intelligence that could save him. He seems afraid it *would*
save him. Isn't that odd?"

"Not at all."

"I came to know he not only wanted things to continue as they
were. I came to know that in his special way he *willed* it. It is this
that has defeated me."

Arleigh nodded, more in assent to his own view than acknowledgment of hers. He could still hear the crash of the Great Bear Spring
Water bottle that dreadful morning in the Morosco.

"I think that my sympathy," she was saying, "at the very beginning
anyhow, was spontaneous. I know it was direct. I loved him. I think—
away back there at the beginning—my own successes frightened him.
Threatened him. They were tiny successes. But they were real. We
lived on them. I think he felt a threatening there, somehow. Not long,
but enough to damage something."

"Seton's always been *seemingly* anxious for me to go on writing.
And at the same time fearful I might. About Hollywood—I've sold
a few magazines stories to pictures. I've been offered work out there.

When the matter comes up he winces. Pretends I'm kidding. His own uncertainty about what I *should* do seems to anger him. Makes him fearful. I seem to set up a problem he knows he should resolve. Perhaps he secretly knows he shouldn't look at it as a problem at all but look at it as an interest. Yet his indecision about *me*—what I might be or do independent of himself—is a constant worry. So his encouragements and his comments about my own writing have always been neutralized—one day 'Do it,' the next day 'Do it but beware the penalty.' What began quite early in our relationship as honest sympathy I had for a complex but gifted man"—here she looked down at her hands and twisted them—"I'm afraid could deteriorate into a kind of patient but sterile pity. The disappointments—we've carried these all right, I think, the same as any couple. But the humiliations—I've had to shutter them up, and what is living in those rooms today, more and more I'm afraid to go in and look."

Though there was never complaint in Jill, there always seemed a plaintive note even in her most sanguine moments. Her sentences often came to surprising endings, to end on minor chords, to trail off and fade away without really ending at all—like madrigals, thought Flowers, leaving the listener enchanted, unprepared, disturbed, unsatisfied, and dreaming.

Her voice fell to a whisper as she added one more sentence:

"That is where we are now."

"Are you frightened?" Dr. Flowers asked.

"Yes."

"You might lose your husband, you know."

"Lose him?"

"To some other woman."

"There is no other woman," Jill said. There was a curious inflection to her answer. It carried the positive overtone of: "I wish there were something as definite as another woman."

"There is always another woman, Mrs. Farrier. Your husband is a vacuum. The only thing that abhors a vacuum more than nature is marriage."

Jill shrugged slightly, turning her hands in her lap.

"Oh, he has women. There was the girl Holly—I suppose he still sees her. And there's the woman Tanager. He paddles about in the shallows a little. He never gets in deep. But I am his woman."

"Tanager is here, you know?" Arleigh said, easily, casually.

"*Tanager!*" Jill jumped. "What's she doing here?"

"I don't know," Arleigh answered truthfully.

"Have you seen her?"

"Yes."

"Don't you think your husband is vulnerable, Mrs. Farrier?" Dr. Flowers asked her. "That some woman, perhaps this very one, might pull him in deeper than he wants to go?"

"I think my husband is naïve."

"What is the difference?"

"Perhaps none."

"Seton could be involved with Tanager without wanting it. You know some that have," Arleigh made it sound calm enough.

"I think I've made the mistake of considering only him, never us," Jill told them. "And of allowing him to do it. It's gotten away from me now. I respected his gifts. I wanted to protect them. I do now. And I think I half understand the forces that fuel him, the turn of the mechanism that keeps him operating. It hasn't been the shutdown of himself from me as a person. It has been his forever running away from the things he should most hold on to—to Sean most of all. And now—the baby I'll bear in a few months."

"The *idea* you can't tell Seton!" Arleigh murmured.

Strange phrases came from Jill.

She spoke of his "brief solicitudes," of his "hooded cheer," of his constantly writing her of the lovely places he'd seen as a guest of the wealthy, the inevitable "You'd love it—we must see this together"; Belmont, Spring Lake, Deal, Tuxedo Park; of her never seeing any of them and knowing she never would. And, now, of owning such a place all by themselves, yet not having it at all.

Distillations of living, bright and hard, accretions of regret and wonder, tiny bursts of hope, and a steadying glow of self-assurance, of acceptance at least, flecked the material of her talk and flickered across her brow as her great struggle to speak honestly, and to listen usefully, advanced through the late afternoon.

Flowers felt strangely insecure and frightened. He felt he might

fall in love if the magical privacy of these three were to be long
continued, or if it went on, even briefly, with her alone. An urgent
resentment toward Seton broke through all his other feelings: "How
could a man live with that and not know what he had!"

"He can do the great things but not the simple," she was saying.
"It isn't easy to live with a genius, Doctor. And it makes it no easier
to know how many women might think I'm lucky. I'm sure Tanager
does. Arleigh knows Seton well. But Arleigh is a man and men—in all
their affairs—can come and go. It isn't the same for the woman who
lives with it. Day to day, or night by night, a genius is seldom kind. A
genius is seldom funny. A genius is rarely companionable. A genius
is never interesting.

"Their selfishness is absolute. My husband's obsession with his
work is fanatical, this I understand. But there is something else even
stronger than his obsession to write. It is his self-obsession. Geniuses
are takers, not givers. They take from those they know and give to
those they know not."

Club members and their guests began coming back from the water,
from bridle paths, from tennis, golf, skeet, prayers; from a pageant
rehearsal depicting the Peace Palace at the Hague. The three who
talked hardly noticed. And Arleigh didn't care whether Tanager was
lurking about. He'd made his point. He'd put her actively on Jill's
mind. He'd set a fear where he knew there should be one.

"I suppose what I really fear," Jill said, "is that I *could* make so
many accommodations that my self-respect would smother."

Flowers said: "If you feel compelled to make up for the lack of
manliness in your husband and if you *do* make up for it, you become
less a woman. You may become more of a person but you will surely
become less woman. Your appeal to others will change. So also will
your responses."

"I've felt this a few times. Wondered what I might be, married
to a man quite different." Then shyly, "Or might be now, involved
with some other." Both men tingled just a little.

She put this vagrancy away quickly and returned to the distresses
that were in her life now. "Not that I can't endure the next bender.
Or next neglect, or dereliction. But I keep feeling the awful moment
might come—perhaps in a wild irrevocable suddenness—when I can

no longer live with myself and with him and *allow* him to hurt the people he loves. Or that he's supposed to love. At least, the people he lives with."

Jill could never successfully hide all her own hurt. It was too big to hide.

Arleigh saw it again. Seton, the dragon, slid into a clearing of Arleigh's memory now. He *was* a dragon, somnolent, slow of motion most of the time, immobile, watchful—then in scenes and seizings most awful, in slashings and snappings and the flash of teeth, he could leave death and wreckage about, the earth gouged, the water blackened.

But Seton was such a solitary being, a person who had to be known over so long a time, Arleigh wondered how much of this the psychiatrist could guess at; whether Mortimer could credit such reptilian eruptions without seeing one of them. And there weren't many to report them, for after his jungle wildness Seton left no survivors.

Arleigh himself felt like one of these. Seton's last affront—Arleigh had brought in his greatest triumph and a stunning profit of more than two hundred thousand dollars—had been the one too many, even for Arleigh. ("You no longer understand what I'm trying to say in the theater.") Arleigh had recovered and cooled. It was Arleigh who was now and forever through with Seton. Not through with Seton the artist but forever through with Seton as a problem in human living. It was Arleigh's unique integrity in the New York theater, and Arleigh's incomparable sensitivity and cunning in the uncharted realm of play building, that would not again be at the disposal of the dramatist.

What Seton did not seem to understand about himself (and it was at this moment fully and for the first time understood by Arleigh) was that once Seton had thrown someone out, the separation was permanent from their point of view too. He wondered now if this was the condition that Jill's own emotional starvation had reached.

Dr. Flowers had a mannerism of lifting his eyelids without lifting his eyebrows, opening the eyes to such an exaggerated wideness he took on the look of a somewhat startled but completely interested child. He often did this after long silences, when he had come to a conclusion or when trying to put himself on the track of one.

"I think what you ought to do about your husband is something I fear you are quite unable to do."

"I've tried everything I can think of."

"I'm sure of it. But there's a very perverse impulsive structure here. I don't like to try to untangle artists. I don't believe artistic endowments are analyzable. Not even in the primary sense, much less the psychoanalytic. But your husband's violence, his contrition, his weeping, his despairing over things lost, his show of dependence upon them once gone although they had no meaning for him when they were present—his father is a good example, the son's not liking him until the old gentleman was dying—the rages and the childish penitence, this is not unfamiliar. It's the classic triad of discord—dependency, guilt, aggression—very hard to live with, dishonest in its every tone and contour. Your husband needs you when you aren't there. He's hostile when you are. His plays are clues, good ones. He's starting to write the same play over and over—the same themes recurring—man's utter dependence on illusion in the face of proof of its futility; loss of identity, loneliness, self-doubt, estrangement from the community, poetic sensitivity seeking beauty, man seeking God, seeking love, man seeking his own meaning but never finding it. Then into his plays the acquisitive mean-spirited materialist comes along—sometimes the hero's own brother—and picks up the marbles or the girl or the farm, and all the plundered people and the muted poets go plumb to hell unavenged, robbed by fate, betrayed by the very morality they served, and Evil escapes to prowl once more in a new play. All your husband has to do is arrange new names for the old fixtures. For a dramatist this is all right. Because these are the great themes. But other things show through very clearly."

"What other things?"

"I mentioned the psychic structure of the man imprisoned, Mrs. Farrier, and said that a lot of them are a lot less wretched than sociologists want to think. Or want *us* to think. A lot of criminals commit crime in order to *be* punished. They *long* for punishment. They demand it. If they don't get it, they inflict it on themselves. In your husband's own activity—the psychic side of it—this is already happening, at least in one form."

"What form is that?"

"In the continuous activity of his work. It is a sign of suffering. It is a sign of expiation."

Jill thought this over quietly, then blurted out:

"Am I good for him? Or bad for him?"

"My dear woman," said Flowers, his head inclining, his eyes full on her, "you are his whole balance. You maintain the environment that makes his living possible, that assures the continuation of his labor."

"If he lost this?"

"Something would quickly disappear."

"Something valuable? Vital?"

"Yes. Indeed yes. Not the sanity of the man—such as he has. And it's enough," he added quickly, "but more probably the energizing focus of the artist, the quality of his output as a producer of art. It would be in that area that a change might be expected if the environmental controls were vacated. His need to disassociate himself from the conventional world—this isn't a pose. And it's as old as beauty. Old as God. Alienations, rejections of many kinds, are just another bewilderment to us. But to the artist—Kafka, Proust, Joyce—men of today—or Dostoevsky, Rimbaud, Verlaine, Henry James, Jonathan Swift—men equally well scrutinized but better understood today than they were when living—these same neurotic structures appear, the same contrariety, the same extraordinary degree of affectivity. Now, if you left him (and I am assuming it is in your mind and that it has been there before), and if no one filled the vacuum right away, the man would grow ill. I would guess—knowing his past history from Randall Cedric—your husband might redetermine his whole tuberculosis pattern. He might even seek the infection. He'll *arrange* to get sick. Then he'll arrange to have the familiar so-called nervous breakdown. He works in a constant state of breakdown all the time. It merely doesn't break him down. In the sense of bodily response and responsibility I'd think Seton Farrier would go on living more or less all right. And go on working. But I think the artist will die. I think he'll write little more that matters, no matter how much it might be. Something essential would be mislaid. What makes him special—unique—may perish. What this is is the atmosphere, the circumstance, the environment that you maintain *for* his work. Or that you put up with. *That* is what you do for him. Of course he does not know this. Artists never do. They know very little about themselves even though they think about themselves with a most consuming fascination all the time. They only know when they can work and when they can't."

"Couldn't some other woman do the same for him that I have?"

"Of course. At least it is conceivable. Another woman—a woman like you—could preserve this climate of estrangement, put up with the furies, pay the bills, shake the furnace, cut the grass, keep the world off his back, keep children out of his room, provide the personal tranquillity he needs, keep bad news away at all times, allow no one around except the few he wants to see—the people who *do* things for him—stage designers, producers, doctors. More doctors than anything else, and I notice from the correspondence, if they can't find him a sick man, he fires them." He smiled at this in sudden enjoyment and the smile went over to the others. "But a woman who will put up with all this—it's unlikely he'll find *her* again. He'd be more likely to be *found*. To be commandeered. By a tawny bitch like Tanager."

Arleigh was glad the doctor had used the word. It was obvious that Jill refused to feel threatened. At the same time it was unthinkable a woman of her spirit would yield her place to a poacher like Tanager without a struggle.

"Seton could get any woman if he went looking for her. He's a willful man."

"Willfulness isn't strength, it's weakness."

"But women—especially considering who he is, who he's become—would be easy."

"Not in the way you think. Willful people aren't perceptive. We're often victimized by our own skills, Mrs. Farrier. The greatest salesmen are always the most gullible, when the picture turns around and someone sells *them*. The life of the party is always the worst sport. Your husband will continue in flight. He can do nothing else. Your husband wouldn't go seeking, he'd be grabbed. He isn't a person who can find things, not in the normal sense. Your husband was born to be gulled. Born to cower. You must not be alarmed by this. Most of us want to run and hide. Most of us want to, most of the time. But we fight it off. We grow away from it. We grow out of it. In the letters I've studied, in the plays by your husband that I've seen I don't find any of this. I don't find any capacity for inner development. The mechanism that cranks most of us up to our shaky maturities—in Seton Farrier is missing. And it isn't a malfunction. It just isn't there at all. He knows everything now he'll know at sixty. And what he *thinks* now, he'll think at sixty. How old is he, about thirty-five?"

Jill nodded.

Dr. Flowers reflected on this briefly.

"He was just as good a thinker at *twenty*-five. Just as bad, too. I saw three of his plays ten years ago in a single season. He was just as sure, just as vital, just as perceptive within his limits as he is right now. And just as immature. Life can't teach him anything because he can't learn anything from it. He has to see it his own way, never the way it is. He has to see it the way it *isn't*. And report it that way, too."

Flowers leaned back and lighted an Old Gold cigarette. The delicious aroma of fresh tobacco, slowly burning, hung companionably over their table. Presently the words resumed.

"His neurotic impressions coincide with impressions of the world—impressions of life—that aren't at all neurotic. Life isn't neurotic, *he* is. And it is this very astigmatism that serves to organize and energize all he touches, all he wants and that he thinks he can't have. Or all he wants but won't take, which is more likely. But the alteration gives his stories a focus. In the panorama of all living there is a general fuzziness that is normal enough to the rest of us who are normal, but Seton Farrier takes the normal view and sends it back abnormalized. For one side of his stereoscope he steals the public's eye, then pops his own into the other side and makes you stare at something you thought familiar till you see it his way. And sure enough it *is* something else, something so patently real to him that *we* believe it also. Never seeing it the way it is, always seeing it the way it isn't—his way—that, of course is why he is interesting. And that is where he is great."

With unhurried hands Dr. Flowers now turned over some pages that were lying on the table in front of him, picked up one, studied the words by himself for a moment, then addressed himself to Arleigh.

"This is an inscription he had written his wife in the flyleaf of the published version of *Harbor*. "To my dearest love: You have cradled me when I was weak, you have clung to me when I was strong, you have believed me when I did not believe myself, you have laid out my things, you have forgiven me when I was too ashamed to ask it, you have interceded for me with a God I am trying to understand but with Whom I cannot yet speak, Whose face I cannot see. Into the still waters, into the calm harbor of your mind, you have brought me out of the madness of my own. I love you into Eternity."

Flowers now tapped the page skeptically against his chin, doubting what he'd read, and looked up at the sky.

"An expression like that can erase a lot of ugliness——" he began.

Arleigh saw that Jill's eyes were wet. He wondered why Flowers had selected this particular item. Over the years there were more than enough of these inscriptions, as Arleigh well knew. All of them were archly haunted, stiffly suffering, like the man himself.

Now Dr. Flowers was putting the page back on the table—he'd evidently copied it out in order to keep it.

"Erase ugliness—but only at the very beginning of a love affair," he went on, "when the struggle for paramountcy, for identity, is still going on. Yet a woman can go through her whole life hanging to a string like that"—he tapped the paper with his knuckle—"dragged over the rubble, while the selfish, self-eating husband in the balloon not giving a damn for anything in the world but the view below and the security of the basket he's riding. He's being carried and that is all that matters. I don't like to sound like a psychiatrist. And I don't like to tamper with artists. But I *am* a psychiatrist and your husband is an artist, and there are certain things in your situation—in his—that are terribly clear to me already. Look at the days of his roving. Surely he never wanted to *go* anywhere. Isn't it possible the ships he sailed were his mother and nothing else? Their pumps her placenta? Their fires her womb? In the ships he felt safe and warm. Most of all he felt carried. Carried. That is the main thing. Someone in charge, telling him what to do. Delivered upon a beach, between voyages, he was lost and useless. The same attitude is present today in all his actions. Cities for example. Delivered upon a city, between plays, he's lost and useless. On a foreign shore without a ship all he could do was cry and quiver, whine and whimper, stumble around getting in trouble till he was re-enwombed and carried once more. Cities have wombs.

They're saloons." Flowers looked at the grand scenery, and extended his arms to it. "This may be the Adirondacks but it makes no difference —your husband is waiting for a ship. And he's between voyages in more ways than just being between plays. His partial crack-up over Patrick is a factor. But his encounter with Dr. Cedric, this time, has been the real shock. It's been a perfectly awful letdown, a frustration of the most immobilizing sort. To any man as determined to be picturesquely ill as your husband nothing can be so offensive to the ear as to be told you're just fine. It's just as certain your husband will remember to insult Randall Cedric, the best thoracic man in the world, whenever he speaks of him as it is certain he'll forget to pay him when the bill comes."

Mortimer Flowers was a masterful simplifier. The points he wanted to make rolled out amiably like a throw of dice and sat straight up on the green-baize expanse of his mind in a kind of black-and-white impertinence waiting to be tallied, or cupped and shaken and tossed again for a new combination. He could bring a prefatory speculation to sudden count; he could subdue formalism with slang, sharpen a phrase with a finger movement, or reach into the cloud of another's uncertainty and pluck out a distillation.

His smile, which always seemed near, was guileless, all-enveloping and alight with charity whenever it really opened.

"The promise of tuberculosis would carry him. This appears to have been sufficient for many years. He came here to *preserve* his illness, remember. He didn't come here to lose it. So, when the specialist he came so far to see—Cedric the Great—the specialist who is supposed to detect complications that are black and to suspect implications that are blacker, when Dr. Cedric pronounced your husband sound in every way and then *dismissed* him!"—here he suddenly flung his arms wide, scattering the air—"it was ever so much worse than insult. It was dethronement! The great artist suddenly relegated to the vassalage of public health."

"You mean he hasn't *been* threatened with tuberculosis—all these years?" Jill said.

"No. Not at all. Just something to ride on."

Jill grew very still.

"What was it, Dr. Flowers"—she was speaking with effort now—

"that you were about to tell me I should do but that you feared I was unable to do?"

"To punish him."

"How do you do that?"

"If you don't know how, I'm afraid there's no giving it to you. It's a matter of energy controls. For all the years of your marriage, you've made all the accommodations. Supposing, for a time, you were to make none at all?"

"Like what?"

"Suppose you had refused to come up here with him on this therapeutic expedition? Suppose you stop running his errands? Begin to live toward him as he has always lived toward you—as a convenience."

"Seton has control of the money, Mortimer," Arleigh interposed, giving Jill an instant to touch these new temperatures.

"What of it? They always do. But there are three imposing factors in the situation, all of them quite special to it. The first is your husband's susceptibility to control. His longing for disciplines to continue, when he lets go his own. The second"—here he acknowledged Arleigh—"money. There's a lot of it now. More to come. If you can't have what you need, cash some checks."

"But my husband——" Jill shook her head. "I don't think this would work."

"Why?"

"Bills are allowed to run till I'm embarrassed to be seen in a shop. Stores have to threaten to sue."

"But the payments are finally made?"

"Yes. Always. But always protesting. Sometimes I've paid them with earnings of my own, just to avoid this awkwardness. Sometimes I've paid them by check and told him, only to have him stop payment on the check. This is 'to teach me a lesson,' he says. You know the phrases. All the horrible old phrases: 'I'm not made of money'; 'Making fast and loose with my checkbook.' It's degrading to think of, humiliating to talk about. He has a serf's terror of poverty but a poor-mouth pride. And mixed up with it is an awkward desire for elegance—imagine our having a Pierce-Arrow, a car we'll have to put in dead storage when winter comes. We have nowhere to *go*.

And it isn't so much that he *wants* things. He's had the tennis courts put in shape. But Seton doesn't play. It merely has a correct look. In the Rotogravure on Sunday. What he really likes are fights and six-day bike races. In the whole world of creative expression in all its forms, there's very little Seton can respond to. Musically he's responsive to nothing but jazz and marches. Galleries and museums bore him. My father, whom Arleigh met a few times and who was the founder of the Modern Art Group, was a painter of some note, and a pupil and friend of Thomas Flesch. But the proximity of such an interest—pictures just don't interest him."

Dr. Flowers was listening closely.

"Yet your husband reads a great deal," he interjected.

"Always has." Arleigh broke in here. "First time I ever met him his coat pockets were stuffed with books, small-size and secondhand."

"Do you remember what——?"

"Yes. I remember especially Strindberg—the collected plays. As a kid of eighteen he could recite whole scenes."

"He can now," Jill said. "But I don't think he's ever been what you would call a general reader. It's all tragedy and pessimism. I've never seen him read a novel. He's spent this summer going through the Greeks. Before that it was Freud."

Swiftly she went back into her memory and rattled off titles that came back now. "He reads the same way he writes. In a week he can go through *Conflicts With Oblivion*, *Revolt of Angels*, *Unmasking Our Minds*, *The Birth of Tragedy*, *Faust*, and *Primitive Society*. Arleigh just mentioned his love of Strindberg. But his love of Nietzsche —more accurate to say his enslavement—is the most powerful *single* influence in his life. It's possible that my husband's torment— the part that is self-inflicted—may lie in this area, where he'd like to adopt the whole Nietzschean rationale, including the *Ubermensch*."

"He seems to have at least two of the principal traits, the will to truth and the will to power," Dr. Flowers observed.

"That is true," Jill agreed. "He has much of the rest of it too——"

"Contempt for mediocrity?" Flowers suggested.

"Yes, that. At least for his own view of mediocrity. Of morality too, perhaps. But he *sees* no truth, even when he's on it. And this is where he misses."

She looked sideways, directly at Arleigh. "The will to power? Now that he's won his way to it, it doesn't appear as anything he's really wanted. Not even anything he can use. Don't you find it so?"

Arleigh nodded, and transmitted his understanding of Jill's comment in his own words to his friend:

"Suddenly it's nothing. Suddenly it's a mere ability to tell the world to go to hell and get away with it. To make the world take it."

"That is more than sufficient for many men," the psychiatrist observed.

"Of course it is, but even when he wasn't able to get away with it, Seton told the world to go to hell anyhow."

"That is true," Jill confirmed, "but the self-assertiveness in the superman that Nietzsche talked about—and I'm sure it coincides with Seton's own concept of himself and makes up a large part of his daydream—don't you think the question of *where* this assertiveness occurs is a key to something?"

"How do you mean?" the psychiatrist asked at once.

"I'm thinking—I believe I am—of such things as rehearsals." Here Arleigh winced and smiled. "I'm thinking of the very *few* places where assertiveness has any meaning at all. The theater is one. Our living room is the other. But if someone barked at him on the street, he'd run. The concept of boldness, a concept that implied plan and action on the grand scale, that envisioned new goals for civilization, new techniques for mastery so effective they'd be exalted in generations to come—this kind of self-assertiveness, at the heroic level, isn't there."

To his uncommon interest, she told Flowers now of Seton's exciting plan to machine-gun Seventh Avenue when the revolution came.

To the psychiatrist the quality of Farrier's infantilism seemed extraordinary. And there seemed something incorrigibly feral about him too, something that not only resisted being civilized but resisted being refined in any way.

"Seton has the discipline and the will and the accomplishment," she said, "but for him to be free—free in the Nietzschean sense, to be accountable to no one, to *use* what he's won—he doesn't at all know how. He's free only in the domestic sense."

"An extension of his early truancies," Flowers appended.

"Yes. My husband will always be immature. Most artists are. My father was. But that's all right. Most art is the expression of a sensitive man trying to grow up or fighting off the challenge to try. Art has no place for the mature man. Nietzsche's ideas had nothing for artists but the pipe dream. And Nietzsche's superman could operate only on three stages—industry, politics, and war. Seton would be a joke in any one of them. His idea of the world of affairs is so creaky it keeps falling down by itself."

"How do you mean? When?" asked the doctor.

"Whenever he puts a tycoon or a soldier or a politician into one of his plays and gives him something to say."

"Or take it out of the world of affairs," Arleigh submitted, "and put it in the world of daily living. Seton's never had a believable child in anything he ever wrote. Or a marriage problem ever experienced by married people."

"Yes—these are worlds he can't live in. Doesn't see. But Nietzsche's superman—the man born to be master, the man who is as hard on himself as he is on others, the man with the unbreakable disciplines— the mere *idea* of transferring such a thing to an Irishman is ridiculous!"

"Power concepts are attractive to us all," Flowers suggested. "Especially to ambitious people who are weak."

"But Nietzsche's superman—as I understand him——" Her voice dropped to a parenthetical aside that sounded more like a comic apology than declaration. "Nietzsche bores me stiff——"

"Nietzsche bores any grownup," Flowers encouraged.

"But his superman must never lose control of himself, even when he's alone. Isn't that right?"

"Yes. The emotional shutoff must be infallible, the control absolute."

"Well, with Seton—it's all there but the main thing. The *real* hardness isn't there at all."

Dr. Flowers wanted to know how early in their marriage the recognition came to her that Seton Farrier was a special personality.

"I think I knew very early that it was not to be a marriage like most." Then she added, with the light mockery that often went with her most covered thought, "Though I suppose there's never been a marriage like most others."

"No, every one is different, quite different," Dr. Flowers conceded.

She talked of Seton's sudden, intense, and saddening assurance of his need for her. She told of his daily, orderly, tireless output in the vast silence of the Cape, in the companionable silence but in the great malevolent roaring that was the tunnel of his mind; she told of the industry of that mind; of the mordant visible suffering that had made his dramas, fashioned the thought of them, architectured the agony of their movements one by one.

As she looked back over the swift years, looked back at the peace they'd had together at the Cape (and there had been some), it appeared more as a well-weathered dullness, a truce observed but undeclared (through shame for the need of it?) than as a tranquillity achieved through faith.

As these scenes came back to her here under the soft splendor of this Indian-summer twilight, she saw that her love for Seton had not been the love that other women have for men and want to give them.

Her love had been an isthmus that she had thrown across the reaches of his lonely preoccupations, across his immense but opaque unhappiness, his infantile and phobic rages. Her love had been a strip of communicating land, narrow perhaps, but safely above the tidal scour and the black water that bit away at the shores of his temper, yet a love strong enough (because she worked at it) to support the traffic of their daily living.

She had had this much love for him. And now she hadn't. She loved him still but loved him differently. Now she saw, in speaking so openly to the two men, that it was her own forbearance that had built the isthmus from the first day. It was, as Dr. Flowers had said, an accommodation. That relations between Seton and herself were as much in Seton's keeping as in hers had never come into his mind. Seton was a person pleased or displeased. Mostly she had pleased.

"One day I began to think of my husband as a curiosity," she said to Arleigh and the doctor. "Many times since that day I've had to think of him as a nuisance. Occasionally, too, as a boor."

Though she made no mention of it, Dr. Flowers kept trying to guess how much of her womanness had flaked off by Farrier's unconscious use of his wife as a servitor, his casual assumption of her bondage, her fealty, and her constant strength.

An appalling revelation came from Jill, conveyed without any feeling at all.

"One night—we were living in Connecticut—I went into New York to my sister's. Her photographic studio had become quite a success. She had a party, a good one. I got home about one-thirty. Seton was up. He was furious. At that time I had just completed the novel that was only half done when we married. He struck me. Then he rushed to the cupboard by the bookcase where I kept my manuscript pages. He grabbed the whole stack and flung it in the fire. Then he held me while it burned. Later, of course, he was so ashamed, he was painful to be around. He tried to make amends. But there is no way to make up for anything like that. Nothing is ever the same again. Of course he suffered. Dreadfully. And I'm sure he winces today when he thinks of it. But this is where he doesn't measure up to Nietzsche's *Ubermensch*. He's out of control almost all the time that he's not actually working."

"Sometimes it's hard not to walk up to this rogue and just cut out his eyes," Arleigh shouted, an unfamiliar ferocity coming into his face. Flowers, though obviously impressed and equally outraged, was more subdued.

"Do you remember anything specific that your husband offered? I mean, in the way of amends?"

"Oh yes. He said he was going to arrange for me to sit for my portrait."

"And did he?"

"No. But he arranged to sit for his own. You know the portrait. It's the one they always use now on the cover of the playbill. For any new production of his."

Mortimer Flowers, who realized that doctors walked through most of their own lives behind partitions, nonetheless felt that he and Jill could achieve a rapport of real use to her, felt that they might already have done so.

Her reticences—and she had them—were in the right places, and certainly she wasn't trying to make out a "case." Quite the reverse. She was hoping there was a solution for a situation so ugly, complex, and progressive it was obviously insupportable right now and might soon be dangerous.

Dr. Flowers now asked a few rapid questions that changed the mood of their talk.

"Has he ever tried to kill you?"

"No."

"Has he ever tried to kill himself?"

"No. At least, I don't think so."

"Has he ever lashed out at you when he was cold sober?"

Here she delayed her answer. "No, never cold sober. He can be glum and hateful, he can be terribly short-tempered. But he's never physically violent unless he's had something to drink."

"Is he aware of this?"

"I think so. He keeps a strange sort of chart. Symbols. They seem to indicate something about his own attitude toward his drinking. I think that *he* thinks it's going to kill him the same as it killed Patrick."

"He's a runaway Catholic, isn't he?"

Jill nodded.

"Who ridicules prayer?"

"I don't know." This question tortured her. "In the strange record that he keeps about his drinking—he keeps all kinds of records, how many strokes in swimming, pulse after exercise, knee bends, rope-skipping—well, you *saw* the punching bag. But in the little book of symbols I suppose the 'D' is for drinking—he'll put a 'D' in the corner. Sometimes no other notation at all. But there might be quite a few esoteric marks, like a lodge code book—crosses and swastikas and circles with dots. Sometimes circles inclosing two triangles. And once in a while"—it was hard for her to say this—"a few words."

Mortimer Flowers sounded as casual as if he might be asking a recipe. "Are they drunkenly entered?"

"Oh no. With great care. Meticulous. The same way he writes."

"Do you remember any of them?"

There was another pause. "Yes." Her voice was very faint. "One was 'Jill is praying.'"

Arleigh stirred uncomfortably but Flowers didn't want to lose anything here. "Any others?"

"There was another: '26 days. My last, I pray. O God, I pray.'"

"My last what?" the psychiatrist asked.

"My last drink, I suppose."

Dr. Flowers got up then and walked around behind Jill's chair, patting her shoulders. She felt his strength. She was glad they had said so much. She did not feel she had betrayed Seton.

"That is very hopeful. I consider that very hopeful," the doctor said, leaning down above her.

"How can that be when he goes right on drinking?"

"Because he doesn't *want* to go right on. He wants to quit and he doesn't know how."

Dr. Flowers walked around in front of them again.

"Your husband is a mystery that I shan't try to penetrate, Mrs. Farrier, the mysterious kinship, the dangerous imbalance of the artist and the neurotic. It isn't new. In the case of many—in the case of your husband, he puts his neuroticism aside when he works. Or perhaps it's better to say he puts it to work, makes it work *for* him. It is the primary characteristic of the true artist—at least it appears so to me—that he can somehow cut through everything and fashion his own work in his own way. That he can *get it done*. That nothing matters until it *is* done, and that those who get knocked about while this is going on—and it makes no difference that they are his own family—are nonexistent. There's nothing neurotic about your husband's writing habits. And there is nothing neurotic about his output. If there is something about its content, very well, for the *man* is a neurotic. It is the artist that is not neurotic. And the artist, when working, is all man. Do you see this? It is important that you try. When not working, he becomes the cultural and social nonentity he was as a child, sassing the world but sassing it from the safe side of the fence. He strikes you. He breaks glass. He kicks. He gets drunk. I asked you if you thought you could punish this and you said you would not know how; that is answer enough. About his drinking, no psychiatrist has ever helped a man with a drinking problem; all but a few would deny this, and nearly all but myself will take on the problem, especially when the drinker is interesting enough to have money. Or to be famous. The man with a drinking problem who comes to the psychiatrist for help is never a man who wants to quit. He wants to drink. This phase of your husband's problem—and mind you, I don't see Mr. Farrier as being a problem to himself at all, I see him as being one of the most astonishing and one of the most durable successes I ever saw—the drinking I won't touch. He'll never quit merely because he's ashamed of the way he treats you when he's drunk."

"But some men *do* quit drinking, Doctor," she insisted hopefully.

"Of course. And he might too, if he could realize that he is not giving up anything; if he could realize he is getting rid of something. But he would have to see it as something that was very much in his own selfish interest as an artist. As an artist, not as a person. He doesn't care what kind of a slob he is as a person, provided the world never finds out and turns him in for it."

He stretched his arms, then relaxed them and looked down gently at her.

"I am thinking more about you, Mrs. Farrier. I can't do anything for Mr. Farrier. You've done it all. Done it well. V*ery* well."

"I don't feel I've done anything."

"The very point."

"Does he hate me for bringing up the matter of his son Derek? I know I shouldn't have. I just couldn't help it. I couldn't stand it."

"Of course. Hates you for seeking him out at all. Desolating reminder of duty. Drop it altogether. It's too much and it's too early. Obviously he's kept this first-born son out of his mind for so long he's *almost* succeeded in disowning him altogether. Now *you've* brought the basket to the doorstep and rung the bell. What else *can* he do?"

There was a taut silence, then Jill's voice cut the air:

"*But it's his own son! He looks just like Seton!* And he's in trouble! We have everything in the world now!"

"You have a good deal. And I'm glad for you. I know you sometimes pray for this man. There's quite a pretty little Catholic chapel a few miles from here. A town called Keene. I thought you might just like to know of this."

"Yes," Jill answered, already regretting her outburst. "I'd like to stop there. I'll go over. I'd like the drive."

"Someday in the future you may find the older son a companion for the younger. I hope so. It sounds so, too. But not now. Anyhow it's no route to their father."

"What is the route, Doctor?"

Dr. Flowers took both her hands and held them warmly.

"My dear Mrs. Farrier, there is no route. Your husband is what we call 'unstructured.' You've made his life possible. You've allowed the artist to work. He's made your life impossible. He can't do anything else. He *isn't* anything else."

Jill blinked, looking up, but said nothing. Mortimer Flowers asked, "When are you going to tell him you're carrying his child?"

"I don't know. Soon now. He'll *see*. I'll have to." She dropped her eyes and took her hands from his.

The psychiatrist was silent for many seconds. He seemed so serious she looked up finally to see if he would say anything more.

"Mrs. Farrier, I think you've earned a little time to make a few plans of your own. That is the third factor in your situation. I mentioned your husband's probable susceptibility to control; control through punishment. This seems unsatisfactory to you. We've spoken about money. You seem defeated here as well. But you have abilities of your own. You have just as much right to put them to work as he has. I think you have an important decision to make."

Now he stood very close to her, looking down with a kind of hard intensity. "In order to make the right one I suggest you stop thinking of your husband either as a husband or as a man or as a person. *Your husband is not a person.* And except in the crudest sense of the bed and the kitchen, he is incapable of seeing you as one either." He started off, then turned back with a quick question: "Why don't you accept the next offer you get from Hollywood and just go?"

He walked off then, up the slope toward the club.

In his own room he opened the letter that Seton had written to Arleigh; the letter Arleigh had mentioned when the two had talked long distance the night before.

It had sudden humors that the psychiatrist was in no way prepared for. All its bitterness seemed more than justified, and all in all it gave him an unexpected close-up of a tortured man.

March 10
—and so it hardly comes as a surprise to me, your quick interest in the (to me) worn-out stage version of "Joseph and His Brethren." I keep getting inquiries about it from others. It is one of the hardiest of the perennials of my experience.

I have certain views of it, and after setting these down, I feel you will understand me better than you do; at least you will understand where I stand in regard to the colorful Joe of biblical history, what he means to me as a factor in my own life, its bearing on that life, and the destructive emanations it has breathed forth upon him who touched it most—my father.

I doubt if it would succeed any more, not that it wouldn't "go" with someone other than my father in the holy bathrobes in which this sad farce is always played.

I just think it is worn out and passé. I think it belonged to a "time." It belonged to the special and the peculiar uses of the more pseudo-imaginative vaudeville in the bigger cities. And (of course—since it had been dowsed in holy water) it belonged to Chautauqua. (It's still being done in the latter, so I am told, and I believe Will Connor is touring it right now.)

I loathe the property. I actively hate it. For the sake of accuracy, do you know it is about seventy-five years old? Of no known authorship? Mark Twain's own father saw it!

I hate it not at all because of its antiquity and its obvious indestructibility, but because it represents, in my child's memory (still acutely active and dependable), my first sight of a stage. More precisely, my first sight of "backstage." I identify Joe and Potiphar's permanently available but seldom-taken old lady (maybe she had a wart or some missing teeth) with the chill of wings in towns like Sandusky, Ohio; I identify him with the chill of ice-cold toilet seats, of heatless registers, the chill of hotel breakfasts placed on shabby tables and left there to wait for me without anyone being sent to get me. I identify this wretched piece with the chill of the men's room lavatory on every single one of America's Pullman trains. I directly trace my constipation right smack back through unbroken generations to Egypt, and why Joseph couldn't have been left to rot in that damn cistern I don't know.

You have remarked that I wear sweaters all the time; that I can never get warm enough. Blame the Old Testament!

To me—and I am quite serious—Joseph means tin basins, loneliness, other's laughter that includes me not, gawdy parties overhead, battered trunks, drying sweat, my mother's weary joys and frozen hysterias—the smell of train smoke on everything I wore, and the tireless importunings and tedious "don'ts" of an endlessly tedious woman my parents picked up in some God-knows-where town in Missouri; a woman (she was my nurse) who seems now—as my mind scurries about in that awful darkness, that perpetual tumult of one-night stands (excuse me! one-night Triumphs), solitary suppers (for me), solitary baths in hotel tubs always just a little gritty with Bon-Ami—who seems now to have been the only companion I had, day and night, summer and winter, moving or stationary, for the first seven years of my life!

Do you begin to see what it is that I hate?

Let me come a bit closer to you. As Father's friend.

I said destructive and I meant it. Father sold out himself for it. It was as sure-fire as "Acres of Diamonds." (And no wonder!) He spent seven minutes in the one big scene with Potiphar's wife. (The Old Testament only gives the old pot 3 verses!) You could go as far as you liked, since Joseph spent all this time running away from her! Even missionaries could attend. Missionaries—hell, priests went!

I can tell you I have been dandled and fondled and lullabyed by some of the strangest Egyptian women that ever come out of Sioux Falls. No, Arleigh, Joseph is dead. He stole my childhood, but worse, he took my father's manhood. Try to understand this.

> *Sincerely yours,*
> *Seton Farrier*

Part Six

23

BECAUSE MARION VOGEL NEVER CAME TO THE CLUB
but spent all her time in The Castle—an elegant timbered pile that
was her summer home and that occupied the high point on the
smaller of Lake Placid's two islands—rumors of her new "captive"
were sure to be as widely believed as they were inexact.

Tanager's greatest skill was getting herself talked about. In the
town of Lake Placid, in its own way quite as self-sufficient as the
club, and a place where Tanager Bolt was as unheard of as rice
planting, she nonetheless managed to deliver one of her Town Hall
lectures in the high-school auditorium and to be widely noticed by
the Adirondack papers for revealing ("from personal knowledge"),
for the first time and to the world, that Rudolph Valentino was
sexually impotent, a circumstance made all the more interesting because it was at such variance with current accounts of what he was
supposedly doing most of the time when not being photographed.

Marion thought Tanager was individual.

As to herself, Marion was rich, reclusive, handsome, and oddly
fastidious. Spirited rather than mannish, she had set a few legends
in motion before she was sixteen by being the first female to drive
a Harley-Davidson clear across the United States. The following
summer she took a Charles River deck canoe through the white water
of the Richelieu, something never before done by man or woman.
That same year she had gone to Paris to study the piano and had stayed
for four years. She had become an accomplished player but had
never recitalized. At least she had never done so in the conventional
sense. When she had first broken upon the public's attention as a
performing musician she had been one of four young women, all of

them first-class players and all of them of striking appearance and
steel nerves. As the "Flying Pianos" these four young players had
been seen suspended on slender cables, their pianos suspended like-
wise, from tracked slots in the high ceiling of New York's famous
Hippodrome and whirled about over the amazed heads of the
audience in an eight-hand rendition of the "Hungarian Rhapsody."
Except for the girls who dived into the tank and never came out,
the four girls who flew about the air playing the "Hungarian
Rhapsody" was the greatest act ever presented in New York.

It was commonly believed that Marion, though highly sexed, had
never married. She told anyone who asked her that it was because
she'd never met anyone as interesting as she was herself, and this
may have been true. She was a Lucy Stoner and a suffragette. She
had borne two children, both boys, but with such indistinct knowledge
of their true fathers she'd had no notion what to call them and had
resolved the problem of the first merely by calling him Bill. The
second had resolved his own problem by disappearing.

Marion liked people who were startlingly different or pleasantly off
center (Tanager fitted these specifications, at least mechanically) and
kept inviting them up to The Castle. Here there wasn't much to do
but talk and swim and climb the Adirondacks. Sometimes she never
saw her guests, who were supposed to ignite each other anyhow and
who understood this. Occasionally people appeared she didn't even
know. Marion's father, still alive at eighty-five, though no one knew
where, had made a fortune in Canadian furs, impartially skinning
the middleman along with the beaver, and was spoken of with respect
throughout the Adirondacks not for his money but because he'd put
up most of The Castle himself, using a broadax to cut her carrying
beams. His activities in northern Canada before 1900 had brought
him in contact with a few Eskimos and here he had also made
acquaintance with his first kayak, an enthusiasm he brought back to
America and transferred to his daughter Marion.

It was in one of these kayaks that Tanager Bolt was now paddling
about on the smooth and reflecting surface of Lake Placid. Marion
had gone into the woods with an alidade, a sextant, and a party of
state surveyors to start the plotting of a projected auto road to the
summit of Whiteface, the road being a popular proposal in the Albany

assembly at the time and the governor's answer to Pikes Peak. Marion's self-appointed addition to the gang of surveyors created a situation embarrassing to the New York Highway Commission but one about which little could be done since Marion owned the mountain.

This activity had kept Marion from her guests. For Tanager's purposes these absences were very welcome.

Tanager knew more about Seton than he might have supposed. And she'd brought to the Adirondacks the scrapbook of theater clippings on which she had spent so many months.

It was quite true Tanager had made a flashing impression on Seton Farrier when they first met. Tanager impressed everyone. It was also true that each time he had run into her since—and these occasions were never the gay fortuities he took them to be but planned interceptions—her natural liveliness had renewed this impression. Though Tanager was known to hate the theater or perhaps to fear it as a trespass upon her own audiences, she had come to a number of Seton's rehearsals. In between times he had never thought of her. Seton never thought of anyone he wasn't with or didn't need.

And he did not yet know she was at Placid.

It is therefore hard to say whether at this moment he would have been flattered or alarmed to realize that Tanager had scoured the shores of Lake Placid with binoculars, hoping to catch sight of him and that she had been doing this several hours each day ever since she came up.

When not looking for him, she improved her proficiency in the use and handling of the light kayak. And she confidently counted on her womanly charms—which were considerable—and counted as well on the delightful unexpectedness of her arrival to recapture his interest.

Now she merely had to make sure of one thing: to float by at a time when he would be sure to see.

At this moment, looking down from the balcony of the Lake Placid boathouse Arleigh's eye caught the flaming image of Tanager, gracefully, purposefully, yet somehow stealthily too, coming across the water in the kayak.

Arleigh had walked over here with Mortimer Flowers to watch the life guard introduce Sean to his first ride on a surfboard, Jill having rented a powerboat for the purpose. She knew it would have been a

waste of time to suggest to her husband that he might like to take
his son into the water. Sean, though only six, had pleaded to be
allowed to try the sport, and Jill had agreed.

In the pine-scented afternoon warmth of Indian summer there
was the sound of a few boats but at the moment no sign of Sean and
the life guard. Either they hadn't gone out yet or they were being
towed about on the far side of one of the islands.

Directly below Arleigh and Mortimer, Seton was leaning against
a wooden pier bollard. He was wearing maroon trunks and had
draped himself in a towel. He looked tan and lithe and hungry.

As usual he was alone. Now into the dark circle of his preoccupations
skimmed Tanager in her little kayak. She stopped paddling and looked
up, lightly waggling the double paddles, then gently dipping them
again, moving closer. Seton's fine head lifted slighty and he saw her.

"Hello there!" she shouted happily, in rich surprise.

He was stunned and delighted. He stood up quickly, ran his fingers
through his hair.

"I thought *you* belonged to the oceans," she went on, quite close
to the dock now, her mouth wide, her expression friendly, her eyes
taking his inventory an item at a time.

Seton was nonplussed but manifestly pleased as well, not only
with her and the sight of her but with the gay and bouncy novelty of
the skin-covered boat she was in. It was hardly more than a shell.
Seton saw right away it would hold two.

"Well, I——" He thought he would tell her about his tuberculosis.
Then the disease plus Randall Cedric and the examining room of
Saranac all fled his mind. "What do you call *that?*" Then he looked
right down at her. Tanager had slipped the shoulder straps of her
bathing suit, something not done at Placid.

Seton's excitement mounted. "Of all the people I never—— Where
are you staying, Tanager?"

"Why don't you get in?" she said easily, maneuvering the kayak to
the foot of the ladder. "Be careful, it's tippy."

Arleigh could hear no more. Seton had started down the ladder.
He popped back once quickly to grab his towel, and in the next
moment Tanager was propelling him rapidly away.

"Who was *she?*" Mortimer asked, impressed as much at the grace of the tiny episode as by Seton's response to it. He sensed the element of prearrangement. "Daytime assignation? Was he waiting for her?"

"Other way around, I'd think. Perhaps she's the woman you described yesterday to Jill at the tea table."

"I don't remember describing any woman to Mrs. Farrier," he said honestly.

"You described the *kind* of woman who might take Seton away from her. That is Tanager Bolt."

Then Arleigh told him much of what he knew of her.

"You think she's planned this for a long time then?"

"Yes, I do."

"But she's a woman of uncommon beauty as well as tremendous fascination."

"A lot of men feel it. Women too, for that matter."

"Why hasn't she married?"

"Everyone wonders. Hundreds of chances, of course. But in her odd way she *has* had a career. Spurious maybe but quite satisfying. Club dates, name and picture in the paper, interviews, trips abroad. Sexually——" Here Arleigh's mind roved through the farrago of Tanager's improvisations, from items as sordid as Patrick's unspeakably cruel lockout of her to the more idyllic cruise a year ago with Somerset Failing, who was so rich nobody dared challenge his conduct but who was so old no one thought to. And now Marion Vogel, by no means Tanager's first liaison of this nature, a linking in with a nest of sexual unclassifiables and social marauders.

"Sexually lawless," Arleigh said at last.

"Even so, why Seton?"

In the cedar chairs of the top portion of the boathouse, while Tanager got acquainted with Seton in the kayak and permitted him the first of a list of premeditated liberties, Arleigh looked down at these two, then up at the mountains that contained this loveliest of all lakes, and tried to reacquaint himself with Tanager—and Seton, too—and to convey to his friend some of the things he remembered about the past, about the two principals now deliciously confronting each other and quite lost to the world, and some of his thoughts, unformed as yet, about what they would do to each other.

"Tanager has many of those qualities men seek in women, as well as many of the qualities women seek for themselves yet fear in each other."

Great physical beauty was one of these, he said, adding that she knew this and not only wore it well but used it well.

Fifth Avenue photographers, a profession lately sprung up after the war, were happy to give her a prominent display at reduced rates any time she would sit for them. It brought business—and her face, briefly familiar each winter on posters in front of Town Hall, could be seen at various times all year in one or another of the fashionable windows of Bachrach, Winburn, Muray, Pinchot, Pach Brothers, and Hal Phyfe—looking out upon the passers-by. She was the first beautiful woman to have her photograph colored by an artist and publicly displayed *as* art, and it was truly said by Charlie Westover that no woman since Mona Lisa had managed to move ahead so fast merely by sitting on her butt and smirking.

She knew how to use people. She knew how to deal with the times, including her own special ineptitudes in regard to them. Because she was crude, she kept to crude people. She had a technique for putting others on the defensive. She treated men with a camaraderie so free and easy it served to imply a concealed disdain for the sex, or, at the very least, a discomposing refusal to acknowledge the male as anything very special. Men sensed this at once. It made them put out their best feathers, which had of course been the effect she sought since it kept attention away from her own imperfections.

First among these imperfections was the matter of her legs. She had terrible legs, the legs of a peasant, almost grotesque.

A plinth for beauty in every other way so real and celebrated, they were so pitilessly incongruous that the misfortune would have destroyed the personality of any other woman. But Tanager was not destroyed as a person, although the grotesquerie of her legs had unmistakably altered her as a woman.

Even so, or perhaps because of it, the emerging personality itself was so projective, its accompanying assurance and self-assertiveness so positive, that both these characteristics were always mentioned in the advertisements that announced each new series of her lectures. (It had been at one of these, Arleigh interpolated, that Marion Vogel had first met her.)

For a number of years Tanager had been appearing in the late
afternoon in the Town Hall before groups who had paid admissions
for the purpose of improving their own thought, if they had such, on
unrelated subjects like "Man's World and Today's Woman," "Sub-
jective Ways to Inner Beauty," or "Philosophical Treasures of the
East." The themes didn't matter. Tanager was the thing, and her
discourses sauntered about amid snatches of poetry, light sprinklings
of French epigrams, quotations from the Upanishads, from Tagore,
Keats, Kipling, impromptu witticisms memorized from early copies
of the *Literary Digest*, and a few simple breathing exercises which
gave her a chance to turn sideways to her audience, then lift her
breasts, a movement that always brought the men quickly back from
Tagore.

For these lectures she wore a plumed hat and a gown of white
tulle with a gold lamé stole. The garment was cut like a toga and
was semi-ecclesiastical in its effect. She made her entrances carrying
a thoughtful mien and a bushel of red roses, the thoughtfulness
giving way to a muscular smile, quick and dental and surprised, as
the applause reached her.

There was a histrionic blessedness about the whole thing.

Tanager breezed across Town Hall's generous stage breathing into
the roses as she bowed, then placed her giant bouquet amid a semicircular bank of other flowers on a low curved table near the footlights.
It was behind this stagy little coronal that she stood and delivered
her talks. It was just right, as Arleigh now saw, for it hid her legs
while letting her move about.

Aimee Semple McPherson, wearing dark glasses, had studied this
entrance many times and had gone West with it to her considerable
profit a season or so before, adding organ music, a spray of long-
stemmed trumpets and a publicity wing. The same entrance had
also been appropriated by Michael Strange, who twice a year used
it to embellish her false but arresting magnetism when she rented
Carnegie Hall and a Swiss harpist and recited a quantity of poetry
no commercial house in New York City had the courage, or perhaps
the perception, to publish.

Actually there was something pitiful and unfinished about all three:
they felt compelled to perform, to appear before people, to personify

beauty, to carry wisdom, light candles, excite people, see their names in the paper, hear themselves talked about, and when they could not win audiences through their own accomplishments, buy them out of vanity. The three together, pooling all they had, couldn't assemble a thirty-ounce brain. It was both sad and funny, for they were as empty as they were famous.

In the beginning days of Tanager's uplifting discourses Charlie Westover had drifted by and stopped in out of curiosity. Arrested by the undeniable beauty of the woman on the sidewalk poster (he had never heard of her before), and for seventy-five cents though seated near the back, he had been so transfixed by the Tanager entrance, then by the voice and face and regality of manner, that he'd kept returning, finally getting Arleigh himself to come, an errand he managed more from affection for the young director than from any expectation of being aesthetically fulfilled or spiritually fattened.

But the vividness had been there all right. There was no doubt about that. And Charlie had used the exact word: Tanager was "auroral." The image stuck, once stated.

From Arleigh's snapshot accounts, his acerb humors, his fine respect for reality, his blistering contempt for crudeness, Mortimer Flowers had the sensation of being taken into the presence of a woman of total command, of superconfidence and absolute rule, so powerful was the effect—as Arleigh conjured it up—of Tanager's platform control and manner.

"I always paid attention to what people were saying, whether I had paid an admission or not, and I'm afraid I came away from Tanager's Town Halls—as they came to be known—with feelings quite different from my friend Charlie's. I kept my judgments to myself, not wanting to hurt Charlie, but I had to share it all with someone. In those days I played billiards twice each week with old Dermod Farrier at the Lambs. Of course Tanager was an outrageous fraud, and the outrage—as is always the case—did not lie in her being a fraud but in her getting away with it. I told Dermod one afternoon about Tanager. I remember describing the 'philosophical message' part of her program to the old Irishman—I remember calling her a 'mail-order Rosicrucian.' He exploded with laughter and came to the next lecture himself. He added a word of his own—'Floc-cinaucinihilipilification.' "

Arleigh grinned affectionately.

"There is no such word," Mortimer said confidently.

"Yes, there is. And it describes what you would see if you looked into Tanager Bolt's brain."

He stretched, looked down again at the water. The kayak had come into view again.

"She has unnaturally large aquamarine eyes, Mortimer. Eyes more green than blue. They have an extraordinary holding power, given them by the mydriatic size of the pupils."

"Coppery hair too," the psychiatrist noted.

"Yes. Women always speak of the hair. But it's the eyes men never forget."

"He seems to like it already," Mortimer said. "And I suppose the money—now that he has some—is attractive. Is there a great deal?"

"Not in the Wall Street sense. But he's made over half a million in two years. But it's the setting, Mortimer. Tanager is a woman that likes a setting. The best setting she ever had is the very property that Seton Farrier now owns."

"How do you mean?"

"Cecil Watrous domiciled her there for two years."

"What happened?"

"Watrous threw her out finally. Same as the others. Quite painless —Aix-les-Bains plus ten thousand. She likes to be the person in control. But she lost it there. And with Charlie Westover, she never really had it at all. He's cleaning up in Hollywood by the way."

"I always heard he was serious about Tanager."

"Charlie's serious about everything. While he's on it. Goes all the way. But he moved too fast for Tanager. Tired her out. The house was full of people she didn't want to know. Or couldn't compete with. Women as beautiful as she was but brainy too. There was a hell of a fight one night. I was there. She tried to throw out his friends. Instead, he told her to pack up and get out. She wouldn't move. So he brought out all her clothes into the living room. It made quite a pile. Insults passed back and forth like dirty pictures at a convention. She accused him of all the misconduct there is. He admitted it and added to it. Then he cut her in two. 'But I never accused you of being a woman!'"

Once more the kayak crossed before them. Tanager was now sitting on the bottom, facing Seton, giving him his first lesson.

"Just as an engineering problem, Arleigh," Mortimer Flowers said, admiring, his eyes alight with mischief, "with those two facing each other in this innocent little boat and their heads only three feet apart, doesn't she *have* to dispose of her legs by putting a scissors around the Irishman's middle?"

Arleigh grinned.

"Well, she'd know the way. She has a pelvic skill never learned on horseback. And she's working against time. Remember that. I think that much of her effectiveness"—the psychiatrist glanced over at the sudden tone of sobriety that had come into his friend's voice—"is her cold-blooded practice of something women know but seldom use."

"What is that? Woman as pursuer?"

"Yes. Most men are too timid to *seek* any given woman even when they're powerfully attracted to her. Yet most any woman could have a sexual experience with almost any man at all merely by asking him."

"Do you think Mrs. Farrier will stand by? Allow the scarlet Tanager to fly in and take over?"

Arleigh didn't answer at once. "Jill's had very little but rebuff, disappointment, anxiety. Hurt, too. But she's never going to allow anyone to hurry her. Not till her baby comes. Then I think she'll leave Seton no matter what he does, what he says. Or what he thinks he wants."

"Then why does she pray?"

"She never prays for the marriage. I'm sure of that. She prays because she believes in God. She prays because she cares about anything that's living and that's in trouble. You made some big points with her yesterday, Mortimer."

"You feel so?"

"I'm sure."

"I just wanted her to begin to think that there would not be anything wrong if she left him cold."

"Yes. I think she feels now that she's been too pliable. And I'd guess the mechanical event of her next childbirth will be the last item of exchange between them. Except maybe a quarrel over money when they separate."

"Oh, I don't agree with that at all," the psychiatrist responded.

"Then what?"

"He's hunting for something to kill him. The brother did the same thing and found it. The same search, in many ways. The death wish is here in this man. But his doctors are giving him a mighty poor time."

"So?"

"I think he's going to commit suicide."

"When?"

"Very soon."

Out on the water it was quite different. It would have amused the seldom amused Seton to have heard this talk. He felt strong, quite daring. For the first time in his life both picturesque and masculine. The warm touch of Tanager's heel, and the whole of her calf lying against his bare thigh, sent a surge of blood into the region of his stomach and put new strength in his paddle strokes.

He realized he was having a perfectly wonderful time. The surprise, the boat, the time of day, the charred feeling of nerves now cooling, the beauty of Tanager, the visible hunger she seemed to feed, the unoccupied part of him and the unoccupied moment she seemed to fill, the rare but special carnal esurience that gnawed at him when he drank, the sudden rise of sexual greed that came after a bout with liquor and that now saw hints of satisfaction in Tanager, all this enlivened the prospect of his afternoon and gave his eyes new brightness.

There was nothing at all he could do about the way he and Tanager were sitting. They had to sit that way. It was either that or paddle the kayak the way Eskimos did it, the bow paddler with his back to the one behind. That way it would be quite impossible to talk. And not at all polite. Furthermore, he should be doing the work, as he was; not the woman.

A few yards away a fast mahogany boat called the "Snapshot"

thundered by elegantly, its power muffled. It was towing a surfboard thirty yards behind. A man and a boy stood on the board, one behind the other, the bigger one balancing with easy assurance and from time to time steadying the youngster in front of him. But Seton would not have recognized his own son, not then, if he had been swimming alongside.

There was a stabbing delicious transfixion about this hour, a new feeling, a feeling of being engulfed in love and beauty. For Seton there was a serene sadness that moved over the surface of the water, floating vaporously to them from the shore beyond without ever quite arriving, quite touching.

He wanted to quote Swinburne: "Eyes colored like a water-flower, and deeper than the green sea's glass, Eyes that remember one sweet hour, In vain we swore it should not pass, In vain, alas."

He was about to recite these lines when Tanager, trailing her finger tips in the water, turned her eyes to the great green rift in the mountain, and, keeping her face averted and as if addressing something revered and mystical and unseen, began to recite lines to him— a poem that was at once familiar but that he could not quickly identify.

Then suddenly he realized it was one of his own!

How blessed of Tanager to be here! And to have known this poem! To have carried it in her heart! Where had she ever *found* it?

> *I hear the ripple*
> *And see the reach*
> *Of sky—*
> *I lightly vault*
> *The spindrift,*
> *Flicking and licking*
> *The curl of breaker,*
> *Nimble as the sandpiper*
> *Hop-skipping the spent wave—*
> *I fly to the same shore*
> *But on my wings more*
> *To carry than the piper—*

Summer flies—
My love lies
Resting by the willow—
Twilight closes.
To you I fly—in you my life reposes.
Though the sun's fire diminish
And the moon's ride finish—
Though love is gone before its heart discloses—
Be warm in me—ashes of summer's roses.

When Tanager finally turned her head back from the mountains and looked at Seton she was startled at the effect she had made. His head hung down, tears had wet his cheeks. She leaned forward quickly, seizing his hands, then, inclining her own head, pressed the backs of his hands hard against her cheekbones.

"Take me to the island, Seton. I shouldn't have done that."

They were close to it. Some of Marion Vogel's guests were swimming at the boat landing, a hundred yards away. Seton headed for it.

"No, not there. Off to the right, Seton. Where that little strip of beach is. I left a bathing wrap there. And slippers."

He saw the wrap on a birch stump and paddled up into the shallow water. The kayak grated lightly in the sand.

Tanager jumped out and was instantly covered in her wrap, a splash of turquoise flowing cotton. Serviceable too, Seton noticed—it went clear to her feet.

"Where did you learn that poem, Tanager? How did you find it?"

As he looked at her standing quietly on the shore, the wild contrast of the copper of her hair and the blue-green of her beach wrap, a light drifting odor of pine needles from the hill behind, the sound of water slapping at the shore and a soft sad wind in the Norways, all the aeonian longings he had felt from times he could first remember —train smoke, crossing bells, the sound of people clapping for his father, the sound of church, of grownups laughing, of pails set down in the halls of dim hotels, of clerks dinging bells, "Front boy!", of the florid, smiling petulance of his nurse—hurried over him, to smother, and possess his senses. He wanted to sob, to flee, or vault to the sky, or be held—forever held. He wanted to touch Tanager. Even more, far more, he wanted Tanager to reach out to him and take him, lead him, deep into the woods. He wanted her to say the poem again, his poem.

Nearby there was a low rickety boathouse with no door. Inside on gantries, turned over, were other kayaks.

"Shall I put this back?" he asked, touching its bow with his foot.

"Oh no. You keep it. How else could you get back?"

He laughed uneasily.

"I'll swim back," he said. Then he whispered: "I'd love to swim out. Tonight. Late. Meet you here. Meet you somewhere."

"Would you? Would you really?"

Her eyes had a wild quick look. "There's a place. Right by. Come, I'll show you."

It was a rustic bridge of unpeeled cedar, spanning a sharp cut, now dry, that carried off the thaw and rainfall from the foot of the Vogel rock garden beyond and above. Seton stood at one end. Tanager walked to the middle of the bridge, ten feet from him, leaned back against the poles of the railing, and smiled shyly.

"If you'll come—I—I have a present for you. I've had it a long time."

"A present? But why? Why a present for me? I don't understand."

"Seton, I—I think you're a great artist. And I think everything you *do* is important. I think a record should be kept."

She left the railing now and walked to the end of the bridge, putting her hands lightly on his shoulders. The pressure of her hands increased. There was a firmness about all she did. He sensed it, and the strength behind it.

"Because it should be kept, I have kept it. I want to give it to you, Seton." Her hands touched his head now, and she whispered: "I want to give you—a lot of things. Oh, Seton."

Seton clutched her to him in a wild eagerness, kissing her hair and eyes, pressing his face to her temples, slipping his hand through the soft cotton of her wrap and curving his hand hotly over her breast. Quietly but strongly Tanager broke away from him and walked to the other side of the bridge. Here she turned, her eyes hurt but appealing, her mouth open, her bosom rising and falling in quick breaths. She put both her hands on the railing.

"Seton, you are lovable and valuable. I wish your wife knew that. I wonder if she really knows what it means——"

"What *what* means?"

With a hint of archness she could not quite conceal, she finished a sentence she had planned for a long time:

"—what it means to be—*Mrs. Seton Farrier.*"

She ran on up the path. Once she turned and called:

"Ten o'clock!"

From somewhere he could hear a life guard's whistle. The surface of Placid was choppy. Boats had gone in. A few people stood about on docks, looking up. There was a whistling sound in the air and a sense of suction near where he stood.

He decided to swim back to the mainland now. The water was roughening, leaves of the birches fluttering. The sob and sighing in the high pines above turned to a thundering of tympani and crashing horns in some dreadful symphony of the Druids.

It was a sudden windstorm, puffed down upon Placid and the region round about by an immense cloud that had materialized over Whiteface, rolling in from the west, and now opening itself like a black umbrella flung up on a sunny sidewalk.

The wind struck the little kayak at Seton's knee and kicked it over. He picked it up and took it into the boathouse, finding the empty crossbars where it belonged, and slid it into place. The shack shook with the wild caprice of the wind.

Seton stepped back into the sun and as he did so, the giant cloud overspread the water before him, reducing the day to a darkness that was frightening and dramatic in the speed with which it struck. Columns of moving air, driving down Whiteface, came on like attacking cavalry, dragooning the hills, scourging the top branches, tearing out their leaves. Hitting the water, the blast scoured the surface, instantly prodding its celebrated repose into a convulsion of protesting ridges of wild water, haystacks of sounding foam, waves so steep and erratic no boat could escape capsizing even for a few seconds.

To the natives and to seasoned vacationers the phenomenon was as recognizable as it was respected, and it explained why sail-boating was forbidden by law in all Adirondack waters.

But what was so fearsome to others aroused something strange in Seton.

The scream in the air and the power the wind carried; the malevolent sound of it and especially the unannounced cunning of its arrival—these were elemental forces in his own darkness. Answering, they suddenly broke the surface, exhilarating his sense of contest and assertion. All his motor responses were quickened with the lift of these recognitions, the sight of nature broken out of her cage. The pelagic in his muscles, the elegiac in his mind, the passional in his spirit, rived and sang and met the wind, clapping the mouth of its impudence.

He was thrilled.

He felt the chill on his limbs now as he leaned into the wind and drove his body, half crouched, along the beach to the deep water at the Vogel's boat landing.

The few swimmers who had been there when he'd paddled by with Tanager had gone for cover and stood back in the boathouse—just as Arleigh and Dr. Flowers were doing a mile away on the mainland—bent against the wind, their arms linked around corner posts, watching in a kind of horrified fascination, but from their own safety, the satanic fury of this surface fermentation—green water turned black and white in fifteen seconds and by the same power that oceans pile up a tidal wave and hurl it a hemisphere away.

Then they all saw Seton at the same time.

He had walked out to the end of the narrow pier. Here he put his arms around a cluster of pilings that secured the deep end to the lake's hard bottom.

Within the woods behind was a crashing of branches coming down, a whole confetti of leaves, twigs and pine cones. But the central roar, the real core of cyclonic disturbance, was overhead, and it was into this center that Seton Farrier seemed to be staring with a fixity so impersonal as to seem scientific; seeking out, as it were, the very eye of its terror. From above, invisible tongues of air currents struck down on Placid's back, whistling and cutting her open like a bosun's lash, actually biting into the water and scooping out dollops to fling them up again where they were instantly atomized. Whitecaps were shored off as the crests curled, their lips razored clean. Then down they went again with a sweep and a whoosh, like grain in a field where the scytheman is out of sight.

Seton felt altogether alone, strangely serene. He was infused with a sense of competence. The awfulness of the sound, so incongruous to the setting it had invaded; the frightfulness of the spectacle—at least to any eye but Seton's—seemed placed here before him for his special use: the pacifying of equivalent furies he had no way to unleash, as the surrounding storm was so grandly spending its own.

He joined it.

Here for him but for no other was a fullness of expression, a resounding satisfaction of experience beyond the need of others.

Perhaps Marion Vogel would have understood it. In any case, to the total disbelief of those who saw it happen—and Marion did not—and in their later report of it (for it was at once circulated and became one more stone for the cairn that marked his legend), Seton Farrier with a calm—some said an approving—look about at the delirious confusion of wind and water and sky, climbed to the top of the pilings, took a deep breath, and dived into the boiling bowl of Lake Placid.

Swimming underwater he did not surface until more than seventy-five feet from the end of the dock. Then, lifting and falling as his body's buoyancy was worked upon by the undulations of the water, he began methodically to swim in unbroken rhythm for the mainland.

Howsoever much the heave or the jaggedness of waves might lift or toss or momentarily overwhelm the swimmer, his progress through the water was never for a second delayed or baffled by the commotion upon it. He was part of the water, not part of the storm. It was the wind that was impostor here. The trouble it caused was a mere impertinence, deserving the contempt it already implied in his venturing upon it with the same rude lack of notice that had come with the storm itself, dispersing boats, tossing birds about, forcing trees to bow. The storm had pounced without warning upon this innocent landscape. He could not repel the intrusion but he could at least scorn the intruder: each stroke had an insolent defiance of its own.

On the high porch of The Castle, Tanager snatched up the binoculars and watched him till she grew ill with dread. Then hearing
others coming in, she ran down the path where she had left him, and,
lying down there upon a rock that commanded some altitude but
hid her from others, kept her eyes on his movement, counting his
strokes, her tensions locking the muscles of her back and biceps, her
breathing accelerating to shallow gasps at the top of her lungs.

Arleigh Brayce and Mortimer Flowers stood with a small cluster
of other vacationers on the mainland pier of the club's boathouse,
watching the swimmer. Jill, who had come over to pick up Sean, at
once recognized her husband. She'd caught a fragment of talk—
"Nobody saw a boat go over"—and went up to Arleigh.

"It's Seton. He's all right."

"I wouldn't have thought it possible," Arleigh said. He relaxed
a little, seeing that Jill had no more concern than the swimmer.
Mortimer Flowers was fascinated.

In Jill's face there was a kind of pride, a recognition that something that was elementally Seton's was being properly managed by
him. Of all on earth except the man himself, Jill would not have
been surprised had she been in the water close beside him and
heard him singing. But it was true. It was watery and it was croaking
and wildly tuneless but there was a rejoicing in it. She'd seen Seton
in the water in every mood known to the Atlantic. She'd seen him
enter the water when there was ice on the shore.

Sean and the life guard were close to the edge of the dock, looking
right down at the swimmer. Jill went up to them. They glanced at
her in quick but silent recognition, including her at once in the
common interest.

Seton's arms reached up for the ladder's lowest rung and he came
up with a kind of patient, dignified weariness. With a remote but
bemused dismay he looked at the little knot of people his swim
through the wild water had attracted.

Now a gust of cold air struck his wet nakedness, stippling his
skin. For a dizzying instant Arleigh saw Seton completely covered
with scales. He half suspected gill slits along the column of Seton's
neck and Seton's breath escaping there.

Dripping and gleaming he stood absolutely still by the ladder, breathing deeply, looking at the people with a curious kind of courteous disinterest. Jill knew the look. He didn't want their notice and they weren't up to his.

Jill moved over close to him. "Sean has just had his first lesson with the surfboard," she said. Seton brightened at once and looked about. He reached down and touched Sean, lifted him up by the elbows and set him immediately down again.

"Aquaplane," he corrected. "You're brown as a butternut, boy."

"You're cold, Daddy," Sean said, putting his hand on his father's forearm. He passed him his own towel. Seton dabbed at his face.

"I left my own towel on the island," Seton said. He turned from them and looked calmly across the stretch of water.

"Rough water—there's no risk in it," he said to nobody. "It's trying to fight undertow that's dangerous. And there's no such thing here."

"The life guard took me on the surfboard," Sean offered, wanting his father's notice. "We're going again tomorrow."

"So that was you?" he said, firmly but pleasantly to Sean.

"I've brought the car over," Jill told him.

"Good. Where is it?"

"Just here."

Perhaps Seton saw Arleigh and the doctor. Perhaps not.

They began walking away from the water. Seton dropped his right arm over Sean's shoulder. The boy reached up with his hand and took hold of his father's wrist. Sean tried to walk in step with his father, stretching out his small legs to bold, comical strides. He had to make little hops to make each step go the distance. Jill walked on the other side of her husband, and looked down at Sean—at the boy's brief absorption. She'd seen the last curving sweep of the two on the surfboard as she came to the water from the car, and a warm feeling of accomplishment livened her step. Seton might enjoy the sport. Abercrombie and Fitch had such a board in their Madison Avenue window right now. And the Farriers had a lake, a lake all to themselves.

It would make up for a good deal. It could.

"Wasn't that Arleigh Brayce? Standing on the boathouse stairs?" he asked Jill, as they reached the Pierce-Arrow.

"Yes, he's here. Comes every year. Very old friend of Mortimer

Flowers. I believe they're both on the Board of Governors of the club."

"Flowers seems like an all-right sort."

"He's a lot more than that," Jill answered, slipping behind the wheel. (She did most of the driving.) Seton sat with her in the front seat, Sean tenting himself under a blanket in the back.

Seton patted his wife's knee and left his hand resting gently on her skirt. It meant he was going to be all right for a while.

Arleigh, at the same time, turned to Mortimer.

"Maybe she's found a way to pull it all together."

"Never."

The psychiatrist said it with dead finality and at once. "There's nothing living whose love he needs or wants." He slung a jacket across one shoulder and they began to walk.

The wind had stopped. Boats began to appear on Placid.

Watching the car lumber into the friendly gloom, Arleigh, who counted the money and who won Seton's scorn for it but who saved Seton's plays by it, had no bitterness over their long voyages of the few swift years just ended. They had found new lands together—taken audiences to regions never before seen—Seton who built the ship and Arleigh who took her through the reefs and brought her in.

But to Mortimer Flowers, who was also watching, the Pierce-Arrow didn't look like a ship. To him it looked like a funeral car.

24

ONCE A WEEK RANDALL CEDRIC CAME OVER TO THE
Lake Placid Club from his hospital at Saranac to enjoy the sight of
people in fine health and the quality of a cuisine that had made the
club's dining room as popular and widely known as the summer golf
or the winter toboggan run.

Now he sat on the great west porch with his former colleague Dr. Flowers and with Arleigh, quietly digesting his duck. Seton Farrier's phenomenal swim had been mentioned. Cedric hoped that the playwright, though he'd already shown up in the talk, would at least keep his person at a distance.

Although Dr. Cedric was a slow eater, mentally he carried about with him an economizing celerity of procedure: when one of his patients healed, he quit thinking of him.

Thus Dr. Cedric, who had given the cold verdict of perfect health, was quite aware that Seton would not be able to bear it. As a physician—when he had weighed Seton's reaction to this news, then weighed the reaction against thousands of verdicts (death warrants, a lot of them) that he'd been compelled as a chest expert to pronounce upon people with many times the personal courage of the playwright —he could bring no sympathy at all to the problem of Seton's collapse. He wished only that Seton would pack and return to New York. Or perhaps shoot himself.

"Why *do* people keep babying this Irish ingrate?" he asked with a slight rise in his voice. "All he needs is a swift kick in the ass. It's all he's *ever* needed!"

Arleigh grinned. It was something Charlie Westover could have said a couple of years before.

"Farrier's lungs are fine," Cedric went on. "I've no interest in the man. His twitches can be dealt with by you psychiatrists, Mort. You can dangle him forever in these suspensions of self-pity. Not me. I'm all through with him. Glad his plates are negative. I was annoyed as hell he hunted me down here in Saranac. But I suppose he'll keep showing up year after year.

"You know the real reason Seton Farrier came to me in the first place?"

"He is always going to doctors," Arleigh said. "He never had to have a reason. Never will."

"Of course. But there's something else in the pilgrimage. Farrier found out I used to be the captain of the Harvard wrestling team. He seems to feel safe with strong people. Physically strong people.

"I tried to give him up as a patient many times. But his mother would always write. Politely, of course. Rather sentimental. Remind me that her boy was always more at home with New London doctors. So twice a year I checked him. And twice a year there was nothing wrong. Nothing."

He lighted a cigar and turned to Arleigh.

"Perhaps my affections don't have much durability, Arleigh. And for the disturbed marriages of today I have none of Mortimer's sympathy whatever. I'd be a poor psychiatrist. Mighty poor. At least I'd try hard to be a mighty poor psychiatrist. Psychiatry spends too much energy working up a thorough understanding of someone who's useless to start with. It's robbing the Western world of its self-reliance. It's making special cases out of nonspecial nuisances. It's patching cripples who were already in retreat when they fell. It's watering the whole arterial system of our sense of adventure and tapping the blood that made us bold. It is Psychiatry, not the Times, that is the great Emasculator."

It was difficult to tell how much conviction accompanied his jabbing sarcasms.

"You think nothing should be done about Farrier?"

"Nothing at all. He's well, let him live. He's tormented, let him produce. Think how *lucky* he is! He's become world famous out of his damn conflict. And the worst writer of English ever to make a good living out of it!"

Cedric held up his hand, amiably shielding himself from an expected counterattack from Mortimer Flowers, but he got none. Flowers was amused. Cedric went on.

"You psychiatrists, you're wrong in all your dynamics. Resolve a conflict and you make it possible for us to live with ourselves. Keep us from suicide. That's the view. But what's the victory here? It's *my* view not nearly enough people are *committing* suicide. I'd like to see its popularity restored. I'd like to see its dignity returned. Subsidized maybe. But with Farrier—what can the man want! He's got a conflict unresolved. He's got a neurosis to run it. And he's tough as a shoe. What more did any artist *ever* have! You repair him, you ruin him! Does he insist on secondary bisexuality besides? Well, by God, he has that too, and he has it to a very marked degree!"

"Where do you see signs of that?" Arleigh asked. It was something he had never thought of.

"Many places. His interest in me as a wrestler, for one. In his calisthenics. In his body-building and his body-wasting. It's observable in the way he describes his women. He doesn't—he can't describe his women, not as other men would describe them. Nor show them to us even as they are seen by themselves. He can't because he doesn't know what a woman *is*. The stamp of his own projection is on them. The stamp of his own projection is on himself, too, as hero. In every play. He's always his own hero. He merely changes the hero's name from play to play, not even bothering to change the description. And always more woman than man. Seton wants to *be* a woman, even though he's very much a man. But he keeps fighting it in his conscious mind. With punching bags or dumbbells or long swims or push-ups. The kayak incident is part of this, as you tell it. Manly stuff. Whisky. Whores. But he doesn't *really* belong at a ball park or a track or a fight. He never follows a sport the way a fan does. He'd miss Zach Wheat's batting average right now by a hundred points."

He dropped his voice.

"Seton's had little experience in love affairs and only the crudest kind of experience with prostitutes. One time, after one of these, he came to see me. Clear to New London. Afraid he'd been hooked. He was all right. Didn't have a thing. But he wanted to talk about it. Wanted to throw something ethereal around the whole sisterhood. I got a glimpse of it a year later. I came down with some rough boys from the submarine base. Some of us drifted on downtown and wound up at a dive called the Taffrail.

"Seton was there. So were three or four of the girls. I can tell you their attentions to this man were remarkable. Not the least whorish. Quite the reverse. Quite motherly. No doubt from time to time he took them upstairs and paid their fees. But there was something wrong. Seton brought them things—tickets for concerts, volumes of verse, flowers, face powder. The night I was there he gave one of the girls a Bible. He was quite gallant about all this. Bowed. Called them ladies. I've felt ever since that night that all he was seeking was to be mothered. Re-mothered. He never had much."

Dr. Cedric waited a moment for strollers to pass their corner. Then he went on. He had become serious, as all did who spoke very long of Seton.

"I find when I'm in New York now, I can't go to his plays any more. They keep saying the same damn thing to me."

"What is it?" Arleigh hitched in closer.

Randall Cedric was still for a moment, assembling his answer. Then he turned himself into an actor, jerked loose his tie, flourished his hair. He stood up and faced them, crouching over, his face close to theirs. He was a huge fellow, and he looked both sad and menacing.

"Here's the message," he said, his face tightening, his voice taking on a secretive and mock-mysterious intensity. Before he said any more, he peered about to be sure their little group was not to be invaded.

"Now imagine me in a pin spot," he said, setting his own stage, "the gels and the ambers giving me a dead and ghostly look."

Here Cedric struck a match and held it close to illuminate his face. The teeth showed, the eye drooped, the lower lip turned in a curl of self-pity. He was a caged ape.

"I am the soul of Farrier," he aspirated, distending his nostrils and stretching out the words to give them a lading of sorrow: "I am the articulator of his torment. I will now put this in italics."

Cedric's voice now did this for him. It became another's and it came from the dark. With a strange querulous nasality, he intoned:

"'I, Seton Farrier, will punish myself for what I've done, but *you* I will punish more for what you would never let me be! Again and again I will punish you. For not recognizing what I was. What a beautiful thing you've rejected! What a rare canvas you've smeared! How can you be so cruel! Look what it's done to me! Aren't you ashamed! Aren't you ashamed and sorry!' Here the physician shrank back, waving off imaginary aid. 'No—No—— Don't offer sympathy now! It's too late—— Too late. I've been and gone. You should have caught the splendor of me while it was passing. You should have saved it then. You should have felt my need and filled it. You should have taken me into the warmth of you. But you *never touched me!* You looked and passed, and *left me dying!*'"

It was a remarkable, miniature tour de force.

Randall Cedric sat down, tapping ashes into the grass.

"That's Farrier," he said, sardonic and surgical, yet momentarily caught in the image he'd just brought the others. "The root of him."

"The *very* root of him!" Arleigh exclaimed, marveling at the unexpected cogency of the display.

The talk turned to Tanager. It always did sooner or later, and Tanager was never a woman who could be reviewed calmly in the mind. There was too much raging vitality.

To two of the three men here on the porch, all of whom knew Tanager separately, if variously, there seemed nothing else but to believe she had come to the Adirondacks at exactly the same time Seton had come (and, since Tanager was known to be fundless just then, must have come at the price of whatever compromise Marion Vogel might expect or exact of her) for the bold but ancient reason of stealing a husband when she'd had no luck in drawing a rich one in the public lottery of Manhattan courtship.

Marry now or marry never—time is up.

Randall Cedric thought it was rubbish. He said no woman would make this kind of play in a neighborhood new to her. There were too many people around her that she could not control. There were too many factors she couldn't anticipate.

He added that it was already well past the end of summer, that the weather was holding up by some freak of meteorology, that it would turn cold any minute and that no woman, no matter how self-confident, would risk a prize of Seton's value in a time and a setting so chancy.

"These things take time," was Randall Cedric's view.

"No. Just opportunity," Flowers said. Then to be completely clear, he added: "And ten minutes."

"Less than that," Arleigh said, thinking of the kayak.

For him the kayak had clinched it. Even though he didn't know about Tanager's long wait with the binoculars, this was an encounter that was more than luck. It was a crossing of lines through the most careful planning. It had to be.

But Cedric clung to his first conviction. He said that Tanager had been tempting Marion for years.

"Quite a number of women possess nude photographs of her," he told them.

"Quite an uncountable number of men possess the same poses," Arleigh countered.

"You don't say!" said Cedric. "How did she hide her legs?"

"She sat on them," Arleigh said at once. "Maybe you've noticed her skill here, if you've seen her in the water. She's always in hip-deep if anyone has a camera. If she's on the beach she's got a robe pulled up. There's never any loitering in the shallows. She's in or she's out. At parties she always sits on low stuff and tucks her feet under. When she's standing up talking to a man, she stands so close he can't see anything but the hair and the eyes and the bosom."

Coming so far with no money and with so many other hurdles to clear—and Seton's sobriety would be one of these, always as fickle as the weather that Cedric had just mentioned—all seemed to represent a reach of such audacity and dimension Arleigh could hardly credit Tanager the detail of preparation it must have taken her.

Yet it must be so.

Cedric said: "Suppose you're both right. Suppose she gets him. It will save Jill from a situation you say is killing her."

"Jill would do better with another man. There's no doubt of that," Arleigh said. "Jill is a woman who needs to be married."

The psychiatrist agreed. "But most, she needs to discover that it is morally all right for her to let him go. To be rid of him. Not to *get* rid—just to *be* rid. That she's made his own self-realization possible. She doesn't owe him a thing. She can do no more."

"Well," said Cedric, "then it really doesn't matter a damn bit if she *does* leave. Or if Tanager takes him right out of her bed. He's your worry now, not mine. The man's mark is made, for many generations to look at."

"You really do think it will come out right, don't you, Mortimer?" Arleigh asked, turning to Flowers.

"Yes. Yes, I do," he answered after a pause. "I think it was splendid—I can think of no other word—that it was a woman like Jill who was first; to have these years. If it had been Tanager at the beginning, perhaps he would never have started. He would have killed her, then himself. Now he can have it done for him. Now she will kill him and he will help her and bless her for it and see that she is protected against the interference of others to consummate this act for him. He is longing for it. If he has any friends left, he'll throw them out just to be sure Tanager is going to be left whole to kill him.

He *wants* her to kill him. That is what he is seeking. That is what he has been seeking for a long time. I told you earlier he was going to kill himself. Now, through her, he senses it can be done for him."

It came out in such a measured way that both the Saranac specialist and Arleigh Brayce looked closely at him to see if he weren't twitting the convoluted simplicities of his own profession. But he was not.

"Tanager will kill the artist first," Flowers continued, "as she was killing it in Westover when she lived with him. Or trying to. Her vanity and condescension are so large, she thinks she inspires others, lifts them beyond themselves. Perhaps to her own level, not realizing what an absurd reversal of aestheticism that is. In fact, it is Tanager's strength never to know her absurdity. Her legs have taught her a whole system of concealment, not just how to hide the legs. Without ever knowing so, and believing the reverse, she'll turn off the flow of Seton. Jill has never done this. She's let him flounder. And it is this that has allowed him to work. But Tanager—she'll bring in the hard disciplines of the lecture circuit. She'll have plans. And a revolutionary idea about money. She'll miss the whole main idea of the man. Less than ten years ago Freud spoke of the 'flexibility of repression' in the artist. Of the huge capacity—psychic and artistic both—that grows out of a predisposition that is dangerous in itself. That the individual's protection against this danger lies in his capacity for sublimation. In Farrier both are marked. He's continuously filling up, continuously emptying. He never dawdles. He never stops. Jill seems to have understood all this from the start. In her own words, Randall, out here on the terrace she's been telling Arleigh and me much the same thing for the past two days. And I've seen the letters."

"What letters are those?" Randall Cedric inquired.

"Four years of their private correspondence. Full of courage and heartbreak and meanness. God, what a monument to the human predicament! But if Tanager moves into the scene, she'll bring a firm conviction with her."

"What conviction is that?" Randall wanted to know.

"She will think—she does so right now—that she could manage Seton's house and life and career a lot better than it is being done for him. That she could manage *him*. And what I suspect most is— there's no doubt at all that she could."

"What will that bring him to? And how soon?"

"It can have only one result. Seton will be briefly happy. Then permanently useless."

"Perhaps," Cedric conceded after a long silence. "Yet it still leaves the great mystery," he added, mostly to himself.

"The mystery of what? Of his power?" Arleigh asked.

"No. The wound. The great horrible gash. The cut that went too deep to heal. The mystery of what it was. The mystery of who delivered it. The mystery of why it never closed. Why it's still bleeding."

"Yes," Flowers said softly. "There's the secret that will never yield. Ironic in Seton's case."

"Why is it ironic?" Arleigh asked quickly.

"Because," said Flowers, "everything that has happened to this man, this artist—all that could hurt him, all that could frighten or disperse—is so well known. Yet something *did* happen—something invisible—something much more terrible than anything that has ever happened to us—or indeed to any that we know—and this something has left him forever a graveled and disintegrated man."

Then Arleigh spoke, and with such solemnity the others looked up, their own thoughts put aside.

"I believe," he said, "that everything that has happened to him is *not* known." He decided to tell these doctors all he knew.

"And do you think you know what it is?"

"I *do* know what it is. I merely don't know what it means. It's too horrible. Even if you hated Seton . . ."

"Tell us what it is, what you think," Cedric urged.

"The thing that shattered him began happening to him before he was born. And this same thing—this horror—went on for a few hours, perhaps a few days, maybe even years, after his birth. And I believe there is no repairing the damage that was done him."

"Do you mean," asked Cedric quickly, "some horrible clumsiness at the time of birth? Some injury?"

"Injury in a sense, yes."

"Were you there?"

"I was," Arleigh told the doctors. "And if I were a doctor instead of a producer, perhaps I could bring it its proper meaning."

"Wasn't there a doctor present at the time of his birth?"

"Oh yes. And a good enough man. My own present understanding of human physiology isn't quite so ready as either of yours, so suppose I put a few basic questions."

"Good idea," said Flowers. "What is basic number one?"

"Does the unborn child have the same blood system as the mother? A common blood stream?"

"No," Cedric informed him. "The blood streams of the mother and her unborn child are separate."

Arleigh looked a little disappointed. "Then this means that the condition or content of the mother's blood stream would have no physiological effect or reaction upon the unborn child?"

"Oh, it doesn't mean that at all, Arleigh," Flowers told him. "It could have a tremendous effect. It does normally. Constantly."

"But if the systems are truly separate?"

"They're separate, yes. But they're intimately related."

"Well, then—another question." Arleigh pursued his thought. "Supposing the mother was a heavy user of liquor. Suppose the mother was a drunkard?"

"Was Seton's mother?"

"No, she wasn't. The question is hypothetical."

"Well, to answer the question: the effect of alcohol that had been taken by the mother would necessarily affect the child. Through the simple process of osmotic transfer, or diffusion. The membrane is permeable. Because of this, the interchange of fluids continues and tends to equalize; to reach an equilibrium. So the alcohol *does* reach the unborn child as if the blood streams were common."

"If the mother is stone drunk, then the baby is stone drunk in the uterus?"

"Yes. But you said Mrs. Farrier was not a drunkard."

"It was much worse than that, I fear. She was a morphine addict."

Both the doctors gasped.

"At the time Seton was born?"

"Yes. By then her addiction was desolating. Incurable they thought. She was not an addict at the time Patrick was born ten years earlier, though that is when she began using morphine."

"Used it all during her pregnancy with Seton?"

"Yes."

The two doctors looked at each other. They were thinking the same thing. Flowers put it into words:

"It means, Arleigh, that Seton was himself delivered into this world a drug addict. It means that the first few hours of his little life were spent in screaming his way through the awfulest agony that is known to the human constitution. It means that his first experience as a viable product of biology was the unspeakable pain of being cut off from the only comfort he knew—morphine. And, once born and thus cut off, the symptoms of withdrawal—these would start to plague his frame in the first few minutes after he began to breathe."

"Did she nurse the boy?" Cedric asked.

"Yes."

"God. That would just prolong it all. High concentrate of opiate in her breast milk. Make weaning a matter of unbalanced dynamics hardly survivable." Dr. Cedric said an unexpected but endearing thing: "Poor little fellow."

He looked out at the dark hills.

"This could have no other effect but to destroy him. Destroy the mechanism of his central nervous make-up. Destroy the whole structure of his emotionalism at the very commencement of his life. It would be bound to smash his personality—a trauma so deep—so—so evaporating—I'm surprised he's alive at all."

All three were silent for many seconds. Time and darkness waited. Lights were going off, windows opening. Whippoorwills took charge of the woods. On the water, far away a ukulele thrummed and a girl sang, "Somebody loves me, I wonder who."

But the thoughts of the three men who with their separate skills and sympathies had caught sight of the greatness of Seton Farrier; who despite themselves had been in some measure forever changed by him, and who as men of courage and compassion had, each in his way, touched the skin of Seton's affliction and tried to heal it— their thoughts kept turning over the hideousness of the story that Arleigh Brayce had just told. They began rearranging their judgments as the impact of its meaning—the horror and the pity of its implications—brought itself close to their sensitivities.

"Did the father know?" Cedric asked.

"Yes."

"What did he do?"

"He was powerless. His own horror over what had overtaken his wife—it crowded him into a corner of childish helplessness."

"Does anyone else know this?" Mortimer asked.

"Yes. Charles Westover. I told him somewhat of it. When he was about to quit Seton's show."

Dr. Cedric got up and stood by the railing, his back to the others. A quiet pitying sigh came out of him. "What a world!"

He reached back to the chair, picked up his sweater, and slung it over his shoulder. Then he turned back and looked with a kind of hard professional questioning at Dr. Flowers. "Mortimer, there must be thousands. *Thousands!*"

He shook hands quickly and went off in the dark. By and by they heard his little wire-wheeled Scripps-Booth chugging off to Saranac.

25

NOT FAR AWAY AT THIS SAME TIME, A LOPSIDED moon, late rising, splashed a lemony glow upon the heads and shoulders of two figures standing close together by the bridge. Presently the man reached down to the ground and picked up a burden of some sort. Then he repeated the motion, gathering up the second blanket, and the two started slowly down a path of pine needles to the shore.

Tanager carried her scrapbook under one arm. With the other she directed a fan of light from a battery torch that she had thought to bring, partly to signal Seton her exact whereabouts when she heard him in the water, partly to get herself back up the treacherous hillside to Marion Vogel's house.

He had come, as she had suspected he would. As she had planned. And his fascination at the completeness of the theater story of his life, in the sweet darkness and the forbidden warmth of the hiding place she had prepared was no less real than the fascination the fire in her body brought to the clean chill of his, when she dried him in the dark, covered him beside her with the blankets she'd brought, then covered him with her own body to bring its warmth directly upon his cold nakedness. She seemed as much man as he woman, and her use of him thrilled him beyond bearing.

In his ear she hotly whispered her terror at his entering the wild water that same afternoon, and whispered, too, the talk—some of it her own fancy—that was going around: that Seton was not human but actually lived in a grotto below the lowest ledges of Lake Placid, in depths never before measured, that he assumed human form only in times of cataclysm and would be seen no more till the earth was split asunder in its last upheaval before being vaporized and drawn back into the ancestral sun from which it had been flung when the universe was just beginning.

Both were images he loved and understood: himself as something atavistic, fearsome in strength, yet still in harmony with all the convulsions of space beyond, of water below; of being mighty there, of being alone.

And of course, being Tanager and knowing the Farriers, she'd had the foresight to bring some good whisky.

Now at the shore they lifted out the little kayak from its flimsy shelter. Seton placed the scrapbook in the bow, beneath the protection of the skin deck and stowed his clothes on top of it.

"I'll dress on the other shore," he said. In the dark he glowed like phosphorous.

She stood very near him, her hands against his cool ribs. Then she pulled him toward her, stood on her tiptoes, and whispered something in his ear that neither ever forgot, something that exhilarated Seton, that separated him from his feelings for Jill.

"My darling, my darling—— Good night, good night. You are going to your wife now. And I am not jealous. I am only sad. Not for myself but for you. I am sad because you are great and"—now for the second time came the sentence—"your wife does not know what it *means* to be Mrs. Seton Farrier. But I know. I know."

He had been twisting together the two sections of the double paddle. She kissed his breasts quickly, then ran across the short strip of beach, into the woods, back up the path they had just descended, her pale light winking. Then he could see it no more. But her words had sent his mind soaring. It *was* true. Jill had no *idea* who he was. Or did she?

At the bridge Tanager snapped off the flashlight and rested her hands on the railing to get her breath. Far off, stealthy and rhythmic, she could hear the sounds of Seton's strokes dipping, dipping, taking him farther and farther. Then in the protective darkness Tanager smiled. Each stroke brought him nearer and nearer, not farther. Men were easier to manage than women. It was women that were the risk.

But Jill herself was taking care of the bigger risk. She was a poor hostess for him. She knew nobody, absolutely nobody. *Being* nobody. Jill was a fool. And so sadly unsophisticated. Seton too! Such a fool about his associates. The idea of some little snip of a shopgirl—Holly Something-or-other—of Seton having an *affair*. With someone he'd picked up in Coney Island or Central Park or somewhere. With Patrick!

A shutter went down in her mind when the image of Patrick came into it. A dull sense of fear stood in the back, as if it might come forward were it only summoned.

She began to walk up the path, hurrying just a little.

Once at the porch, she turned. With the massive protectiveness of the house at her back she looked far down at the water. Clear across the lake, at the apex of the V that was the kayak's wake—two ribbons of yellow crepe, twisted and curling—she saw a glint of a wet paddle as the blade turned upon the moonlight and back to her. She stopped thinking of Patrick. Her mind went to the problem of Holly, of just who and where she was, and how, if Seton were still seeing her, she could most discreetly be diminished or dispatched.

Everything had gone very well. Up to now.

Inside the great living room there was a boom of male laughter. Marion had brought the surveyors back.

Tanager slipped up the back stairs and expertly reconditioned her face and coiffure, changed to an austere velvet gown brightened only by a single rhinestone shimmer at the breast. She put on silver slippers, then stood before a full-length mirror inspecting the head that was known everywhere as imperious. She decided the contrast of black velvet and copper hair was too extreme, so relieved it by tucking a white rose from the vase on her dressing table into the deep marcel wave above her right temple.

Tanager was careful about her entrances. She always wanted to look her best. And she always did.

In the enveloping dark the brightness of Tanager lighted Seton's mind. He could hear her—"Your wife doesn't know what it *means* to be Mrs. Seton Farrier."

But *she* would know. She understood him. He'd been in her thoughts for months and months. Years perhaps. She knew his secret heart—his poems. Tanager knew hundreds of little things, interesting little things about him, that Jill never guessed at, never suspected— cast lists of all his plays in every production there had so far been; reviews in papers never before heard of; pictures of Seton, fragments of interviews, predictions, monographs, quotes attributed to him that he could now no longer remember making.

Tanager had found them. Tanager had saved them. Tanager cared. Tanager was fiercely alive to all that Seton meant. And fiercely protective too. A strong, strong woman who knew the world.

As he cut across the slow rise of the long tenth fairway, making his way quietly to Colden Cottage, the quick excitement of her body, the memory of its eager strength and hunger, jerked at his steps, making them awkward and uneven. He wanted to go back there, slip up to her, in to her. It was not possible to believe the stories about her. She was manifestly untainted. Those eyes could never bury guilt. They were too open, too appealing, too communicative, to conceal anything. And that nonsense about Patrick! If he'd seen her twice in his life, it had been the purest accident. In all the world there could not be two people with less to give or to interest each other than his brother and Tanager Bolt.

Wild talk. Old-maid chatter. Started by Charlie. Jealous Charlie Westover, jealous, vindictive Charlie Westover, who couldn't hold her, couldn't hang onto her. There was just too much *woman* there— even for Charlie.

Seton was lucky. That was all. He was lucky he'd gone swimming at that exact time and place.

What was the matter with Jill, anyhow? Didn't even appreciate the place he'd bought her to live in. He was used to her not appreciating *him*. Long, long ago he could see he'd have to get used to that.

Seton stopped in the narrow strip of low spruces that separated the tenth from the seventh fairway. He carefully set down Tanager's scrapbook in the dew-cool grass, leaned against one of the little trees, and took a long pull from the bottle that Tanager had brought to their tryst.

Man can have a drink with a woman like Tanager and not get in a lot of trouble. Not hear a lot of preaching. Be himself.

He drank again, feeling cool and safe.

What's wrong with being yourself? What the hell's wrong? What's Jill all the time at me for? What's she doing digging up a son I never wanted and never saw? And never will! Not my son. Not my idea.

Tanager's right. No rules for artists.

Seton picked up the scrapbook from the grass, balanced himself straight by holding the rough bark of the tree, and walked through the gloom to the deeper shadows of Colden.

He did not go in at once. He went to the window of their bedroom and peered through it.

A spread of light from the bathroom was enough to make shapes and fixtures visible to his eyes. He could see that both his and Jill's beds were turned down, but both were empty. Then he saw Jill's head. Only her head.

And he knew she was praying. He knew she was praying for him. It pleased and soothed his feelings. He wished the whole world might be praying for him. He wished that somebody might do something! The doctors had let him down again. How did they ever manage these days to get licenses? What kind of quacks were they?

Leeches!

Thieves!

There in the dark, outside the bedroom window looking in, he shivered, wanting to go in to Jill to be forgiven for his thoughts of her, to be forgiven for his amorous hideaway with Tanager, now already becoming fuzzy in the alcohol wash his brain was receiving.

A sob rose up in his throat without escaping and he slunk away from the front of Colden, across the fairway. He kicked off his shoes and wandered back to the low firs. Here he squatted down, propping his back against the bole of the largest of the little spruces, and in a spasm of terror and compulsion, of eagerness and abhorrence, he drank and drank.

He had walked away from Jill, but the picture of her on her knees remained there before him like something in a frame. Now it moved slightly. Jill opened her eyes and looked down at him there in the cold grass. She seemed to be speaking. Not begging or supplicating either, just anxious to communicate something, something he realized he was quite as anxious to hear. There had been times in his drinking, brief open spaces in the shroud that kept so much of it out of useful memory; holes in the clouds through which a flying bird might see the warmth and welcome of the earth, see it for a second only but see it for sure; times when with the utmost ecstasy of relief he felt a calm turning away from something he really loathed—from the drink that blinded and derailed, that made him lose his thoughts, lose his pencils, curse his lot, loathe the skin that covered him, loathe his family. Drinking now, and seeking that surcease in just one more, searching his brain and stomach and the temperature of the air for a sign of release, running from an addiction whose seeming cheer, whose gleaming tinkle had deceived him almost to the point of death; knowing the whisky that Tanager had supplied was a poison in truth and in fact, that any whisky at all was a poison so strong and subtle it could cup its carnal hand under his elbow and did so, taking him down the charnel stairwell of his own decay even though at that very instant, in the empty reaches of the grass at his feet and the forest all about he could see and smell the rot that lay where the whisky took him. In the picture's frame Jill drifted away and Patrick appeared. Seton could see and smell his brother Patrick, far below now, stretched out and staring there on the top of the heap, rakish and gutted and deliquescent, a ghoulish clown sprawled on a castle of broken glass.

There he was! There was Patrick dead and broken!

Seton leaped up shrieking.

All about there was no sound but insects at the end of summer. Then the ghostly cry of a loon floated through the trees, shaking the air, waking birds. Briefly it shivered in the dark, then filtered out of hearing, wailing for a friendship it could never find, expecting no answer in the endless orphanage of the forest.

But Jill heard.

Part Seven

26

THREE OF SETON'S "DOWNTOWN" PLAYS WERE NOW
successfully uptown in revival, one at the Waldorf Theatre, another
at the Mansfield, and the third, *The Rim of Chance*—once more a
gold strike—at the Casino. Now he was making his way north on
Fifth Avenue. For the fourth time he was approaching Ovington's,
a strange adhesive perturbation hugging his stride. His problem was
what to buy for Jill.

Seton had no sense of anniversaries but he was sure his wife's
birthday was in November. His own birthday, to which he always
looked forward with boyish delight, had come and gone. Jill as usual
had remembered it, this time with a telegram in the morning to the
Wentworth Hotel, where he now stayed, and a package of food.
Carefully printed on the outside of the package she had written:
"To be delivered by hand—Room 802."

It was Jill's remembering of Seton's birthdays that always reminded
him that his wife's was near. He loved her packages. And the cookies
were still fresh, for Jill always wrapped them in wax paper and put
them in a tin box.

An even bigger thrill came while he was opening the cookies. A
man from Tiffany was at the door. Jill had given her husband
a watch. It had a tiny chime. It rang the hour, then the quarter hour
and the minutes, just by touching a stem by the winder.

He trembled with delight. He had never seen anything so beautiful, so rich-looking. It was something Otto Kahn might buy for his
own use.

It was the first of November and snowing softly, padding the sound
of infrequent horses, muffling the squawk of klaxons, sweetening the

air. Manholes began to steam. The cross-town trolley at Thirty-fourth coasted calmly across the new snow, its windows lighted and almost cheerful. Then it was engulfed by B. Altman.

Seton went out on the street and started south. He had three errands. Ovington was first, for Jill's present. He had never bought anything for Jill. In fact he almost never shopped for anything at all without his mother.

The next errand would be Spalding. There he planned to inspect a rowing machine he had seen in the basement of Madison Square Garden.

Holly was his third errand. He had a five-o'clock date with her.

He had resumed his sporadic and febrile love affair with her. Tanager was too strong. She thrilled him but she frightened him. With Holly it went on as before; trying to pretend it wasn't *really* going on, trying to pretend that each time it was a spontaneous accident, unplanned and always to be the last meeting. Yet each time, with Jill homebound with a pregnancy she had not even yet confessed to, Holly's genuine gladness to see him had won him quickly back and vestibuled his conscience (her praises of his accomplishments in the theater were always so real he felt distinguished, even man-of-the-world). Slipping off with her to the movies (and once to a speak-easy on Forty-fourth Street near Eighth) seemed the most exquisite of adventures; more tremulous, more satisfying than the embracings and clutchings that always followed. These he enjoyed in their quick mountings but abhorred the instant they were over. Sex disarranged him. He didn't know what to say when it was over.

He still preferred to meet her in places, rather than be seen with her on the street. Not that she wasn't pretty enough. Quite the contrary. She got prettier every time he saw her. Sweeter too, and more loving. The matter was with himself and his lack of aplomb. He knew too many people. He wouldn't be ready. He wouldn't be assured. He'd gum up introductions. Or run. He could never toss it off as Patrick would have. He could only be a man of the world when there was no one about. With Pat, who needed the world, it was the reverse. When he thought of Patrick a great sigh, audible to people near him, met the atmosphere and stood there in his vaporous breath as a briefly visible cry of regret. He had forbidden all others, even his mother, ever to mention Patrick's name in his presence. His death was too painful, too personal. *His own brother!* If he were also someone's son, then let that be their lookout, not his.

He turned into Ovington, this time determined to buy the fitted bag for Jill, no matter what.

When the salespeople saw him they found other duties. One of them, who had been patient with Seton while he puzzled over the beautiful display on previous trips, started for the men's room.

"Here comes Old Lady 31 again," he mumbled to a companion. It was a reference to a popular book of a decade before, a book about an old man who wound up in a home for old ladies.

There was nothing uncharacteristic about Seton's incertitude or his fear. Stores bewildered him. He felt as if his money were being laid out and counted, as if all could take his full inventory and all did. Salesmen had a custodial impersonalism, a world-weary detached concern, the same that doctors wore in great clinics. Some clerks even seemed to have police power. All, Seton feared, looked down their noses, and the question: "Do you have an account here?" sent him into such a spiral of doubt, he could never immediately answer. (Once he'd phoned Jill to ask.) There was a corporate strength, an executive rectitude about stores that jarred his nerve and set up the wild fear that he was in everlasting danger of being challenged, even arrested. Jill had told him this would go away if he paid his bills, and he'd slapped her for it.

"May I help you?"

Here were the bags again, the beautiful shiny feminine bags with mirrors, tiny compartments to tuck away cosmetics, places for billfolds, car license, shopping pad, change purse, cleansing tissue.

"She can put a little phial of perfume right under this clip here."

Seton began writing out their Fairfield address. He could envision Jill's delight upon opening such a rich package from such an elegant store. He'd start doing things for Jill from here on. It wasn't so hard. Keep track of what she wanted or needed. Now especially; now that he could afford things.

He went out into the air again and proceeded up Fifth Avenue, passing the stone lions of the library, waiting for the policeman's whistle at Forty-second. His neck felt chilly. He better get a muffler, but he was not at all sure that Spalding carried mufflers. He'd see, anyhow. Spalding was the only store he could enter without fear. He'd bought all his sweaters there. He had twenty-nine of them.

Two detectives who had been following Seton for many days now separated. One ducked into the lobby of the 500 Building to telephone Tanager Bolt. His companion followed Seton into Spalding.

Tanager was not interested in Ovington.

Holly was Tanager's concern.

She'd seen her now five different times. These occasions had not been mere surreptitious peekings in at the window of the Far Cathay. Tanager's boldness, and her sense of plan, had brought her, in a cloche hat and daringly unfashionable long skirt, right to Holly herself. And it was apparent to Holly that Tanager Bolt (whoever she was) knew the world, had been much abroad, Europe especially. However, the itineraries this importunate woman laid down before Holly; the insistence on meticulous answers to the most intricate questions, would have taxed the resources and the patience of Thos. Cook. Four or five times a day she'd phone. She'd make changes in her trip a few hours after a reservation was confirmed for her. She kept adding new countries, while subtracting days from countries where her visas were secured. She took out the Minches to include the Kattegat, dropped Derwent Water to have another day at Montreux, and canceled the Rhine. She rolled the Dolomites around as if they were marbles.

She left two hundred dollars with Mr. Crosthwaite, the ceaseless manager of the Far Cathay, and if she did not earn his respect, she won his attention. She was a special case. Holly didn't know that anything was being set up. All she knew was the woman made her so nervous, routine problems were getting too big for her.

This was Tanager's first objective.

Calendar errors appeared in Holly's work. Holly scheduled an impossible jump—Arles to San Remo in four hours. Tanager blew up. She appeared in person to see Mr. Crosthwaite.

It had taken a lot of patience but it was coming out right for Tanager.

When the three came out—Holly, Tanager, and Mr. Crosthwaite—Seton was seated in a wicker chair in the customer's alcove. He was waiting for five o'clock, holding a sheaf of unread folders, watching the people pass in the snow. Tiffany was right across the street. He thought he might get Holly a small pin, a nice inexpensive small pin. In a Tiffany box. She'd probably never had anything in a Tiffany box. She'd probably never been in Tiffany's. He never had been in Tiffany's either, had never bought a wedding ring for Jill, for that matter: never thought to. But the fitted bag at Ovington lifted him and made him feel urbane, used to wealth, weary of luxury ships.

It was easier now, with money, to stop in at the Far Cathay. He would have Holly book his passages if he ever took a trip.

Mr. Crosthwaite, the ubiquitous manager, spoke to him with deference and—so Holly told him, full of pride—went around to other customers to whisper to them who Seton was.

From behind her counter, crowded with its garish invitations to leave everything behind and go through the Panama Canal, Holly saw Seton sitting there, waiting quietly.

Her heart stopped for two beats. Tanager pretended to see nothing. Holly gave the playwright a tortured grimace of a smile.

She was trapped.

A sound of insensate exasperation reached Seton's ears—a voice he knew.

Impossible!

He froze stiff, afraid to look, afraid to think, afraid to breathe.

What horror was going forward here—*Tanager* and Holly!

"I demand the immediate return of my two hundred dollars!"

Seton half rose from the wicker chair and agonizedly turned to the two backing off, not daring to make the identification he dreaded.

It was like watching a death drama underwater. Without sound it seemed to advance.

He saw Tanager take money from the manager. He saw her lightly slap Holly with the sheaf of bills, saw Holly shrink, suffocated with embarrassment. Then, in her mountainous pique, without waiting to tuck the money away, Tanager leaned clear across the counter and slapped Holly with the back of her hand. It was a sharper slap than the disgracing gesture with the money. But it was the studied deliberateness of her movement that put the edge of contempt upon it, an edge that cut them all.

Turning away grandly, Tanager used a rank word and started for the door.

Seton could not move. He wanted to rush to Holly's defense. Just then she seemed the shyest, most innocent of people and Tanager the most satanic.

He wanted to do something immediate, something manly and equalizing; to fling Tanager into the snow outside.

But he could not move! He could only stand there in a half crouch, travel folders falling from his weak hands, his own face as stricken as Holly's.

He realized that Holly had fled to the rear of the office. Tanager had moved to the street door. Here she turned scornfully, in imperious willful rage, to hurl one more epithet. Instead of speaking, she pretended to see Seton for the first time.

"Seton!" she shouted. "What are *you* doing in this horrid place!"

It was a challenge. It sent a feeling of dread through his whole body. The six or seven who had come into the Far Cathay on their own errands, now looked right at Seton with a bright, waiting interest.

He could not bear it.

He went quickly to the door and opened it, following Tanager.

Here, as far as he could read her attitude, the matter of the moment just before—the calculated reduction of Holly—had ceased to be. Tanager was almost serene. Firmly she tucked her arm through his and walked him away boldly, steering him toward Madison Avenue as if she knew her objective and were generously including Seton on her way to it.

"What in the world were *you* doing there, Seton! I couldn't believe my eyes!"

"I—I was waiting," he said honestly enough, but his voice, over the hum and mumble of buses in the snow, sounded thready.

"Stand up straight, Seton. Don't slouch. You're not old."

She said this exactly as if Seton might be her son.

"Waiting?" she went on. "Waiting for what? Take me to tea, Seton. I've just time."

Seton felt a whole system of controls threatening to take over his own, yet his own were so weak he felt sustained by the momentary transfer of responsibility—of even the need of speaking—to someone else. Nonetheless his mouth whitened with unspoken rage. What gall she had! What a terrifying way of taking charge of his manhood; of his independence, his privacy. She had a terrifying way of taking charge of *everything*, now he reviewed her methods. It didn't matter whose business it was. Very soon it was also Tanager's. Soon thereafter *only* hers.

Goddamn everybody!

He didn't want to take Tanager to tea. He wanted a drink. He'd never had tea in his life. He didn't even know how it was done.

He wanted to tell Tanager the whole story of Holly, to look at her face as he told it step by step: of their special meaning to each other; of Holly's making up for what he couldn't find in marriage.

By God, he *would* tell Tanager. Look right at her and *tell* it right at her! He felt dangerous now. It was a good feeling. He wanted to flaunt it before Tanager, fling it in her face, flick her with it just the way Tanager had flicked Holly with the money. He glared down murderously. It was a feeling he knew, a releasing and a cleansing thing.

"Yes, I know the lady." There was a touch of snarl in the sound of it, the way his furies always began. "The one you had the fight with. Her name is Holly. She's an altogether fine woman in every way."

"You *know* her? You're kidding! She's a stupid little nobody who works *at a wage!* How *could* you know her! You're joking!"

"No!" There was venom in his contradiction.

"But how *could* you know her?"

"I'll have to go back and explain you!"

"Explain *me!*"

"Yes, for being so goddamn rude!"

She was making him walk more briskly than his natural gait. She laughed aloud, rocking slightly forward in her enjoyment. He realized he was being steered right into the main entrance of the Ritz on Madison Avenue.

Suddenly Seton and Tanager were inside. Seton was scraping off his hat. The chandelier made him nervous. He began to tremble inwardly. He wanted to run.

"But she's a *tradeswoman*, Seton!" she said animatedly.

They were going up the grand stairway—Tanager grandly poised—to the Japanese Gardens.

He tried to think of Glen Lochen but his mind stopped at the doors of the rooms that were closed off, and instead of a country estate, he saw a sheaf of bills, he saw Jill praying, he saw a complicated furnace in an immense and frightening cellar.

"You don't mean—you *can't* mean you know her socially! *That* isn't what you mean, is it?"

A hat-check girl was taking his things.

"Is it?" she persisted.

The captain was before them.

"Near the window," she said at once, and followed.

Tanager fluttered her hand from time to time. Bright faces looked up in response.

"Oh, there are the Gish sisters! There's Katharine Cornell! Today's her birthday."

They were sitting down now. His rage subsided. He had to behave here. He knew it. A sense of grandeur flowed through him in warm suffusion. His skin glowed. He wanted very much to look as if he belonged here, to achieve the poised pre-emptive look that Tanager wore. He wanted to look as if he came (at the same time every day) with a beautiful woman.

To his acute distress, but almost equally to his intense inner pleasure, he realized their tiny table was attracting attention. A lorgnette went up. It seemed impossible. It seemed like the movies.

"Socially? Know her socially? Hell, no!" he said, in sudden irritation. "It's the office that takes care of my reservations. I'm going around the world." He said it casually. "It's detail I hate to be bothered with."

At once he felt better, at least for these moments, in this place. That ought to shut Tanager up. Maybe he *would* go around the world.

The décor caught his eye, Japanese pagodas, dainty shrines, a bright parasol over each table, delicate paper lanterns faintly glowing. And everywhere the sound of running water. There were tiny fishponds with live fish actually swimming about, dwarf trees, Japanese wind bells tinkling in screen and lattice.

It was the genteel tradition. He had been seeking it all his life.

Then Seton saw the bridge. It was almost miniature, yet exquisitely and strongly fashioned, and meant to be used. Doubtless so, for a lady—fulsome, elegant, and self-possessed as Tanager—stepped upon it and moved serenely to its other side. The bridge actually spanned a stream of water that tumbled lightly over a two-foot fall.

"That's Jane Cowl," Tanager offered.

"Isn't that Woollcott?" Seton asked.

"Of course," Tanager answered, surprise and impatience in her voice. "Don't you know *him* yet?"

"Well—I——"

"And George Jean Nathan."

The famous actress now joined the two critics, Nathan quickly rising for her, Woollcott pretending to try. But his stub-bottle body jammed into the table and kept him down. "They both raved about her opening last night."

"I didn't notice. What was it? What show?"

"Really, Seton, you're the limit. *The Road to Rome.* The biggest comedy of the year. And a new writer, too. Comparatively. You better look out."

"Look out? I'm not in competition with anybody. Nathan and Woollcott wrote good reviews for me but it hasn't done anything to the way I write plays."

"It's done something to the people who come."

"The hell with them."

"Don't be so crude. You live on them. And for goodness sakes, why don't you get out of that dreadful hotel you live in?"

He looked at her coldly but she looked back with fire and ice.

"How do you know where the hell I live?"

Tanager ignored this. "I mean it, Seton. Get out of that dreary place. Right now."

He felt his legs shift nervously.

"They know me there. And it's near the theaters. I don't come down to this city to enjoy myself." (What the hell is going on here, telling me I have to change hotels!) "And I never go to a hotel to spread out. I just go to hole up. To work. I'm not your kind of a fellow, Tanager."

"You've forgotten Lake Placid. You've forgotten we've discussed a few plans."

"No, I haven't. Lake Placid was a natural place. I could be myself up there. Never here."

"You don't know anything about yourself. Neither does your wife. You go with the wrong people."

"I suppose I should go over to Woollcott's table and say something unforgettable?"

She looked at him then with a mature, mothering patience, putting her hand lightly on the back of his. She had a power. Now he felt it all over again, just as he had when she paddled up that afternoon in the kayak at the end of summer. Things were hers.

"I thought you'd love coming here. I thought you'd love the little bridge, Seton. I thought you might think of the other little bridge. The real one. On the island. In the dark. Of the night."

All Seton wanted was a drink of whisky. No, not a drink. He wanted a barrel of it.

Tea came on a wheeled cart. What was happening to him? Did he *really* like it here? Or did he hate it altogether? If only he could feel socially comfortable! He had seven hundred dollars in his wallet. This made him feel better. He had meant to pay it, part of it anyhow, to his lawyer.

Seton began to feel more and more comfortable in the money. Let the lawyer wait. The lawyer had been making good money a lot longer than Seton had. And there was no risk to being a lawyer. Nothing like plays, when you're always a bum to somebody, no matter.

There was a covered dish of hot canapes over an alcohol flame, tiny baskets of toasted cheese bread stuffed with curried chicken.

Who the hell did this Tanager Bolt woman think she was anyhow? Dragging him out of his life, knocking Holly around! She didn't seem to realize he was married even!

He was a married man!

Some things are sacred!

She had no right!

Hell with her!

Goddamn slitty-eyed slut!

How had Charlie Westover stood it all those years! Goddamn slitty-eyed slut was what he used to call her. Well, he hadn't stood her and that was the answer to that! God stiffen her! Who in the goddamn hell did she think she was, anyhow! His keeper?

Tea was delicious.

"Sit up, Seton. Don't slouch."

Seton sat up. His fine head was poised like a serpent's. Something happened to the total mechanism of him when she spoke, when she gave an order. It had a strange authority. Just as she'd said: "Near the window" to the captain.

She was sure of the world she lived in. She asked for a lot. And she got it.

"Never mind about the bridge. I thought you'd like it. I didn't know what an abtuse donkey you really were. Never mind about you and me, for that matter. It would be quite a victory if I could make you realize only one thing this afternoon."

"What?" he asked quickly, taking fear.

"That you don't have to go over to Woollcott's table and say a damn thing. That he wouldn't have *anything to do* except for you! That you're the most important man in the room. That you're the most important man that ever came *in*. The other tables know it. *They* concede it. But what do you do? You just sit here, bent over like a chestnut worm, glaring at your sandwiches."

She set her cup down with a firm but dainty click.

"You don't have to go to *anyone's* table. They have to come to yours. Don't you know that? Don't you know who you *are*, Seton? Then why don't you expect it? Why don't you insist on it?"

"Insist——?"

"Oh, you're hopeless. Let's get out of here. Just go on through your dismal little life with your dismal wife, having your dismal damn little babies! The hell with the little bridge. It's one we can burn without ever coming to. Such a waste though."

She laughed then. She laughed right at him, and strode out of the Japanese Gardens as if she were the Empress, Seton coasting behind, rocking like a slave under a load of firewood.

At the marquee on Madison Avenue the doorman jumped under her quick invisible nod and opened a cab door. The way things happened for Tanager! How did the man even know she wanted a cab? She'd said nothing.

"May I see you home?"

"Don't bother."

Seton was bareheaded. He knew he might catch cold. It was a dangerous time of year. Pneumonia weather. He looked in as she seated herself. She smiled brightly, exactly the way she had smiled across at him when they first sat down half an hour earlier.

"But can't I see you again? Everything seems so strange here. I'm not used to things."

"Don't hurry." The smile was now light mockery. "There's an invitation in the mail . . . Thanksgiving party. Come or don't come. But *do* stand up. Do try to stand up. You *are* a New Yorker"— here Tanager touched him lightly on the cheek, as one pats a child— and "there's lots to see!"

The door slammed, the gears meshed, a policeman on duty in the middle of the intersection at Forty-fifth Street waved them south, holding back a trolley to speed them on.

What a woman! What a cold, wretched woman, Seton thought, as the car whirled off in the snow. But what he wouldn't give to have her sense of belonging!

It was her world, every bit, and everyone in it was a servant.

To hell with her and her party.

Alone in the snow, alone in the winter sounds of early evening in New York, he turned west. All he could think of was getting a drink. With both his father and Patrick dead and his mother a teetotaler, it was hard to get a drink now. He had no supply of his own, no bootlegger. And he was no collector of speak-easy cards, for he was a lone drinker.

He wanted a drink before apologizing to Holly for what Tanager had done to her; to apologize for not interfering. He had to have the drink, then he had to think what to say.

There was not anything to say. That was why it was being such a problem in his mind. He had just stood there watching, letting Tanager sass and scold, letting her cuff away!

He winced inwardly as the ugly scene kept coming back, coming back, each time putting another lash across his manhood.

Why *hadn't* he done something? Done anything! Why hadn't he acted! Why had he fled? He could have stepped in and broken it up some way, even perhaps just by introducing the two.

He was no man!

"Tanager—this is Holly—my own personal travel agent. What in the world is the matter?" Something like that. That would take the edge off the attack. Then to Holly, "Miss Bolt is a very *intense* person, Holly. I apologize for her. May I help you in any way?"

But Seton was afraid of Tanager and now, after the encounter in the Adirondacks, after her penetration of his private lake at Fairfield and their plans for more in the spring, he couldn't bear letting her find out—as she might—that he was there to take Holly out on a date. He wouldn't have been able to endure the spoken scorn this might earn from Tanager.

Then the essence of his self-disgust became very clear: he would not have been able to take it so he had let Holly take it. Take it all alone.

The Far Cathay was shut for the night. So was Tiffany across the street. Seton trudged on toward Tony's on Sixth Avenue, the only speak-easy he was sure he could get in.

It was dark and smoky but it was crowded and disturbingly cheerful. He hated to jam his way through people. He hated to touch them. He hated subways and street crowds and people in the aisles of stores.

Finally he got to the mahogany of the bar. Shrill women were all about, people expanding, voices rising to dent other voices already in motion. It had the congestion of a foc's'le. Seton had four fast drinks. He thought of his own saloon. It would almost certainly be closed up. Hennessy would never have made the kind of money necessary to meet the pay-offs to stay open. It was probably a cheap restaurant by this time.

All of a sudden Seton wanted to kill himself.

He abhorred everything he saw inside himself and every fixture in the world outside, including all the people he knew. He did not think of his wife, or his sons, or the child unborn. He just wanted to be dead, to be dead, to be dead.

In the Pilgrim Pawn Shop one block from Tony's on Sixth Avenue and Fiftieth Street he bought a .25-caliber revolver, a small hammerless revolver, for sixteen dollars. He put this in his trousers pocket. It felt uncomfortable and conspicuous there and he transferred the weapon, looking foolishly over his shoulder at no one, to his overcoat.

He decided to see his mother before he shot himself. He would shoot himself on a pier near Hennessy's. He'd wait till the tide was going out. Then he could lean forward and shoot himself so as to topple into the Hudson and be swept through the Narrows and out to sea by the current and the scour while the tide was right. He would be dead when he hit the water. He wouldn't have to drown. And the sea would take him, finally and smoothly and forever.

No one was in his mother's apartment.

Then he saw a bottle of Green River, unopened, sitting on the window sill. He opened it at once—probably she kept it about for any of the Catholic fathers who might come to call.

In the presence of the whisky the urgency of the moment receded. It fortified his determination—now a conscious longing—to kill himself, but to do so without making the means of it, or the instant of it, so important any longer. He would do it and be glad of it but now that he had the whisky he could take his time.

He was not afraid.

It suddenly occurred to him that he had bought no cartridges. He wouldn't be able to buy any till the next day. His revolver was useless altogether.

He twitched convulsively in the frustration of this, spilling his liquor on the carpet and on his clothes. He brushed at it carelessly with the heel of his free hand and filled the glass again.

Something was here, plucking at his memory. It was something he needed now. *There was something nearby he had to have. He knew it.* He stood up. He began to tremble. He set down his glass. He forced himself to think. There was a solace here. There was a way of death. Right here!

Patrick jumped into his mind. Incongruously he saw Patrick's head bobbing down into a tub of flowers to smell the hyacinths as they passed a Broadway hotel. Years ago. But something fastened to Seton then that was on him still, something that Patrick had

said and that Seton had tucked into the vault of his mind, something
for him to *use*. Never, never to speak of but never, never to forget.

If he had to kill himself.

The sight of his brother was as clear as life. He could even see the
yellow gloves, the white summer spats, briefly fashionable in Patrick's
ephemeral circle. But what was it he'd *said*? What was it that his
mother did that had then so fascinated and horrified?

It moved a little closer now. It wasn't something she did. It was
something she had, something she collected. In brittle declaration, as
his memory crackled to perform and serve him, a key word broke in
upon his gathering hysteria:

"Dispense."

Then the phrase came back, the whole phrase, and the sound of it,
just the way it had come out of Patrick:

"She dispenses it for toothache. Or lumbago. Hands it around the
neighborhood to anybody that's feeling bad."

It was Veronal.

She never took it herself, not any more. But she kept it about.

Seton began tearing up his mother's apartment. Soon he had ruined
it.

But he found the cache in the bottom drawer of her bedroom
bureau.

Shaking in a most agitated way, he twisted the cork out of one of
the bottles and shook out a handful of pills.

Death was a friend. A *friend*. Death was still. Death was peace.

But he couldn't kill himself right there. His mother might come
in. She might come in and stop it.

He rushed out, grabbing the whisky, forgetting his hat.

You just went to sleep with Veronal. You didn't have to think
any more. You felt nothing. Veronal locked up your kidneys. You
died in a coma with no pain, no noise, no mess. No agonizing inter-
mittent returnings to any conscious concern over what was happening. It was opium sleep without the dreaming, it was morphine sleep
without thirst; quiet, sure, unhurried, clean, irrevocable. You just
floated out softly on the dark river that made no sound, that had no
chill, no turning, and no end.

At West and Fulton, Seton was relieved to find that Hennessy's was not only open but that it held the same comforts he remembered. And not jammed, either, the way Tony's was jammed.

Hennessy saw he was drunk and troubled, but he beamed in real gladness.

"Here's your old sailing mate, men!" he roared. Seton flourished his own bottle and slid it down the bar. "Where you been? Last time you paid us a visit, you had a beautiful young lady. You took down the *Great Admiral*"—here Hennessy waved toward the back room— "and showed her every stitch o' canvas she had!"

Seton's eyes glistened in the strange disharmonies the reference brought him. He'd been drinking in the cab coming down. Yes, he remembered being here with Holly, all right. And vaguely remembered showing her the ship's model, point by point. But little after. All he could see now was the face of Holly, the face slashed by his cowardice, and her eyes, not accusing, just bewildered, eyes that kept moving back and forth, looking at him. And as he watched, the face kept getting crowded away by Tanager's.

Holly was his woman.

"One on the house! All around!" Hennessy was full of delight.

"No!" Seton roared. "Drinks on me! All night!"

There was a good shout. Seton slapped down a fifty-dollar bill, and Hennessy gave him forty back, helping him to tuck it away.

Seton leaned across, close to Hennessy.

"You got a room I can have? Upstairs?"

"The girls—they aren't working here any more, Mr. Farrier."

"No, no. No girls. I just got to be alone, I got to rest. I just got to be away from everybody I know. Day or two."

"Sure, I guess. Fix one, anyhow. For you."

Hennessy left the bar but immediately peered back from behind the curtains of the back room to take a sharp look at his old friend; the man who used to love to come down here, the man who would always be strange. As he watched, he saw Seton shake something from a small bottle, saw the hand toss something to the mouth—three times it went there—then reach for water to wash down what he'd taken.

What made Hennessy wary was the black, bleak, departed look that loomed over Seton's face after he swallowed. He'd seen this

before, just once. He'd seen it early in the morning at Arras, with
men running everywhere and the air exploding with noise, and this
one man, the one with the same look that Seton wore—the vacant
half-friendly surprise that occupies a man's face when death arrives
before pain.

Hennessy went upstairs to check a room. When he returned Seton
was in the same place and smirking just a little, as with some inner
pleasure, or some private victory he preferred to hold onto alone. His
head was nodding sleepily now and then, as he amiably accepted
the obtuse thanks and the worn-out toasts of the men around him.

He drank, then passed his jigger to Hennessy with a flick of his
forefinger. Hennessy quickly filled it, then slipped down the bar to
Eddy, a cargo checker he knew well.

Very quietly and steadily Hennessy said to him:

"Move up on Mr. Farrier, Eddy. When you are on the far side of
him, fish around in the left-hand pocket of his overcoat."

Eddy didn't look like he belonged on the waterfront. He had a
Y.M.C.A. look. And he had a collar and tie.

"You mean, pick his pocket?" Eddy was horrified.

"There's a small bottle in the left-hand pocket. He took a big dose
out of it. Just now."

"Maybe it's cough medicine."

"No. You go do it, Eddy."

"Well——"

"I'll stand you drinks for a week."

"You like this fellow?"

"Yeah. Yeah, I like him. He's a writer."

"What the hell is he doin' here, then?"

"He used to come here."

"I don't get it."

"Just get me the empty bottle."

"Do you think he's trying to croak himself? Is that it?"

"Yeah." Hennessy could see Eddy going with the plan now, for
his glance traversed the distance and his mind began to tighten down
on the chances. Suddenly Seton began to shout.

"Set some bottles on the bar, Mr. Hennessy! To hell with these
little shots! We've had a long v'yage!"

There was a boom of discordant laughing and shouting. The bottles came off the shelf and banged like jugs. Seton held up a ten, which Hennessy took, then turned to the opening of the bottles. The men drank, sang, and swapped stories for half an hour. Then the cargo checker went out to the men's room. Here he handed Hennessy two bottles, one empty, the other nearly so. Neither man could make much of the markings. The bottles were unlike in size, color and shape. The prescription dates were eight years apart.

"Skin up to the Vesey Street Pharmacy. Find out what the hell this is. Call me!"

"It's a hell of a dirty night! It ain't freezin'! Just dirty."

He left. Seton came in immediately then, wobbling with liquor, unbottoning his trousers. Hennessy held the door for him to pass through. Then he asked, direct:

"Are you all right?"

"Yes," Seton answered. But it was a faraway answer, impersonal, lost in the drift of louder talk beyond. His eyes were glazing, his jaw getting slack. There was a room upstairs but Hennessy didn't intend that Seton die in it, not now in Prohibition, especially not now since the man was famous.

Hennessy had enough trouble just staying open. It cost him half his take, exactly half. Not the net either, half the gross. An attempted suicide would close him up. A call for an ambulance would bring police.

He waited outside the door.

"Mr. Farrier, you're carryin' too much cash to be carryin' all that booze. You want me to lock it up in me own safe?"

"Sure, lock 'er up. Lock 'er up. Whassiff-I-care-lock-'er-up!"

He thought Seton was crying. He went back to the bar. He gave five dollars each to two stevedores who frequented his place.

"Keep him walking! Don't let him rest. Don't let him si' down."

"What if he passes out cold on us?"

"Don't let 'im."

"Don't *let* 'im! Jesus! How d'ya do that don't let 'im!

"Rub snow on 'im. Hit him. If you have to hit, hit him. But don't *hurt* 'im. Just to keep him movin'! *He's gotta stay awake!*"

"What's he got in 'im?"

"I don' know."

"Maybe it's just the whisky."

"It isn't the whisky."

Seton came out. Hennessy took Seton's wallet, counted out six hundred dollars, and put it in his cash register. He scribbled a note: "I have your 600. Hennessy." He clapped this in Seton's wallet and put it in his pocket. But Seton was entering a pasture of velvet grass, with long slanting shafts of sunlight giving way before him. He felt the earth yield gently with every step. He could hear music. A woman dressed in white was walking toward him, very pretty, smiling and lifting a hand, as an actress might to get attention for a prologue.

The two dock workers looked at Hennessy. All the men drinking stopped. Hennessy jerked his head quietly toward the door. One man took Seton's left arm, the other his right, and they steered him out.

Hennessy ran to the door and gave one more order.

"Keep goin' around the block. This here block. So we can find you quick. When we know what to do!"

Seton's knees lost their strength in less than a block. One of the stevedores reached down, scooping up a handful of slush. He daubed this over Seton's face, but Seton kept sinking down. They sat him down then on a stone-loading platform of a shed to get more snow and slush but Seton fell off at once.

"Hit 'im!"

"Naw. *You* hit 'im. Only don't hurt him none. Just kinda slap 'im."

"You do it. I ain't never seen this guy."

They stood looking down for a moment.

"Hey!" He nudged Seton with his toe, pushing the hip back and forth.

"Hell, I'll hit him!"

They picked him up and slapped him. Then they walked him over to the edge of the sidewalk and bent him over the gutter. All the gutters were choked with slush, soft, stained by horses and traffic filth. They splashed more slush in his face. It was ice cold. Seton gasped and his eyes half opened. A groan came out of him. The two men slapped him again, encouraging him to wake up and start walking. They told him they were his friends. They poured slush down his neck. They felt very kind and foolish and afraid.

"Who the hell is he?" one of them asked. They didn't like to hit him. But they didn't like their assignment either and they didn't like the way the man couldn't seem to get walking any good so they could exercise him and make him feel better. They kind of liked him. He'd set up a bunch of drinks. But he sure didn't belong at Hennessy's. The clothes. And that roll. What the hell is this?

They both saw the policeman at the same time and they both fled. Seton fell down again, gently flattening out on the corner of Fulton.

Molly Farrier, finding her place turned over, called Arleigh Brayce.

"Do you know that saloon he used to go to?"

"Of course, Molly."

"I've got a feeling he went there."

"I'll go." He'd been there before once or twice. For the Farriers, Arleigh had been in a thousand places he loathed.

Hennessy was glad to turn over the six hundred dollars.

"I had a couple of the boys walk him around. While we got a druggist to see what it was."

"What was it?"

"It was Veronal."

"And he took it here?"

"Right here. Right there exactly where you're standing now."

"But why did the men run?"

"Damn if I know. Scared maybe. Nothin' like this ever happened. We looked everywhere."

Arleigh looked at him and believed him.

"But you didn't call the police."

"No. I got real light protection here."

Arleigh saw the pleading look in Hennessy's eye.

"Well, I'll do this, Hennessy. I'll stop at the precinct. Then I'll go on to Bellevue. But that's all I'll do for you. If I don't pick up anything, I'm going to call the commissioner. And you better remember who was here. Every goddamn one of them. And where they live."

Arleigh walked through the slush to the precinct.

Its blue globes and its drab pillars gave the building and vicinity a London look, London at night. It smelled like the Thames. It took Arleigh back to a thousand nights, to memories of marriage, to the great waste that was always right there to chase after the great effort.

In the precinct they knew about Seton. They provided a police car to take Arleigh over to Bellevue.

In Bellevue, with the tubing rigged to pump out his stomach and drain off the poison, Seton looked like Patrick just before his own death.

Except for the long span of trimmed mustache, unusually black against the bloodless lip, Arleigh realized for the first time that Seton could have been Patrick. Near to death, their resemblance would have astonished them both.

"You a relative?" A Jewish intern was wiping his hands.

"No. Friend of the family."

"How'd you hear?"

Arleigh shrugged wearily.

"Goes on benders. I've expected him to make Bellevue for a long time."

The Jewish doctor didn't say anything.

"He was supposed to sail for Europe this Friday."

Arleigh made it up and made it casual.

"Gee. He could make it. If he had somebody to go with him."

"Somebody is going."

"You?"

"No. Not me. A man named Vivian Sable."

"Vivian Sable the publisher?"

"Yes. Do you know him?"

"Well, not really know him. But I know a lot of his friends. Who's our guest here? I've seen him. His picture anyhow."

"It's Seton Farrier."

"The playwright?" Arleigh nodded slightly. "My God." Though his concern before had been real enough, he looked down again with new interest.

"What the hell is the matter with these guys that got everything? Why the hell can't they handle it?"

He leaned down again, poking about with his stethoscope.

"My God, if I had it, I sure wouldn't be here."

"You're better off than he is."

"How do you figure?"

"You *belong* someplace." There was a pause. "Nobody has everything. I never met any who did."

"You know everybody?"

"Yes." Arleigh felt snappish. "Can I remove this man to a private hospital?"

"Yes. Another day anyhow. Dr. Barret will have to see him. Does Mr. Farrier have a doctor of his own? Here in New York?"

"Oh yes," Arleigh answered, deciding not to go into the matter. But thought at once of Mortimer Flowers.

"That blackness in his face—how soon will that go away?"

"Couple of hours. Cyanotic. Always happens."

"Thank you for taking care of this fellow, Doctor." Arleigh walked out without looking back. At the door of the ward he stopped.

"Here." He handed fifty dollars to the young intern, who shook his head, puzzled but pleasantly surprised.

"Yes, take it. Please, for God's sake. You earn it. Thirty times over you fellows earn it. I know what they pay you. I was going to be a doctor once."

It was Seton's money. It made Arleigh feel good.

He walked down the corridor. He was never to see Seton again.

27

SETON WENT TO TANAGER'S PARTY. HE HAD RECOVered from the overdose of pills. No one knew. He was in rehearsal once more. It was two days before Thanksgiving. He looked at himself in the mirror in Tanager's apartment lobby, then looked at himself all the way up in the elevator. He was wearing the same clothes he had worn the month before when Montagu had made the portraits.

One was in the window right now at Forty-fifth and Fifth. Montagu had placed the head in a frame that was cut and decorated to take on the outlines of a Roman coin. The effect gave austere isolation to the face but great intensity too.

People stopped to stare. Seton could see why. He had a strong face. He'd always been aware he had a strong face.

He pushed Tanager's buzzer. She came quickly, peeking around the side of the door, looking startled, looking a little puzzled.

"Seton!" she said. Her tone was cool, her face had a startled but not unfriendly look. He could see she was wearing something Chinese. The upper frogs were unbuttoned. For the rest, pantaloons was the only word that came to him.

"You're surprised to see me," he said, himself nonplused and a little embarrassed.

"Seton, you're gorgeous but it's *tomorrow!*" She waved at the room; then took him by the arm and brought him in. "See?" A papier-mâché Pilgrim with a papier-mâché blunderbuss stood guard at the fireplace. There were some pumpkins below.

"But you can help!" Tanager had arranged such surprises before. They never failed.

That day and that night and the next day Seton stayed to help. He was in her toils. He knew it and he loved it and he hated it.

28

OWN WIFE,

. . . and I have been quite desperately ill, not that this would be of much interest to you. I realize your days are full with or without me. I guess you didn't like the present I sent. You might at least have said thank you. If you don't like it, you can exchange it for something you might prefer to pick out for yourself.

Darling Husband—

How do you think I can know of you if you don't tell me? I sold a scenario and bought you the most beautiful new watch I ever saw and heard not a thing. I'm terribly sorry you have been ill. I thought after the wonderful trip to Placid, and after your being able to put drinking aside, you would be fine, even for the grinding demands of so many rehearsals.

I'm very excited about the present you bought me! Even more than I am about Barren Goddess. *Of course I'll love it! It just hasn't come yet. What is it? The very idea—that I should ever think of changing it for something else! How little you know me! Just to see you in a store, picking out something for me! It is very flattering. I will cherish it forever. Being a woman I just can't wait to see what it is! I do thank you, thank you, thank you, my thoughtful husband!*

Be sure you have a sleeve sweater (not a vest) at all times in rehearsal. I wrote to your mother. She answered this morning but said nothing of your illness. Did you keep it away from her too?! I asked her to keep reminding you of malted milk. They have tablets now, too (besides the powder). Keep them in your pocket. Wear your rubbers. Didn't the cookies come?

Lovingly, Jill.

29

JILL KNEW THE BABY WOULD COME THAT DAY. SETON had kissed her in the morning and had been very tender. Frightened too. Once, to show her his great appreciation for the watch, he'd crept up close behind her, touched the tiny lever, and held the magical mechanism to her ear while it sweetly chimed. She'd reached behind and patted him and felt very warm and safe.

Now it was four-thirty in the afternoon. Jill could hear the click and clatter of the little rectangular weights that rose and fell in the vertical tracks Abercrombie and Fitch had set into the brick wall of what Seton called his exercise room.

Each day during the winter, whenever Seton was at home in Glen Lochen and after he'd finished writing for the day, he'd spend half an hour in his tiny gymnasium making swimming motions with the chest weights. First he'd do the breast stroke, facing the wall, then, back to wall, he'd do the trudgen. He had a third exercise he called "running in place." When his exercising was over, he'd do West Point breathing for five minutes, take his pulse with a stop watch that he'd bought at Spalding, jot down the figure, then put a yellow tape measure around his chest.

He'd measure his chest deflated, then normal, then expanded, and note this figure too, and the date. Then he'd measure his biceps, a measurement always taken with the muscles up.

Jill knew it was past time. Today he should not have exercised. Or he should have done it earlier. He should have gone for Dr. Gillespie two hours ago. Now her pains were coming every eight or nine minutes. She was glad Mrs. Breslin was at the movies and that Molly had Sean for this week. She was glad she'd be alone with a doctor and a nurse. She was glad there was nothing to worry about. She and Seton had had a long period of peace. She wished only that Seton were being as solicitous about this baby as he had been about Sean.

But from what she'd been told at Placid, she knew Seton felt threatened by her pregnancy and that the actual birth would be a greater shock to him than to her. Even so——

Well, there was no sense in fussing. The baby would come and it would not wait on Seton's solicitude.

The sounds had stopped in the gymnasium. She heard a door slam. Seton never made any sound when he walked, but he slammed doors. He would be up now. He'd be up and they'd be off. She knew he was passing from the pantry, where the cellar door was, through the great dining room. Probably he'd stand there a moment looking again at the Charge of the Light Brigade. He'd become deeply involved in the battle and had named several of the officers. Arleigh Brayce was the one whose head was rolling.

Now at the top of the stairs she called to him. But she got a phlegmy answer.

She called again. Seton walked out into the hall then and stood quietly at the foot of the stairs. He was dressed in a pair of blue shorts too long for him, and a maroon sleeved jersey. He had on a pair of gym shoes, and in his hands was a pair of mechanical grips which he was absent-mindedly squeezing. He looked bony and unlikely. And suddenly, to her, he looked exasperatingly useless. It was obvious he had forgotten all about her condition.

"Is the car in the drive, Seton? It's time we went. I'm ready."

He stared up at his wife. His hands stopped working the grips. He seemed trying to understand her while trying also to retain the thought that her words were replacing.

"Telephone," he said softly. "Use telephone."

"Seton!"

Fear stabbed her, fear and a surge of vexation. He wasn't preoccupied. He was drunk. This shocked and disappointed her, for she knew he was beginning to see his way out of the trap that liquor set for him.

A labor pain seized her. She hung onto the bannister, then sat down on a step near the top of the stairs. Seton kept looking up at her, interested, docile, willing to be used, trying to relate and register. She winced and pulled herself to her feet. She leaned for support on the railing, looking directly at Seton, trying to project hard sense into his mind, all the time descending step by step. When she was near the bottom he began to back away a little. She feared now she would not be able to make the hospital, that Seton might not be able to drive.

"Get in the *car!* Get Dr. Gillespie!" she implored.

Seton seemed vaguely to hear and to respond. He set the grips on the console table in the hall and went out the front door, then came back and put on an overcoat, saluted elaborately, tried to smile, and went out again, leaving the door open.

In the alcove off the hall Jill went to the phone, but the receiver was off the hook. It had obviously been off all during the period of her husband's exercise. The phone was a wall-crank instrument like all the rest in that part of rural Connecticut. Jill returned the receiver to its hook, cranked, lifted the receiver, and listened.

"God! Hurry!" She hissed this to herself. She heard nothing. She kept hanging up, then unhooking and cranking, unhooking and cranking. She could hear a steady wire hum, but the sound was as impersonal as the snow outside. She was afraid she might have another pain before she was able to get back upstairs to her bed.

Outside, she heard the Pierce-Arrow drive away. This cheered her. Even if Seton hadn't made sense to her, he might recover in the cold of the afternoon.

The grotesque indignity of her position occurred to her and in strange obedience to custom and to her habit of modesty, she tightened the edge of her skirt around her knees. At once the absurdity of this struck her and she let her legs open relaxingly.

Sitting there in the cold and in the quickly arriving darkness of late afternoon in the winter, she thought how wrong everyone was who talked of the symptoms and the experience of childbirth. She thought that in the very next thing that she wrote—if she ever had time to set it down—she would correct the whole misunderstanding that surrounded the popular image of childbirth. She'd begin by scotching the rumor about the "bearing-down" pain.

With so many babies born of woman, how could such an inaccurate view of the dynamics of childbirth receive so much popular credence? Because men, not women, did the writing?

Damn you, Seton! Where are you now?

When the next pain hit, Jill was drawing her feet under her body. The wave sent her against the cold plaster of the wall, in gasping silence and taut immobility, as a prisoner lashed when seated. Her body quivered. With her two hands she reached up, clutching the wooden box of the telephone, and pulled herself to her feet.

Once more she cranked the phone, unhooked the receiver and listened.

"Number, please?"

"This is Mrs. Farrier at Glen Lochen. I'm having a baby. I need help. Call Dr. Gillespie. Call anybody."

"Mrs. Farrier?"

"Yes. Please. Call the hospital. Call Dr. Gillespie."

Now she realized for the first time that she might have to have her baby with no help. She was more furious than fearful. She knew the baby would be born whatever she might do or not do, and in the slow climb up the stairs she began to think what she should have near her if she were to be all alone for this ordeal.

There was not much time.

In her feelings, staring at the ominous bulge she was lugging, she wished she could somehow separate herself from Seton physically for as long as her sense of humiliation was to continue.

She hated him.

Her pain would visit, then mysteriously, mercifully, take its leave. Outside, there was a cemetery stillness, but inside, her mind roared. She felt her back would break; that cleavers had entered the spinal column and were being screwed from outside.

When pains hit her now they began to bewilder her. She could see, but while they lasted she couldn't think. What am I *trying* to think? I am trying to think—how will I cut and tie the cord? What will I do if the baby won't come? If I have trouble? If I have a breach?

What will I do if I have a breach?

What will I do if I hemorrhage? That is what I am trying to think. Please God, be near.

To cut the cord, get some shears. Use the sewing basket, Jill. Use the sewing shears. And thread. Use Number Two thread. You have some. That is strong.

But she could not find the sewing basket. She remembered seeing it in the kitchen. She remembered Sean's taking it to Mrs. Breslin in the kitchen.

Now for the first time Jill's fear began to spread.

How comforting would have been the sound of a motor, the slam of a door, the clicking open of the latches of a doctor's grip. Would he bring chloroform? Yes. Of course. He'd have to. Right away he'd see she was in no shape to make the trip to the hospital, that there wasn't time. But suppose he forgot to bring any?

The phone rang, their own ring—three, then two—but Jill knew she could not make the stairs. The last climb was all she had in her.

She picked up two towels from the bathroom, putting one over her pillow slip, tossing the other to the middle of the bed. She took off her robe, then while slipping her nightgown over her head, a new pain possessed her—the worst and the quickest to arrive—and it racked her arms, half raised as they were. The sight of her bedroom was briefly blotted out by the nightgown she could not lift from her face. She sat on the edge of the bed. She felt sweat run down her face, down her ribs, run off her thighs onto the sheet.

She heaved her dragging ungainliness onto the bed, shoved the pillow up against the headboard, wedging it there, then reached up to grip the carved decorations on its top. Her knees opened.

Now her back was on fire. The small of her back. It was exactly as if an unseen hand had forced a red-hot poker up through the mattress and laid it flat and searing on the small of her back. She could feel herself reel while half sitting. She realized she was descending into a stupor.

"Oh, come! Oh, do come!" She tried to say "Dr. Gillespie" but nothing intelligible formed in her mouth and her breath, blown out in quick gasps, tossed saliva to her chin and mouth corners.

Her head rocked.

For three hours and a quarter she tossed back and forth.

Between pains she realized her hands were exhausted from clutching the headboard. Then a new pain, engrossing and stealthy, would freeze her mind and send the hands wildly, reflexively back again for something to grip.

Though she could not hear them, she knew that groans were escaping her. Pains that had come every few seconds were now striking in faster sequence so that she could scarcely find breath between. Torment was greatly magnified with each contraction. Through the whole region of her groin she now felt a pulverizing pressure that must soon split the pelvic bones.

Suddenly her whole back seemed to disintegrate. It felt as if the backbone itself were being pulled right out. She had no fight left. She had to let everything go. Dizziness blurred her eyes. The room dimmed. The ceiling rose and disappeared. Racked and laid out, Jill's hands and arms fell down limply. Just before the baby's head emerged, there was a violent rupturing of membranes, an unbelievable quantity of water burst forth. It made a loud gushing sound. The baby's head came out at the same time. One more violent contraction and the baby was pinched forth. Shoulders, chest, belly, hips, legs, doll's feet—the body slid forth with such force and yet with such a controlled steadiness it seemed to appear as by mechanical impulse. It seemed not a new life at all but a marvelous toy with an invisible spring to steer it.

The pain was too severe and enveloping for Jill to know the instant her baby came into the world, but she had a half-conscious realization that some awful crisis had just occurred.

She opened her eyes in the dark, rousing from the stupor of what had happened, struggling to act, to think, in whatever remained of the emergency.

It was not over.

She heard a strange splashing sound. She looked quickly down between her legs, heaving her body back. The day's light had long ago gone. She snapped on the reading light. Her baby was there in the middle of the bed before her. About ten inches of cord was showing. Then Jill realized her baby was drowning in a pool of amniotic fluid. She turned sideways to the edge of the bed where her weight made a depression that ran the water off the bed and onto the floor. But she was still carrying the afterbirth and she knew she could not stand. She seized a towel and dried the baby's face, opening its tiny nostrils, wiping its mouth clean, crying to it. But the baby was limp and silent. Jill wept. Then came one more contraction, like a shuddering of the earth—the one that was the one too many, she felt—a smothered cry came into her mouth, she fell back halfway to the pillow, and the contraction, with the spasmodic reaction of her whole body, brought the afterbirth.

She sat upright at once. Her baby was still motionless. How long had Jill been unconscious? How many seconds, how many minutes had the baby's head been immersed in the very water that had for so many months protected this very same life?

She prayed and worked.

She wrapped the ugly afterbirth in one towel, her baby in the other. She set the two bundles beside each other in the middle of the bed. She stood up. Unexpectedly she felt able to move freely. She walked to the bureau. She picked up her manicure scissors and came

back to the bed and unwrapped her baby. Attentively she snipped
at the umbilical cord. It seemed very tough. She cut at the cord,
making tiny, quick motions, finally separating it about four inches
from the baby's navel. Blood oozed from both ends of the tube. She
grabbed up some unfinished knitting from the night table, tore out
two feet of stitches, snapped the yarn and tied the cord at each of
its severed ends.

Now, looking into her baby's face with a wild urgency, trying to
breathe her own breath into its body, piteous little cries came out of
Jill, begging the strange creature to come to life. Lovingly she dried
its face again, patted its back, its miniature buttocks.

Suddenly it wailed, showed its gums, and in full face turned all its
six pounds of disapproval and vitality upon Jill.

Jill had another little boy.

She carried the placenta to the bathroom and set it down in the
tub. Then in the basin she gave her baby his first bath. She put a
fresh towel around him, carried him back to the bedroom, looked
at him all over, opened Seton's bed—her own was ruined—and put
the baby carefully down. Then she cleaned the floor, stripped her
own bed, and got out a fresh nightgown.

Many hours later Dr. Gillespie came in but there wasn't much
for him to do. It seemed a pity to wake Jill.

Forty miles away Seton was yelling "Bro-o-o-o-cco!" with the rest
of the crowd but he didn't know why. He could scarcely see the
bicycles or the bent backs of the riders and had no idea who had
won the last sprint.

He drank for four days. Then he was afraid to come back. Unexpected interest in his newest play took him to California. He was
glad to go. He wrote every day. His contrition was so anguished, Jill
began to fear the man would break down again. His remorse seemed
beyond expression.

Then with no warning, a single letter changed everything.

*I loathe California and I loathe especially this smug rich
empty subtropical palm-fronded Pasadena-that-looks-more-
like-Cohoes and I am hardly sane considering the strain of
this trip, and the suspense of having to deal with zealous*

*incompetence. But added to that is the alum taste that your
actions (only just now reported to me) have put in my
mouth and that have been reported to me here from Hollywood. It is therefore most painful for me to hear, on the
very best possible authority, that you are carrying on just as
if your own conduct were your own affair, lights on all night
at Glen Lochen; as if I didn't exist, as if you had a right to
come and go, with whom and where, at any hour of the
day or night; that you'd hired a man to drive you back and
forth to New York with God knows whom and for God
knows what, as if you had not a care in the world nor any
responsibility whatever to the increasing host that I am
supporting.*

*Jill, I am just plain shocked that you can even think of
having cocktails, of even wanting them, in public or in
private. After what I've been through! And a brand-new
baby! A baby I've never seen! What kind of hypocrisy am I
living with that you can make such a fuss over my drinking
and throw such a handy disguise over your own! I forbid you
to drink ever again! And you are constantly being seen with
men! Suppose the newspapers got hold of this! Just as I am
to raise the curtain on my greatest effort—perhaps my last?
They'd kill us! Do you know what my plays are doing? What
is being said? A hell of a lot you care! Even Tanager is more
attentive than you. She's keeping a daily scrapbook."*

Dear Seton,

*I would feel freer to talk about you as a dramatic artist if
you gave me the same privileges you extend to others. You
have locked this away from me, yet chide me for not knowing
the things you have withheld. I've never seen a Seton Farrier
opening with you, and only seen two with Vivian Sable. Two
out of sixteen. I've missed all the fun. I would be proud, as
would any wife, to be seen somewhere, anywhere, as Mrs.
Farrier; to be beside you. When your producers or scenic
designers or directors come down here I am the boys' nurse,
or the chatelaine, or the truant officer or the girl who goes*

*down for the mail, or the old-lady-with-market-basket. Per-
haps Devereaux is the most exciting imagination in today's
theater (you and I both think this of him), but in the three
visits he has paid you here at Glen Lochen I have been
permitted to be present at meals. I have never been present
for any of "the talk."*

*But did you know that Devereaux did the sets for King
Vidor's new picture—with Clive Brook and Pola Negri?
And did you know, if you looked closely and quickly at the
opening credits, you would see another name there that you
know? Mine? I am of interest to these people, Seton, to
some of them. And even of use. I did the scenario. (I have
just finished another.) I do nothing grand. But what I do is
quite real. So am I.*

*About being "constantly seen with men," I have seen
exactly one, one that you imposed on me by a telegram last
month—Junius Thorpe, a crude bore and a waddling oaf.
I took him to the horse show in Danbury. He barked at
the waiters, spat in the grass, bothered people in the next
box (they got up and left, and so did I right after). He will
never come here again. He doesn't write well enough to be
that much of a boor. No one does. Our application for membership at the Somerset has been put aside for another year
because of his gross behavior.*

*As to my drinking, please go to hell. I'm nursing your son.
Do you think I am a fool? You believe any gossip you hear,
provided—in your delight to "get" things on those who are
closest to you—it is disgusting enough. In this craven weakness, you become as disgusting as the people you listen to.
In your savage protection of your reputation, you should not
imperil it yourself. Two weeks after we got back from Placid
I went down the cork path to the boathouse. I had decided
to tell you we had another baby coming. I wanted to be
alone with you. I knew you were rowing. I could hear you.
I had wanted to tell you at Placid, when the doctors were
there, but Mortimer Flowers said you would not be able to*

*"accept" this new situation so I said nothing. (I do not know
how you could have so long avoided seeing my condition.)
Then I realized you were not alone in that Eskimo thing
that Tanager sent you from Placid. There on our own dock
I heard her paddling about in it with you in this lake. Later
I saw you, both of you. This will not interest you. But something else will: Mrs. Breslin also saw you. She is a local
woman. I have no idea what she will do with her information, but I imagine she will have people to carry it to. And
do you know why? Tanager was one of the many "friends"
that stayed here from time to time with Mr. Watrous, only
Tanager stayed here for two years. Mrs. Breslin was house-
keeper then as she more or less is (or has been) for us. I say
"has been" for a good reason. You are quite right about the
lights being on "till all hours." I have closed the house. You
can get the key from that bubbling-over little Mr. Horner. I
shall never come back here. I am blind with fury.*

Seton knew this was all true. He could not endure it. Reason had
left him now. He could go to any extreme. And there was only one
more:

*I have gone over my diary and our correspondence and
find this interesting disclosure: not out of my suspicion but
out of your own mouth and record you are condemned. And
in your own handwriting. It is physically and biologically
impossible for me to have been the father of your child! I
was in Detroit when this child was conceived! I don't know
who the father is. (Perhaps you don't either!)*

*—and so, dear Seton, let us terminate this ugly charade
that others have called "our marriage." We cannot relate to
each other, ever again, in any way. Let us, therefore, have the
courage to stop trying, to make the amputation, to smother
our cries alone. That is about all we have been doing together for nearly ten years anyhow. I have no doubt of your*

*greatness but as for me, I doubt if there has ever been a
woman in any marriage so lonely as I, yet so willing to have
been a faithful partner to all its promise.*

30

WHEN JILL GOT TO NEW YORK SHE CALLED UP DR.
Celce. She wanted a nurse to help her through the next few weeks.

The nurse was a calm, sanitary, severely starched German woman
of fifty named Helga Taussinger. In her blunt solicitude, in her
unhurried but relentless practicality, she seemed to Jill to be trying
to make up for all the evils the Germans had committed during
the war.

Her first action was to put Jill to bed.

Over Sean and the new baby Helga asserted a severe but pragmatic
blessedness that had them both on schedules of her own selection
within twelve hours. By the end of twenty-four, Sean was her victim,
for she had brought him the excitements of the Harz Mountain
fairy tales, all with endings most bloody and desperate and, for a
six-year-old-boy, quite satisfactory.

Dermod eyed her once as she powdered his little bottom and he
seemed to smile. This pleased Helga, though she knew, with babies
that young, it was more likely a gas pain than a smile.

The shock of having Dermod the way he had come was now
beginning to retreat for Jill. But the shock of losing Seton was beginning to emerge and to take hold. Not losing him in the conventional
sense that women lose their men; losing him in the way that loss is
sustained when a person deeply loved, intensely inhabited, breaks
up spiritually and shreds out on the stony beach of his own personality; when the breakup is his own doing.

It seemed to Jill—after the devastating letters—that her husband had suddenly declared himself unfit to live any longer, just as Patrick had done. Unfit or unwilling. She guessed that the drives and the endings for Seton would be about the same as his brother's had been.

Her woman's instinct told her that their own baby was already disowned. It came to her now—its meaning clear for the first time —that Seton had not been compelled to go to California at all, at least not then. It occurred to her for the first time that Seton's son was named for Seton's father and that Seton either did not know this or did not care.

Jill knew what it meant: the infant Dermod was now and forever disinherited, even as Sean and Derek had been, and not because of the letter in which Seton had disclaimed paternity but in the barbaric pattern of rejection that was the mesh and tissue of his real make-up.

She felt that the net was closing in forever on itself, making Seton his own captive. In her mind now, before she was caught, she looked back just once into the darkness, then with painful but sure resolution swam clear of it.

There in bed, looking at the ceiling, and with the sound of Helga's kind authority for the time taking care of Sean, Jill felt herself break away from Seton, from the web of Seton himself and from the much vaster invisible snare that kept him under the waters of life. He could breathe there but she could not.

She wanted one thing and one only: the safety of her children. If to win a victory over Seton's pitiless abandonments she must herself abandon him, or worse, stand still while she watched him abandon everything that was his own, then living without Seton was not something that had to be struggled over. It was an eventuation already coming up on the calendar.

Coming up? It had come. It was here. It had already happened.

Sean tiptoed in and seeing his mother awake crept up close to her. He was full of curiosity about the new baby.

"Did he really come from your stomach?" His eyes were great searching orbs, capable of any truth or wonder.

Jill slipped her fingers into his curls and smiled.

"Yes, he did, dear. It is the way all babies come."

"Is he ours?"

"Yes. He's ours forever. He's your own brother. You're to help him grow up and see no harm comes to him."

Sean thought about this a moment, then a look of another interest came into his eyes.

"Did I come from your stomach too, Mommy?"

"Yes, Sean. Just as your little brother did."

Then Sean's look changed suddenly to one of childish roguery.

"I want to go back in your stomach, Mommy."

"Why, dear? Why do you want to go back in my stomach?"

The grin turned to a strange impish mysterious glee.

"I forgot something."

He ran out of the room giggling, hunching his shoulders.

Jill was delighted at the antic originality and unexpectedness of his child's fancy. She wished she could share this delicious caprice of mind with her husband. But Seton was not interested in what children said or did or were. What wonderful treasures she had to share! What poverty was her husband's that he could not take them!

Jill got up and dressed. She needed to get out, even though the March day was wild and cheerless. Out in the plaza the nymph in the dead fountain seemed to shiver. Central Park was deserted. Even the sea lions had gone inside.

Why not be grown up about everything? she thought. Why not let Tanager have him?

She walked through the thick carpeting to the elevators, then unfeelingly through the rich lobby of the beautiful building, a hotel she had never been in until four days before when she had moved there. Once she'd said to Arleigh, complaining about the extravagant absurdity of Glen Lochen: "I don't want to be grand. I just want to be congruent." Now it came back to her. And something came with it: the cold and absolute knowledge that, Seton or no Seton, she was now and forever through with poverty.

Walking past the Powder Room in the main foyer on her way to the steps facing Fifth Avenue, she knew her mind was made up: that she was getting rid of Seton and not the other way around. She'd seen the item in the New York *American* that Tanager Bolt was in California.

Well, so be it. Welcome to him, Tanager. Welcome to what you can find there. Perhaps more than I? Perhaps the same. With fleeting maliciousness her mind darted to a corner that Tanager might dread: Are you past childbearing, Tanager, and must you finally own up? Or will your deceptions again serve you as conveniently as before? How old *are* you, dear Tanager? I am thirty-one. How will you look in ten years? In five? How much weeping—in your commercial dedication to gaiety and *haute couture*—will you be able to stand? Seton weeps, you know. And snores. By what controls of muscle and temper will you hang on to your aplomb when Seton appears at your first soiree, cursing and unshaved and in his sneakers, and tells all your guests to get the Christ out of his house and stay out?

How are you at lugging chest weights about? Would you like me to show you how to fix the pump that blows up the bladder for the punching bag?

Jill went down the steps and around the little half circle of the plaza. A great awakening came to her, calming and desolating at the same time. Was not a stab of jealousy supposed to accompany the special pilferage of husband stealing? She searched herself but she could feel none. None at all. She even felt vaguely disappointed. She must be deficient in the mechanical inventory of feminine reactions.

Jill knew that if Seton were ever to catch a glimpse of what Tanager had represented in the life and death of Patrick, there could be only one of three actions: to kill himself, to kill Tanager, to marry Tanager. Marrying her, he could deny it all. Marrying her, he could prove that everything the world said against Tanager was a lie. If it weren't a lie, how could he marry her?

When he was cornered, Jill knew his rationalizations could be as primitive and as crippling as this.

Layers of revelation began to unfold. As she passed the opulent windows of Bergdorf Goodman, she realized that she had been married all these years to an artist—perhaps a great one—but never to a man at all. She wondered what it would be like to be married to a man, to be in his bed, to be beside him on a beach, to be beside him now in the wild air of New York, to be in a theater with him, to be included in his thoughts, in the exchange of ideas and experiences and memories that make up the talk of civilized people.

She had been married all these years—how many?—to a child; to an angry, self-pitying boy, a refractory little urchin kicking at hedge roots, yanking his nurse's clothing, soiling his fresh collar, refusing to recite when called on, sticking his tongue out, throwing his Sunday-school money on the nursery floor, throwing his blocks in the toilet bowl, daubing the mirror, spitting.

All his life Seton had been doing the same thing: he'd been trying to beat the world to death with a chair rung.

And it would not be beaten. It just kept on being the world.

Jill waited for the Fifty-ninth Street trolley to pass, then walked across Fifth Avenue and studied the exciting windows of F. A. O. Schwarz. The main window was completely occupied by the Southern Pacific. Every once in a while, quite magically, a puff of steam came out of the tiny stack. She would stop there on the way back. In the suite she had taken there was plenty of room in the Plaza to set up all that track for Sean. It would be fun to do it with him.

She began walking south, preparing her mind and her thoughts for their final leave-taking with Seton, however it might happen.

Sadly, and with some pity for him, Jill knew it was always going to be getting worse with Seton. He had written twenty-three plays of theatrical power and dramatic originality, some better than others, all crude, a few trashy, four of splendid reach. She was trying to think of the *mind* now, not the talent. It came to her that he had never set down an original thought. It came to her that he had never had one. He had never brightened or invigorated the language. And in the millions of words of his that were projected each year with such spirit and scorn and sputter from the stages of theaters all over America, there was never a line that was remembered, never a philosophical truth that would go on living.

It came to her that the great dramatist had never said one thing in his whole life that was quotable.

It came to her that Seton was born to sing man's destruction, while she lived to sing his birth. Seton was afraid of Nature: he was afraid of Man, the creation of Nature; he was afraid of the Machine that was man's creation. And he was the impaled victim of all three.

She saw that it would never end; that she could never lift him from the spike and that neither could the hands of his sons.

Jill now made another discovery that women often make after their feelings have been stretched in such travails, but can't refit themselves to the old sockets.

She was bored.

Most of the time, during the years of Seton's struggles, of his haunted mutterings, she had listened to all he said, had followed his groping, hoping to hear something more valuable, more noticeable, more worthy, more provocative, more penetrating, more nobly compassionate, or more truthful in the enduring sense of life's meaning than his carping and his fractious, captious, venomous vituperations and dismissals had revealed. She had listened for deeper tones but they had never come.

Why? Why?

At the Chaucer Head Book Shop, where row on row of impressive crescents displayed all the published plays of her husband, she pondered a long time. Who could be sure? And what did it matter? One could be a great name in the theater, and still be no thinker at all. The two faculties were not at all involved necessarily. Seton's feelings, which were intense, were also quite as certainly adolescent, and to Jill, who lived with the man Seton and who had privately studied the artist Seton, it seemed now that it was this quality of adolescent introspectiveness that he flung across the footlights to each beholder; that darted out as a tongue of self-pity which each viewer could enjoy without having to acknowledge as a weakness; that each might say "How true, how true" when it was wholly untrue, not even representative or characteristic or plausible.

To Jill, private response from the individual playgoer in Seton's audience was not unlike the reactions that a man who is a drinking problem and who knows it, might have when, upon seeing the pitiable condition of a passing inebriate and finding himself haply sober, he feels cleansed and acceptable and benevolent and lucky and briefly comfortable.

The cold air exhilarated her. The old days swept by. Jill felt plowed

and harrowed and all smoothed over. She wished she could remain
so for a time. She did not want to be planted.

She thought of Sean safe in the big suite in the Plaza, and of the
baby Dermod safe with the calm and military nurse. A terror ran
through her when she thought of losing either one. What *would*
happen if they lost Sean! What comfort could Seton bring her? Did
Seton suffer? Yes, he did. But she began to think he didn't suffer
more than others. He just met it ineffectively. He postponed it. He
met it in weeping, in recriminating, in running, in prowling the dark
for anodynes. He always handed the burden to someone else, always
would. There seemed a special ostentation about his loneliness. His
griefs too, when they came. His was the grief that was private. Though
it might be the same grief for all—as it surely was with old Dermod—
though it might be worse for another than for himself, Seton could
never register such a thing; no realization that Molly had lost more
in the death of Patrick—indeed lost most of what she had left—than
Seton had lost.

None suffered but Seton. As if none was allowed!

Jill crossed Fifth Avenue again. She was grateful to be alone, to be
walking, to have no set goal. There was nothing she had to do and do
right now, and there had not been many times in her life like that.
Reflecting objectively and without hurry upon their days and years
together, she realized that not only she, Jill, but no woman living
could be Seton's wife and be a woman too.

She was grateful to be alone, to be walking, to have no set goal.
There was nothing she had to do and do right now, and there had
not been many times in her life like that. Reflecting objectively
and without hurry upon their days and years together, she realized
that not only she, Jill, but no woman living could be Seton's wife
and be a woman too.

Mistress, yes, though mistress only, as far as a woman's femaleness
went; but even then, only in the exact and measured moments of
their mating, increasingly mechanical and unloving; anonymous even.
All the rest of the time Seton's wife (whatever kind of woman she
might be; Jill, or someone altogether different and distinct—someone
as different and distinct as Tanager) would not be his wife but would
be Seton's mother or Seton's cook or Seton's strong but scolding

nurse, depending on the quality of immediate danger, on the trigger of impulse, on present need or momentary appetite, on who was at the door. Seton's wife, whoever she might be, would move from room to room and role to role, from bonnet to toque to apron, knowing she had never been known for what she really was, never would or could be; that she never would be needed for what she really had; worst of all, knowing that the best of her as a woman—her essence as Woman—would never be seen or taken; never seen, never taken, never even sensed, never valued, never understood.

On her solitary walk down Fifth Avenue that early afternoon in March, Jill's love for Seton died. It died with a kind of surprised suffocation. It died in the enduring kindness that is fatal to all loving. Because she knew she could never be unkind to Seton no matter what he might do or not do, she knew it meant she could love him no more, no matter what he might do or not do.

Pity stayed in her heart and stayed after.

Strangely, resentments drifted from her. She felt the peace of a tired swimmer, safely through hostile waters. The world began to integrate. Things would fall into place. The struggle to go on living began to lessen. She could even think dispassionately about Tanager. Or she began to think she could, if she could keep out of her mind any picture of an actual physical embrace.

If Seton was a great artist, she rejoiced in it; but he was also an irrecoverable cripple and she could not live with it. He would never be different. He would never be able to do any of the things that men all over the world did all the time and thought nothing of. He would never be able to know his children, handle money, keep friends, or meet the world on any level except in those cases—rare as solar eclipses—when the world's acceptance and his own mood were in brief conjunction.

She did not know how to leave her husband, but it was this knowledge that brought Jill the quiet resolution to do so, the cold realization she must do it to save her own children.

Chimes rang with a sharp coldness from the bell tower of St. Thomas's and were distorted by the wind and whirled off. It was quite cold. Tea would be warming and refreshing. Maillard was quite near.

Then Jill got the shock of her life. She had come to the window where Seton's picture was prominently standing, the portrait that was framed to look like a Roman coin. Now, right beside it in a companion frame, as Calpurnia to Caesar, was a portrait of Tanager Bolt! Bold, *haute*, chin out, eyes exulting, eyes looking confidently through the laurels of her own frame into the brooding eyes of Jill's husband!

It was then that jealousy hit Jill—jealousy and rage and shame. In the middle of Fifth Avenue she felt slapped and spat upon. Her sense of outrage exploded. Flashes of slights from days past, pricks of humiliating discourtesy, burned in her eyes and aggravated her pace. She wanted to smash the window and mutilate the picture that sat there so smugly, so sure of itself, insulting her.

Jill knew one thing: now her husband would *never* get Tanager Bolt. Never, never, never!

How she could prevent their living together she did not know. She knew she couldn't dislodge her with the story that Patrick had told in the asylum. Tanager would just deny it, deny it convincingly.

She'd have to think.

The first thing she did was reckless but it was also humanly feminine. If she was going to have to fight Tanager she was determined to look as well as Tanager. Only twenty minutes before, Jill had passed the irresistible windows of Bergdorf Goodman. Now she went in. She identified herself. She had a bankbook and the registration card for the Pierce-Arrow. She was indubitably Mrs. Seton Farrier and she immediately began to receive frantic attention.

In a few minutes less than three hours Jill spent twenty-nine hundred dollars for new clothes.

She charged everything to Seton.

Then she walked under the trees back to the Plaza and telephoned Arleigh.

In a burst of monologue unfamiliar to her, she told the pleased but astonished man that Tanager was in California with her husband now. She said she wanted a lawyer. She said she'd left Glen Lochen forever, that she'd brought Sean and her new baby to the Plaza. She added that she was so mad that she was afraid, if she ran into

Tanager anywhere in New York, she'd jab her in the eye with a knitting needle.

Arleigh was a good person to say this to. He laughed shortly, didn't interrupt.

But now, with her first pause, he broke in.

"Jill, you knew that Molly died."

Jill gasped. "Molly! No! When?"

"Two days ago. I tried in the worst way to find you."

She felt numb.

"Molly! Oh my God! I—Arleigh, I was *right here!* But you couldn't know. Of course. And I purposely *didn't* call Molly. Not this time. Oh, Arleigh, you poor man!"

"I'm all right, Jill. How are you, is the thing."

"Oh, I'm so sorry. I wish I could have helped you. You especially. The Farriers—they always seem to leave you stuck with it."

"Me! They leave *you* stuck with it."

"Does Seton know? Is he here?"

"He wasn't here. It was very sudden. I've wired him. I think he's on his way but his telegram is quite ambiguous."

"What did it say?" Jill asked, trying to steady herself.

"It said something like 'Terrible, terrible. Will try to come at once. Get me a room McAlpin. Take care of everything.'"

There was a pause.

"When is the funeral? I suppose there's a Mass?"

"Dear Jill, it's all over. Even the interment."

Her voice broke then and she said: "I guess you took care of everything, Arleigh."

He caught the irony of it, knew where it was directed. He wished Seton might have heard it. He wished Seton could know, even for a few minutes sometime in his life, what was thought of him.

Jill said: "Arleigh, I saw something I just can't get over. On Fifth Avenue."

"What was that, Jill?"

"Tanager's picture displayed with my husband's. In identical frames. In the same window."

So, she'd seen it herself! And he could imagine the sharpness of the slap. Well, there was no sense in trying to minimize it. It was surely the most brazen thing Tanager had ever done, at least in public.

"It's getting a good deal of notice, Jill. The papers have picked it up."

"Well, that might get her picture out of that window even faster than I can get that vile woman out of his life. He *hates* gossip. He loathes it!"

"Seton isn't running the show, Jill. Tanager is."

"Do you mean he doesn't *know?*"

"I'm not sure."

"Oh, it's so selfish of me even to mention such an ugly thing! I mean, in the same conversation about Molly."

"Don't feel guilty about that, Jill. There's nothing you can do about Molly. You were the girl that was there for Dermod. And Patrick too."

He thought he could hear Jill crying.

"I'll be glad to let Seton go." She was saying everything with difficulty. "But *Tanager!* I'll never give him to Tanager. Never!"

To Arleigh she sounded completely friendless and desolated.

"Jill, do you want me to come over?"

"Oh, Arleigh. *Can* you?"

He was there in fifteen minutes.

He was unchanged, graceful, limitlessly courteous. It had been that way through his life. It would go on that way, Jill knew. He was the most civilized man in the theater, one of the few "greats."

Just seeing him again made her feel better.

He met her in the Terrace Room, where they ordered tea. He looked sharply at Jill while she was being seated. She looked composed. He leaned down and kissed her. He could sense the tension but he couldn't see it. He wanted to break the tension but did not quite know what to say first. Then the right item came out and came at the right time:

"Charlie Westover's here. Sent his love. He still wants you to come out there and write some pictures for him."

"Really?"

"I mean it. And you better think about it. Charlie sent you a very specific message, Jill."

"He did!" This cheered her. "Well, what was it? What is it?"

"Charlie told me to tell you he still thought you were the berries." Here Arleigh's great black brows lifted amiably.

"The berries? What does he mean?"

"He means you're the snake's hips." He smiled boyishly and looked down at her as if the remark made everything clear. It seemed incongruous and comical that such phrases could be tumbled from a man so distinguished. Jill laughed.

Inside, Arleigh sighed with relief. Jill had gone around a corner. There would be others but this was progress.

Tea came. Jill began to pour and pass.

"What's Charlie doing in New York?" she asked.

"Première of a new picture. *Sunrise*. A new title for the old Sudermann story. May MacAvoy and George O'Brien."

"Did Charlie direct it?"

"No. But he brought some magical lighting to it. Charlie's quite big now, you know."

"He always was, wasn't he?"

"Yes. Here. The best in New York. But he's surviving out there too. Getting his way. Not easy." Arleigh folded a piece of nut bread and ate it. "I'm glad I was able to miss it."

"You're glad? I should think any studio on the Coast would feel lucky to get you."

He said it again then: "Dear Jill." Then with real affection he picked up her hand and bent low and kissed it just as he had done at Molly's party so long ago. And that day at Placid.

"Thank you, Arleigh. I hope I can see Charlie. He was so—so *alive!*" She put her napkin aside with sudden impatience.

"Oh, Arleigh, why does everything have to be such a mess! When it could be such *fun!* When it finally came in for us. For Seton."

"You're not a mess, Jill. And there's no fun for Seton. He isn't here to be happy. I learned that a long time ago. You're in a bad time right now. But you're coming out of it. You've already made the most important move of your life."

"What is that?"

"Closing Glen Lochen. And doing it all by yourself."

"Was that important?"

"Yes. It freed you."

"But I hated the place. It was spooky and freakish."

"Not from the place. From Seton."

Very quickly Jill told about the impulsive purchase of the great estate in Fairfield, the hysterical inefficiency with which Seton tried to cut down overhead by dismissing the staff; of the vastness of the house in the day and its creakiness at night; of the arrival of the kayak, of the nocturnal visit that Tanager had made just a few days later; of the agony to which Seton had drunkenly abandoned her when the baby was coming; of his flight, of her own recovery and rebellion; of her making her peace with her husband in her own mind, peace in her decision to leave him, even leave him to Tanager if that were what he thought he wanted.

Jill's description of her own *volte-face* in regard to Tanager, when she had run head on into the picture, quickened Arleigh's pulse. He now felt there were two people who could kill this vain marauder and have not a thing on their conscience.

"How are you going to get rid of Tanager, Jill?"

Jill now told Arleigh all the details of the last hours of Patrick in the asylum near the little town of Falls Bridge, and that it was Tanager who had delivered the blows that had brought Patrick to his end. For the first time Arleigh heard all the details.

"You couldn't use that against Tanager."

"No."

"She'd lie. She'd have to."

"I'm sure she would. I merely thought I might tell Seton."

"And let him either believe it or not believe it?"

Jill nodded.

A strange and almost malevolent firmness set about the mouth and jaw line of Arleigh. He stood up without any statement, laying money on the table.

"Get your things."

He strode out ahead of her. He had never done such a thing. Jill was startled, apprehensive. When she overtook him in the foyer he was already into his own coat and with his hat was impatiently waggling at the doorman to send over a cab.

It wasn't yet four o'clock.

"Gramercy and Twenty-first," she heard him tell the driver. Jill had never been to Arleigh's home, but once when Arleigh had taken her to Ladies' Day at the Players, he had pointed it out to her, an amiable red-brick place, quiet, aristocratic, and as uncharacteristic of the rest of New York as most of the other structures in the pleasant square, and twice as charming on that account.

Arleigh paid the driver and they went up two flights to his floor. A fire was burning. There seemed to be a manservant. Highball makings were already sitting out. Jill shook her head when he gestured to them. Arleigh ducked down to a cupboard behind the piano and below the bookshelves and came back with a large brown envelope. His hands were agitated. He pulled out a picture. Jill's hands trembled as she took it.

It was the corpse of Patrick, pitifully scourged, pitilessly exposed. Arleigh was in the picture, standing at the head of the embalming table upon which the unclothed body lay. Another man stood at the center, dramatically pointing down to the five stripes that lay in a row across Patrick's back. Patrick's eyes were open. They seemed alive and begging forbearance.

"Who is the man with you?"

"The coroner. He had the record of the asylum doctor. Was his name Sommers?"

Jill nodded.

"When a body comes in from a place like that, with a tag that says 'acute alcoholism' besides, they don't bother much. If there isn't a complaint."

Arleigh poured himself a large drink with a short splash of soda, picked up the picture, took Jill's arm, and went down the stairs with her again.

"She couldn't lie about this," he said, waving at the Gramercy Hotel doorman. A cab started over.

"What are you going to do with it, Arleigh?"

"I'm going to stick it under Tanager's nose."

"Do you want me to come?"

"Do you want to?"

"If you need me, I'll come. I'll go alone if you'll give me the picture. Do you know where she is?"

"Yes."

The cab drew up. Jill started to step in, then turned back to Arleigh.

"I'd sooner go alone, Jill. Why don't you just take this one back to the Plaza? I'll call you sometime tomorrow."

"You take it. I'd sooner walk around the park anyway. You have the errand, not me."

Arleigh didn't argue. He tipped his hat quickly, bowed shortly, stepped in, and they drove off. Jill fluttered her hand. Soon the cab disappeared.

Edwin Booth looked down at her in his iron dignity. Gramercy had a snug beauty, even in the March twilight, even though the trees were bare and the beds empty. It had the elegance of a loved widow, well provided for; the repose of chastity, the serenity of good remembrance.

Jill walked around the park, then up Lexington to Twenty-third, where she stepped into a cab. She instructed the driver to take her to Schwarz.

The maid who answered Arleigh's knock at Tanager's present residence tried to keep Arleigh from coming in.

"Madame is dressing," she said with embarrassed irritability, as she saw she was to be overrun. "She isn't expecting anyone."

"Then I'll be quite a surprise," Arleigh said. He could take on the flatness of Scotland Yard when he had something dirty to do. "You can tell her it's Mr. Brayce and that I've been here before. She may remember."

The maid retreated a little more, angry, beginning to take fear. But she didn't start for the bedrooms.

"You tell her I'm here or I'll go back in and get her!" With that he gave her a hard shove that put her in rapid motion and made her scream.

Instantly Tanager was in the doorway. She was clothed in a worn wrap-around, her hair was bound in a towel, and she had applied a quantity of cold cream to her face.

"Arleigh! What do you mean by this?"

"What I mean is quite simple. Leave Seton Farrier alone."

Tanager unwrapped the towel from her head and began wiping the cold cream from her face. She felt unsettled but she didn't know why. She knew she wasn't showing it. She wished she looked well but she was glad to have such plausible business with her hands.

"That's the second time this year that some bounder has broken in on me and told me to stop seeing Seton Farrier."

"I know about the other time."

"Then you know how far it got him."

"Yes, I know," he answered cryptically. His eyes never left her. "Why don't you ask your maid to pull up a chair and join us?"

"All right, Marie. I'll call you if I need anything. I know you couldn't help it."

At the door Marie turned. "If you want me to get the police, I'll be glad to do that, ma'am."

"That's an excellent idea, Marie," Arleigh said with judicial force, "and I suggest you do so at once." He picked up the phone and rammed it at her.

"Just run along, Marie," Tanager said. There was nervousness for the first time. Marie scooted out. "Now in the first place, Arleigh, what Seton and I mean to each other is none of your goddamn business. And in the second place there isn't anything you can do about it."

"I must disagree with that."

"Get out of here, you snooping old man!"

"I'll go when I finish."

He took off his coat and tossed it to a sofa. For a hideous moment it seemed like the drunken Patrick come back again. He was just as unhurried, just as brazenly at home.

"Do you mind if I change into something else?"

"Yes, I do mind. When you're finished with me you won't feel like calling on anyone. Not for quite a while."

Tanager sat down.

"Really. You're quite forceful. Seton and I are getting married the instant he's free from his scrawny little farmerette."

"If you don't agree to leave Seton alone, I'm going to have you arrested."

Now she laughed. It was rich and spontaneous, the kind of laughter others would have joined in had they been there to hear it.

"Arleigh, you are a scream. Really you are." She seemed to mean it, every bit. "Why don't you just stick to the theater? You've had good luck there. You've never had any with your women!"

Arleigh walked over to the chair on which Tanager was sitting and slapped her so hard he sent her spinning onto the rug. He picked her up and propped her back on the chair and went over to his coat and took out the picture.

Tanager stared at it and gulped. Then with quick strong motions of her strong hands she tore it up.

"Prove it," she said with a murderous calm, her voice rich with hate.

Arleigh walked over to the telephone and picked it up.

"I want the Twenty-second Police Precinct, please."

Tanager was ashen. She began to shake. Then she leaped up and put the receiver back.

"No, no!" she implored. "Let's talk! You don't know what he did to *me!* You don't know how *cruel* he was! For God's sake, Arleigh, you *don't* know what you're doing! *I* didn't bring him here. He broke in. He was a dirty rotten bum and whatever he got was coming to him. I only hit him because I *had* to. He attacked me."

"Well, you did a pretty good job, Tanager. You could never square the story with Seton."

She went down on her knees and grabbed the skirt of his coat. Her horrible legs were now shamelessly exposed.

"*Please* don't tell him! It was an awful time! Oh, you *can't* be such a beast!"

"Yes, I can. Now get up and listen to me. If you ever see Seton Farrier again, I'll get a court order to exhume Patrick's body and I'll have you before the Grand Jury for murder in the second degree. You won't be convicted but you won't be worth much to anyone in this town any more. You aren't now. You're the dirtiest leech in New York."

Quietly he put on his coat, then his hat. He tapped his gloves.

Tanager was stricken. She must have known she looked ridiculous; to Arleigh, even repulsive. She hobbled over. All of a sudden she was old, old. She was disheveled, distrait, and defeated. She had not one fragment of poise.

"What will I *do?*" she asked in a strange whimpering helplessness.

"I don't know, Tanager. I just don't know. You might pick up those pieces of Patrick and start a scrapbook on him. I thought you'd rip this one. We took about thirty. You're good at pasting things together. I heard about it. As to what to do"—he opened the door now—"Marion Vogel might have a suggestion. Perhaps you can find a new spa together."

He went out, closing the door with quiet firmness behind him.

31

THE SOUTHERN PACIFIC WAS INDUSTRIOUSLY PUFF-ing about the living room of Jill's suite in the Plaza, with Sean squealing and dispatching and reversing and lighting the headlight and blowing the whistle and wishing that such joys would never stop, when Helga called Jill to the telephone.

Seton was in. He was at the McAlpin.

"Oh, Jill! Could you come?"

She knew it had to be.

"Yes."

He had a typical Seton Farrier room and it was in typical disarray. Some odd piles of California clothes were tossed about, and she could smell bay rum and Baume Benguéy. The analgesic meant he had sore muscles.

Seton looked tired but he did not look ill and he certainly did not seem grief-stricken. He had a fine tan.

"Arleigh took care of things for me," was his first sentence. "I'll never be able to thank him."

Jill sat down in a deep chair by the window. Right across the way she could see Saks-Thirty-fourth. His new play *Scorpio in Libra* was rehearsing in the next block. Already the bulbs were being fitted into the marquee of the Empire.

"I've got such a terrible backache," he said. "You've no idea what an experience it is! How exhausting! Coming clear across a continent. And no preparation at all."

Suddenly his eyes were filled with tears. He flung himself down beside her and began weeping into her lap.

"Jill, Jill, I'm an orphan! I'm a homeless orphan!"

Jill stroked her husband's head and talked quietly while his sobs spent themselves. She saw that he'd brought some sort of electric heat lamp and had tried to rig it at the head of the bed. She realized that if it could be turned on there, the rays would surely miss the areas in his back.

"Why don't you take the rest of your clothes off and let me give you a back rub, Seton?"

"Oh, would you, Jill? I'd love it. We aren't going to quarrel, are we?"

"Quarrel? No, Seton. No quarreling."

He was stark naked now.

"Why don't you get on the bed, on your tummy. I'll put the lamp on for a few minutes and you can tell me where the soreness is."

He seemed very docile and cheerful.

The telephone rang. Jill answered.

"Who's calling him, please?" Then to her husband, while cupping the phone, she whispered, "Acme Theatrical Photographers." He looked at his wrist watch.

"Tell them to come at ten tomorrow morning," he whispered back.

"Mr. Farrier says that ten o'clock tomorrow morning will be all right."

She hung up and came back to his bed and snapped on the light, holding it by its handle above the small of his back, then running the rays slowly across his shoulders, then down the spine and over the firm muscles of his hips. He seemed to be in fine condition.

"How was California?" she asked pleasantly. "Did you fall in love with Mae Marsh or anybody?"

"Oh, that feels good, Jill. I think that's enough heat. It's the muscles across the top of my shoulders that are killing me." She began to knead the muscles lightly. "The doctors out there think I have some strange sort of dietary deficiency. They've given me all sorts of tonic pills. Highly concentrated of course. And they found I was taking too much thyroid. You've got to get the balance just exact, or you're in trouble. But, Jill"—he turned his head to look at her and he had a triumphant gleam in his eyes—"I haven't had a drink. And I haven't wanted one. Not even with the shattering news about Mother."

Under her hands he groaned with delight and relaxation. Then quite suddenly, with the quick movement he was capable of, he reached over and grabbed her and pulled her down on the bed beside him and began hungrily to kiss her, to pat her hair, to whisper, to unfasten her clothing.

"Jill, I want you! I want you! I need you!"

Jill's thoughts were on the loyal revolutions the electric train was making for Sean. They were on Tanager and on the mask her face must have become when Arleigh placed the picture of the dead Patrick before her. Mindlessly she permitted herself to be undressed and possessed. She had no feeling. Even though she knew it was for the last time, she had no feeling. When his brief moment of climax was reached and passed, Seton stretched and looked out the window. Light spring snow was falling. He turned to Jill and squeezed her ankle. He smiled darkly. He was quite shy. Then without saying anything he got up and showered in the bathroom. By and by he came back and sat down and picked up a newspaper. Jill ran a tub for herself and left him reading. When she came back he was asleep in the deep chair, his feet sticking straight out.

Jill knew he was all right; that in his way he was always going to be all right, that he could go on, perhaps forever.

She thought, with the tears stinging and her husband sleeping, how the whole world might have been turned clear over for her right in that same room if, when she had entered, he might have had flowers waiting, or a new nightgown from Hollywood.

But all he wanted was someone to rub his back and bury his mother.

Jill knew she was not Seton's woman. She knew she was not any man's woman. She knew, too, that no woman could be Seton's, for in that single exploding and liberating phrase, "Your husband is not a person," the doctor had said the whole truth of it, for all social and emotional purposes upon this earth.

Jill dressed quietly and quietly went out, leaving him sleeping calmly in the chair.

She decided to walk back to the Plaza in the snow. Tomorrow the photographers would come at ten. Rehearsals would start at eleven. But dawn would not bring a new day, only a new weariness and the old unconquerable competence, the gravelly voice.

For many minutes Jill walked up Sixth Avenue, calming herself in the chill and the dark and the friendly snow. It would be the last snowfall, no doubt, and was already post-season. She could see her husband going about his work tomorrow, head down, eyes up, shoulders hunched, sweater unbuttoned.

Now she passed the Pilgrim Pawn Shop, not knowing it was the same door through which Seton had gone to buy the revolver with which he planned to kill himself, and out of which he had emerged without remembering to buy the bullets that would slay him.

Perhaps Arleigh had arranged another protection for him this very night in driving away the succubus that was Tanager. Who knew what influences were taking care of what spirits?

Now she passed the Warwick Hotel. An orchestra was playing. She wished someone would ask her to dance. Seton never had. But she liked to dance.

Arleigh's picture of Seton as an underwater animal came into her mind. How it fitted! Yes, Seton would be forever palustrine, forever weaving through marsh grass, scudding through streams unknown and currents chill, past the bubbling shallows, then down the black deeps, always steering away from harbor, away from ships that sought the lighted headlands, the marked channel, the final anchorage. Seton would never be there. He would never want to be. With chitin for skin, with a transparent film across the center of his eye, a film that permitted the intake of man's perversity but filtered out the image of his hope, filtered out all the comfortable tints of kinship, Seton would scull and scour, never still, anadromous, blindly driving, dredging the ledges and the shoals, feeding on the ooze of grottoes, until he found the only peace for which he was fashioned: a place where there was no sound, no light, no movement, and no creature with the pulse of life or speech or desire or destiny or meaning. There on the sea's bottom, he might return to the rock from which he had been taken.

There was an orchestra playing in the Plaza, too. Jill hurried. She wanted to get upstairs before Helga had put Sean to bed.

Jill stopped at the mail desk. There was a note from Arleigh. It was short: "I just melted the Iron Butterfly."

32

IT WAS THE SECOND WEEK IN APRIL. CHARLIE WEST-over, driving the Marmon sedan, had run from one theater subject to another. The picture business excited him altogether and it had won every bit of his energy.

It was fun to hear an excited, intelligent man talk about work that he loved and understood.

Charlie hadn't changed at all, not that Jill could see. He hadn't even bought a hat.

"No need to have one out there," he said lightly.

He had volunteered to drive Jill to New London and they were nearly there.

"Say, tell me something, Charlie."

"Oh, I'm good for the whole trip, Jill. Ask me anything."

"You know, at Placid about a year ago, when Tanager showed up, we kept getting oddly informal invitations from that strange woman that Tanager was staying with."

"You mean Marion Vogel?"

"Yes."

"Marion does that."

"But why us?"

"Was Arleigh Brayce there?"

"Why, yes, he was. Part of the time."

"I think she's still kind of crazy about him."

"Marion Vogel crazy about Arleigh Brayce? Are you serious?"

"Serious? Hell, yes. She was Arleigh's first wife. I thought you knew that."

Jill shuddered.

"No, I didn't."

"Fact is," he offered, "I was deep into my own dalliance with Tanager before I found she had an almost equal interest in women. It was Tanager's affair with Marion that destroyed Arleigh's chances of coming out right ever again for himself."

"Poor Arleigh."

"Yeah. Poor everybody. But Arleigh's tough and useful. And he's been well used. Few can say that. Few ever get it in this dirty business."

They were silent after this, except for Jill's directing him through the town's streets to the top of the low hill where her childhood had been spent.

She had to see the place where Seton had kissed her. She had to see the place in the grass where they had lain together that first time. She wanted the assurance that its still being there would bring her.

They parked the Marmon before the big frame house. . . . Jill's mother had just sold it.

Charles Westover sat on the swing on the front porch. The swing was all that was left. The house was empty. There was a Mr. Lathrop that Jill had to see in town. She was to surrender the keys to him.

"I'll be back in a few minutes," she told him. He had brought a new playscript of Philip Moeller. He flicked his finger, then looked down at the pages.

Jill remembered all her little stratagems, even the hiding of the sandwiches that she made the night before; hiding them in the mailbox. No mail ever came on Sunday, not even the paper.

The Thames River was full and bright. The submarine pens looked just the same. A new water tower had gone up—a practice escape tower, she'd heard. But that was the only change across the river.

She walked through the breach that had been the gate of the girls' school, burned down so many years before. Beyond the school, beyond its friendly ruins, some new construction of some sort was going forward. There were piles of new lumber, small mountains of brick, and a great revolving tank, for mixing concrete. She could hear hammering, but it was far away and did not disturb her.

Here indeed was the old greenhouse, its ribs still standing, though rusted through. The rubble of old pots was now moss-grown. Even the odors came back now. Her throat began to choke up. She walked on past the end of the ruins of the greenhouse and came suddenly and quietly to the very place. She remembered where they had stood when it rained. She remembered where they fled the one time her mother had called. She remembered Seton coming out of the water, the fine strength in his arms, the great light in his eyes each time he saw her. She knew that if she did not soon leave she would weep. She looked down into the grass, as if the imprint of their bodies might still be there, pressed forever upon the remembering earth.

Then she heard a voice and turned quickly, startled. It was an old man, a watchman of some sort. He had come over quietly from the pile of lumber. He was wearing a peaked engineer's cap and a light red corduroy jacket.

"I saw you lookin'. I thought maybe you lost somethin', lady," he said pleasantly.

"Yes. Yes," she answered. Her voice sounded far away to her.

"Well, now, miss, maybe I can help you." He began moving about, peering down. "How long ago about was it?"

Jill looked at the kindly old face of the man and shook her head.

"It was a long time ago," she said to him. "Never mind." She looked away for a moment, out over the sweep of the river. The tidal boom was gone. There was a steel marker in the river now. When she thought her voice was calm, she turned once more.

"A long, long time ago," she said, almost apologetically, "I don't think it's here any more. Thank you for offering."

Then Jill turned and started up the hill to the empty house where Charlie waited for her. The old man looked about for a moment after Jill had gone. Then he walked back and sat down again on the lumber.

The End